The Modern
Coral Reef Aquarium

Svein A. Fosså · Alf Jacob Nilsen
———— Volume 1 ————

The wonderful world of the Maldives

Photo: R. Lunde

Credits:

All the pictures, drawings, diagrams and tables are by the authors, except where otherwise stated in the captions. The photos for the commercial products shown were put at our disposal by their manufacturers. They are typical examples available in that line of products. The fact that they are presented in this book does not imply an evaluation of their quality and safety.

The Modern Coral Reef Aquarium, Volume 1
First edition, 1996

© Birgit Schmettkamp Verlag, Bornheim, Germany. All rights reserved.

Original title: "Korallrevsakvariet", © Svein A. Fosså/Alf Jacob Nilsen

Translations: Gerhard Brünner, Hamburg, Germany; Georg Zurlo, Bergkamen-Rünthe, Germany

Proofreading: Julian Sprung, Miami, Florida, USA.

Editors and layout: Dr. Dieter Brockmann, Mülheim, Germany, and
                    Werner Schmettkamp, Bornheim, Germany

Printed and bound by J. C. C. Bruns GmbH, Minden, Germany

ISBN 3-928819-29-1

Zebrasoma xanthurus in a Modern Coral Reef Aquarium

So, in due course of time, nine out of every ten aquaria were abandoned; many of the shops were given up, because there was no longer any custom; and to all appearance the aquarium fever had run its course, never again to appear, like hundreds of similar epidemics.

But there was one element of strength in the aquarium possessed by none of the others. This was the study of nature in one of her hitherto unstudied phases. Those who merely treated the aquarium as a toy soon became tired of it, and cast it away accordingly, but those who saw its real capability became more enamoured of it daily.

J. G. WOOD, 1868: The Fresh and Salt Water Aquarium.

Agents:

* Norway - NorZoo A/S
            Marken 4
            5017 Bergen
            Tel.: 55 31 11 21
            Fax: 55 96 07 28

* UK - Tropical Marine Centre Ltd.
        Solesbridge Lane
        Chorleywood
        Herfordshire
        WD3 5SX England
        Tel.: 0 19 23 - 28 41 51
        Fax: 0 19 23 - 28 58 40

* USA - Two Little Fishies, Inc.
          4016 El Prado Blvd.
          Coconut Grove, FL 33133 USA
          Tel.: 3 05 - 6 61 - 77 42
          Fax: 3 05 - 6 61 - 06 11

Micro-atoll at low tide in the Great Barrier Reef

Table of Contents

Preface 10

Chapter 1:
Natural Coral Reefs 13

Types and geographical distribution of coral reefs 15
Ecology of coral reefs 19
Primary production in coral reefs 25
Primary producers in coral reefs 25
Consumers in coral reefs 30
Zones of coral reefs 31
Microorganisms of coral reefs 48

Chapter 2:
Zoogeography 57

The four zoogeographical main regions 59
❶ Indo-Pacific 59
❷ Eastern Pacific 88
❸ The Caribbean 90
❹ West Africa 98

Chapter 3:
A Coral Reef in the Aquarium 103

Chapter 4:
Setting up and Decorating the Modern Coral Reef Aquarium 111

Decoration materials 112

Chapter 5:
Modern Coral Reef Aquaria 127

Fish aquarium 129
Community aquarium 132
Sand zone aquarium 138
Reef gorge aquarium 145
Cave aquarium 149
Reef profile aquarium 156

Chapter 6:
The Break in Period 161

The break in period of a Modern Coral Reef Aquarium 162
Acclimatisation of fishes and invertebrates 165
Animals impaired by cyanide 166

Chapter 7:
Live Rock in the Modern Coral Reef Aquarium 169

How to treat live rock 170
Organisms living on live rock 173

Chapter 8:
Light in the Modern Coral Reef Aquarium 195

UV radiation and the effect on living corals 196
Light and photosynthesis 198
Light intensity 198
The underwater light-field 199
Moonlight 201
The importance of light for the Modern Coral Reef Aquarium 202
Sources of light for the Modern Coral Reef Aquarium 204

Chapter 9:
Temperature Control in the Modern Coral Reef Aquarium 213

Coral bleaching 214
Heating the Modern Coral Reef Aquarium 214
Cooling the Modern Coral Reef Aquarium 215

Chapter 10:
Water for the Modern Coral Reef Aquarium 217

Salinity of the sea water 218
Osmoregulation 219
Artificial or natural sea water? 220
Chemical reactions and parameters of the sea water 222

Chapter 11:
Biochemical Processes in the Modern Coral Reef Aquarium 241

Bacteria and their environment 242
The decomposition of nitrogenous compounds 243
Phosphorus cycle 247
Reduction and oxidation 247

Chapter 12:
Filtration, Water Maintenance, and Hydrotechnology for the
Modern Coral Reef Aquarium 251

Biological filtration 251
Subgravel filters 256
Mechanical filters 257
Activated carbon filters 257
Protein skimming 258
Reverse osmosis 262
Ozonisation 263
UV sterilizers 264
Water changes 264
Hydrodynamics abd hydrotechnology 264
Combination of filters 266

Chapter 13:
Algae 271

Structure and reproduction 273
Taxonomy and nomenclature 274
Division Heterokontophyta – Class Bacillariophycaea: Diatoms 275
Division Cyanophyta: Blue-green algae 276
Division Chlorophyta: Green Algae 282
Division Heterokontophyta – Class Phaecophycaea: Brown algae 302
Division Rhodophyta: Red algae 307
Division Dinophyta: Dinoflagellates 319
Résumé 324

Chapter 14:
Marine Aquaristics and Nature Conservation 327

Catching coral fish with cyanide 328
Catching coral fish with dynamite 331
Over-exploitation of coral reefs 332
Dangers to coral reefs 336
Death rate of animals in the aquarium trade 339
Coral reef aquaristics – more than just a hobby 342

List of References 347

Index 355

Preface

Even as early as in 1868, the English reverend J. G. Wood noticed that the interest for the aquarium hobby has a tendency to vary. This was the case in the Victorian era, and it is still so, even today. This is particularly evident when certain specific trends within the hobby, such as for example Malawi cichlids, catfishes or reef aquaria, become the "in-thing".

As for coral reef aquaria, many people are attracted to them because of their beautiful colours and exotic appearance. Frequently, new aquarists spend a lot of money on invertebrates, colourful fishes and sophisticated technical equipment, only to discover that it is not as easy to copy the natural coral reef in a closed aquarium system as they perhaps at first thought. In far too many instances the interest disappears again, just as rapidly as it came.

A coral reef aquarium is not necessarily difficult, neither to establish nor to run, but unfortunately this specialized branch of aquaristics offers plenty of opportunities for making fatal mistakes along the road. Since we first started with marine aquaria in the mid seventies, we have tested and observed a lot of coral reef aquaria. We have made our mistakes, and we have had our successes. From our many discussions with other aquarists, and through the reading of literature we have found that the hobby abounds with myths and misunderstandings. For example, we can frequently see recommendations of technical solutions which are absolutely useless if one wants to achieve good results.

We hope that our new four volume series of books, under the title *The Modern Coral Reef Aquarium*, based on the German best-selling series *Korallenriff-Aquarium* will help to clarify what a modern coral reef aquarium is all about, to stimulate further studies and to give our English speaking readers the possibility to share the techniques and trends of the most successful German school of aquaristics.

This volume could never have been made without the help from a lot of people all over the world. For a start we will extend a heartfelt thank you to all the German aquarists who, during our cross-country tour of Germany in 1985, gave us our first real life experience with German coral reef aquaristics. Thus, a special thanks to: Erhard Ewald, Rudi Krause, Dietrich Stüber and the other members of Verein für Meeresaquaristik in Berlin; to the late Peter Chlupaty, Munich; Johannes Birkholz, Linz; Jürgen Spitters, Klaus Klamma and other members of Siegerländer Meeresaquarium Club; Horst Schmidt, Wesel; Peter Findeisen, Witten; and last, but not least Helmut Schmidt and Franz Vennewald, Lünen. The same year we had our first personal meeting with Peter Wilkens, of Winterthur, Switzerland, who has given us much help and valuable advice throughout the years.

Amateur and professional aquarists, scientists, and aquarium business people from all over the world have supported our research and book project through many years. We extend our thanks to: Dr. Bruce Carlson, director of the Waikiki Aquarium, Honolulu, Hawaii, who has taught us a lot about growing corals and supported this project from day one; Jan Olsen, owner of Aqua Design, Oldenburg, Germany, who always is ready to help and who financed Alf Jacob Nilsen's trip to the magnificent reefs of North Sulawesi; Robert Brons, of Red Sea Fish pHarm, Eilat, Israel, who has given many helpful hints; as well as Erling Svensen, Egersund, Norway, and Janine Cairns Michael and Scott W. Michael, Lincoln, Nebraska, for allowing us to select photos from their impressive photo archives.

Our thanks also to Rolf Hansen, owner of Nor Zoo, Bergen, Norway, for providing funds for a study tour through Germany, and to our travel mate and fellow aquarist Ingvald Erga, Orre, Norway. Ove Fosså, Sandnes, Norway helped us with various translation work. Our Norwegian fellow aquarists Øystein Grindland, Kvinesdal; Ingar Gulbrandsen, Oslo; Flemming Jørgensen, Stavern; Leif Lindstrøm, Stavanger; Kjell Nagy,

Flekkefjord; Kenneth Olsen, Oslo; and Karl Ole Dahl, Bergen, must all be thanked for unselfishly letting us experiment with their aquaria, and shoot a lot of photos. Habib Sekha of Salifert BL, Duiven, Holland, has helped us a lot with advanced chemical tests and deserves special thanks.

Furthermore, all the following persons have, in different ways, contributed positively to this volume: Dr. Phil Alderslade, N.T. Museums for Arts and Science, Darwin, Australia; Michael Armstrong, Newcastle, Australia; Dr. Craig Bingman, New York, NY; Jan Carlén, Haugesund, Norway; John Dawes, Corsham, England; Charles Delbeek, Toronto, Canada and Honolulu, Hawaii; Enrico Enzman, Geretsried, Germany; Professor Daphne Fautin, University of Kansas, Kansas; Göran Flodin and Ulf Teräs, Aquaria Vattenmuseum, Stockholm, Sweden; Santiago Gutierrez, Puerto Rico; Dr. Russel Hanley, Hanley Caswell and Ass., Kenmore, Australia; Gordon Howes, formerly of the British Museum (Natural History), London, Great Britain; Klaus Jansen, Cologne, Germany; Dieter Kornfeld, Bielefeld, Germany; Knut Kvalvågnæs, Elnesvågen, Norway; Dr. Jürgen Lange, Berlin Zoo Aquarium, Berlin, Germany; Tor Eiliv Lein, University of Bergen, Norway; Jeff Macaré, Laguna Hills, California; Dr. Hans Mergner, Ruhr University, Bochum, Germany; Christer Olsen of Stavanger Akvarieforretning, Stavanger, Norway; Uwe Richter, Hagenbecks Tierpark Aquarium, Hamburg, Germany; Steve Robinson, California; Karlheinz Sauer, Kaben, Germany; Professor Terry Siegel, Aquarium Frontiers, New York, NY; Eduard Stirnberg and Ralph Slabik of Tierpark Bochum, Bochum, Germany; Professor Dr. Ellen Thaler, University of Innsbruck, Austria; Steve Tyree, Los Angeles, California; Endre Willassen, University of Bergen, Norway; Joseph Yaiullo, The Okeanos, Ocean Research Foundation, Long Island; Dr. Manfred Zahn, Löbbecke Museum and Aquarium, Düsseldorf, Germany; and Frank Osleby, Flekkefjord, Norway.

A very warm thank you to our publishers, Birgit and Werner Schmettkamp of Birgit Schmettkamp Verlag, Bornheim, Germany, who have done a tremendous job for us. First by their efforts on the German edition of the series and now by doing it all over again with this fully revised English version. Without their care and support this project would never have become a reality.

Julian Sprung and Daniel Ramirez, of Two Little Fishies Inc. and Ricordea Publishing Inc., Miami, Florida, have supplied us with a lot of important information and given excellent general support, in particular by editing the English translation of the manuscript. Dr. Dieter Brockmann, Mülheim a.d. Ruhr, Germany, has done an excellent job doing the lay-out for the English edition, and Georg Zurlo, Bergkamen-Rünthe, Germany, translated the German manuscript into English.

Last, but – most certainly – not least, a sincere thanks to our beloved wives, Lise Nilsen and Kristin Fosså, for all the patience and understanding they have given us through the years, while we have spent days and nights in front of the PC, with our heads deep into the aquaria, or away on some remote coral reef.

Grimstad and Hidra in Norway, March 1996

Svein A. Fosså and Alf Jacob Nilsen

Natural Coral Reefs

Coral reefs differ from other ecological systems because of the remarkably large variety of living organisms they harbour. They are exceptionally complex systems as a result of this diversity of species and the many symbiotic relationships. A reef as a whole has been built up by the organisms living there, especially by the reef-building hermatypic stony corals. These deposit calcium carbonate in its crystalline form "Aragonite", to build their calcareous skeletons. When the organisms die, they become porous limestone or "live rock", as this material is called by aquarists.

The first corals developed at the end of the Lower Cambrian about 650 million years ago. Since then the surface of the earth has repeatedly been restructured by great geological changes, which

Above: The corals on the reef edge of Bunaken, Indonesia, have to cope with the burning sun or rain showers when they are exposed during extreme low tides. In the background is the volcanic island Manado Tua.

Left: At a depth of 20 metres on a reef slope in Bega Lagoon, Fiji, colourful gorgonians sway in the current. These gorgonians are totally dependent upon catching planktonic food (Underwater photo: E. Svensen).

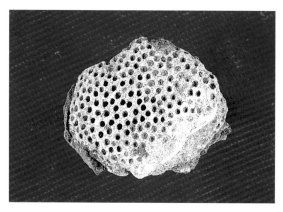
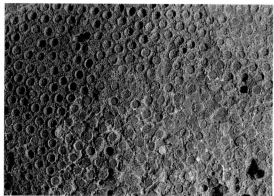

A small fossil *Favoistes* sp (left) and a close up of fossil tubes that once housed the polyps of a *Haliolistes* sp. (right), both from the suborder Tabulata found in fossil reefs surrounding Oslo, Norway.

Photos: H. A. Nakrem and A. Jensen, Paleontological Museum Oslo

A series of mainly Pliocene reefs rising up to about 300 meters on Misima Islands, Papua New Guinea. Photo: Prof. D. Hopley, James Cook University

Ols Sea Stack and Cave at Cave Hill on Barbados. The reef is from the Mid-Pleistocene, about 290,000 years old.
Photo: Prof. D. Hopley, James Cook University

also resulted in a displacement of the reef belt in the course of geological history. 400 million years ago a vast ocean, the Tethys Sea, surrounded the primeval continent Pangaea. With temperatures between 10 and 20 °C this ocean was relatively warm and there were no geographical barriers to keep the corals from migrating. At that time the most luxuriant coral reef fauna was found in the area that is now the Mediterranean.

A total of about 7000 species of corals have been described. More than 5000 of these species, including all members of the suborders Tabulata and Rugosa, are extinct. In species of Tabulata, which existed from the late Cambrian to the end of the Triassic, the polyps lived in tubes. The Rugosa, which peaked in the Silurian and died out in the early Jurassic (about 200 million years ago), contained both solitary and colonial species. The order Scleractinia, which contains the recent stony corals, first appeared in the late Triassic (about 210 million years ago), and diversified greatly during the Jurassic, Cretaceous and early Tertiary periods (200-50 million years ago).

About 25 million years ago – in the Oligocene – the situation changed. The Tethys Sea was divided by a land barrier between Eurasia and Africa. In the course of the millions of years that followed, this resulted in consider-

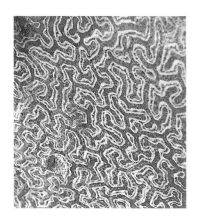

"Key Stone" was once mined from the Florida Keys and used for decorative building material.

able differences in the development of the coral reefs in what today are the Indo-Pacific and the Atlantic regions. In the Indo-Pacific area with the Indo-Malayian region as its center, large numbers of coral reefs with numerous genera of reef-building corals were formed. In the area of the Atlantic Ocean, which was now separated from the Indo-Pacific region, the development was quite contrary. Here a large number of genera of corals became extinct because a geographical barrier prevented them from migrating westward to areas with more favourable living conditions. This situation continued for the next 10 to 15 million years. Then the Western Atlantic was completely separated from the Eastern Pacific Ocean. This brought about a geographical and thus also genetic isolation which has governed the development of the faunal regions in the Indo-Pacific and in the Caribbean. Since then the regions have developed independently (NEWELL, 1959; FELL, 1967; WOOD, 1983).

From a geological point of view, present coral reefs are young structures. Glacial epochs have caused extraordinary variations in the sea-level: from 120 meters below today's (about 15,000 years ago) to 20 meters above it (about 7000 years ago). Coral reefs, as we know them today, were probably formed only about 5000 years ago (STODDART, 1973).

Types and geographical distribution of coral reefs

Today we distinguish between two main categories of coral reefs:

- shelf reefs,
- oceanic reefs.

Shelf reefs

Shelf reefs are found close to the coast, in shallow waters, where the seabed slopes gently down from 0 to 200 meters depth. This area is called continental shelf.

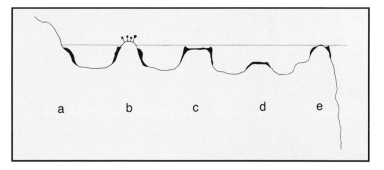

Zones of shallow water like these in tropical areas usually offer favourable conditions for the development of corals. Shelf reefs have a highly variable fauna. Compared to oceanic reefs, their water is usually higher in nutrients. This causes a characteristic fauna and flora, with soft corals and algae often dominating.

Oceanic reefs

Oceanic reefs form in ocean areas off the continental shelf. Volcanic activities cause elevations that rise from the surface of the sea as islands. Examples of such volcanic islands are Tahiti and Hawaii. Unlike the deep seabed surrounding them, they provide favourable conditions for the de-

velopment of corals and thus for the building of reefs. Oceanic reefs are much less influenced by freshwater run-off than shelf reefs. Most oceanic reefs therefore have more abundant fauna with a larger variety of species than shelf reefs, especially as far as stony corals are concerned. Oceanic reefs away from shipping routes display an abundant variety of species, as they are least influenced by human activities.

There are several types of shelf and oceanic coral reefs. The most important are:

- fringing reefs,
- platform reefs,
- bank reefs,
- barrier reefs,
- atolls.

Types of shelf reefs (after WOOD, 1983):
a – fringing reef at the shore
b – fringing reef in the lagoon
c – platform reef
d – bank reef
e – barrier reef

Fringing reefs

Fringing reefs account for the majority of all littoral reefs. The development of a fringing reef begins when coral polyps establish themselves in the shallow water along the shore, provided that there are favourable living conditions. In places where, for example, sea water and fresh water mix, reefs cannot develop. Whereas a large number of coral reefs can be found off most of the coastal regions of North-East-Australia and

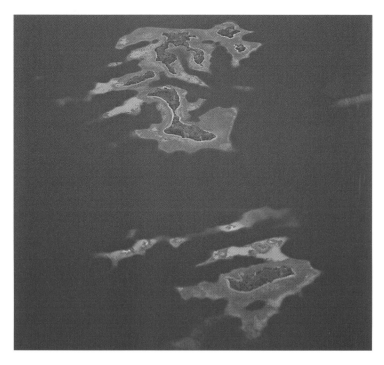

Fringing reefs surrounding small islands close to Sulawesi, Indonesia.

the Indo-Malayan region, there are hardly any reefs on the east coast of Brazil and on the coasts of Surinam and Venezuela. This is largely due to the enormous inflow of freshwater coming from the Amazon and the Orinoco.

The fauna of fringing reefs along the continental shelf may vary greatly. There are also fringing reefs around islands away from the continental shelf, and they may be highly developed. One example of this type of reef are the reefs of the Seychelles in the Indian Ocean.

Platform reefs

Platform reefs or patch reefs are found in places where elevations in the continental shelf reach the sea-level. Under these conditions a coral reef may develop with parts of the reef reaching the surface, where sand cays or limestone banks may form.

The edge of a fringing reef in the Red Sea viewed from below. Thousands of *Pseudanthias* sp. and big colonies of the soft coral *Dendronephthya* sp., both searching for plankton.   Underwater photo: E. Svensen

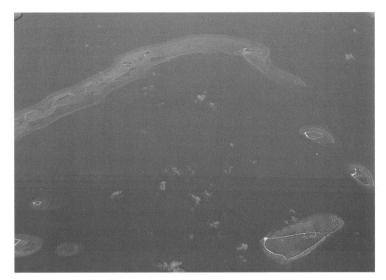

Typical shape of a Maldivian atoll viewed from the air. Note the shape of the outer reefs and the many patch reefs ("faros") with small islands inside the lagoon at bottom left. Also note a couple of deeper bank reefs, barely visible.

Small platform reefs also called patch reefs are also found on the inside of atolls. In such reefs corals grow most lavishly and beautifully. In the Maldives, which by and by have become a very popular attraction for tourists, these reefs are quite numerous. In some places they even reach the surface and have formed small coral islands with fringing reefs of their own.

In the Maldives these reefs are known as "Faros" and are common in the central and northern part of the country. For some reason, they do not appear in the south. It is not fully understood why these ring-shaped reefs have developed so numerously in the Maldives. Two basic theories exist; either the faros are formed as a response to wave action, or they are the result of growth from ancient ring-shaped formations in Pre Ice-Age reefs. See ANDERSON (1990).

Bank reefs

Bank reefs also develop on elevations of the continental shelf. They do not reach as high up to the sea-level as do platform reefs, and the top of the reef may even be found as deep down as 40 meters. The most prolific coral growth is usually on the reef top, where the highest light intensity exists. Bank reefs can also occur in oceanic reefs.

Barrier reefs

The Great Barrier Reef along the east coast of Australia may justly be called the greatest construction made by living organisms on earth. This reef complex can even be seen from as far away as the moon. Experts do not completely agree on how the process of formation of the Great Barrier Reef may have begun. Most of it lies directly at the edge of the continental shelf and forms a barrier between the shallow waters of the shelf and the deep sea beyond it.

The directions of ocean currents are the reason why most of the barrier reefs have formed on the east side of the continents. A barrier reef may also develop from a fringing reef due to subsidence. If they are oceanic reefs, barrier reefs may turn into atolls.

There are considerable differences between the seaward face of a barrier reef and its landward counterpart. Most of the corals on the seaward side are of a sturdy and hardy nature. Calcareous algae thrive here as well. On the landward reef-face we find much more delicate types of

The famous Watanabe Bommie in Flinders Reefs, Coral Sea, is a bank reef with its top about 12 metres below the surface. The schools of fish found here are unbelievable.

Approaching the coral islands and atolls of the Maldives at the end of a long flight and watching them from above, it is hard to believe that these structures were built up by innumerous tiny organisms.

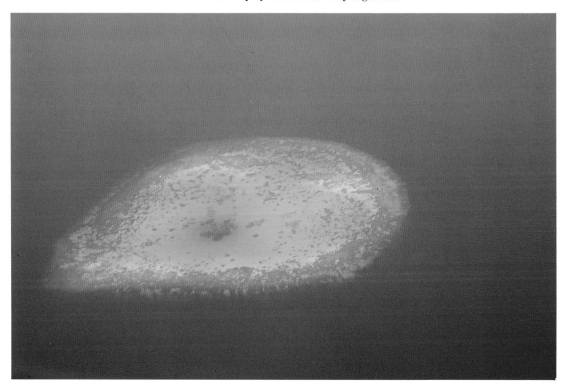

corals that are adapted to the calm water and the weak currents.

Atolls

Atolls almost exclusively form in areas off the continental shelf. Atoll islands, with their more or less circular form, enclose a lagoon. The size of the lagoon can vary considerably. The lagoon of Kwajalein Atoll in the Pacific Ocean has a "diameter" of about 100 kilometres and is about 55 metres deep, whereas the lagoon of Astore in the Indian Ocean measures only three kilometres in diameter and is nowhere deeper than one metre.

As mentioned above, often a large number of small platform or patch reefs can be found within an atoll. The waters of these reefs are very calm and they are the ideal places for marine aquarists to get acquainted with natural coral biotopes.

Living coral polyps are only found in the uppermost parts of an atoll. Further down it consists only of dead material from earlier stages of the development of the reef. DARWIN's theory of how atolls develop is still most widely recognized. The illustration above further clarifies this theory. It shows how a fringing reef changes into a barrier reef due to subsidence and later becomes an atoll.

We have repeatedly visited the Maldives in the Indian Ocean, the atolls which are the closest to reach from Europe. A lot of the underwater photos in this volume (and in the other volumes of this series of books) have been taken there. A bird's eye view of an atoll is an unbelievably beautiful sight. The idea that these incredible constructions have been built up in the course of thousands of years by myriads of tiny little animals and plants is a most fascinating one and constantly inspires us with great respect for nature.

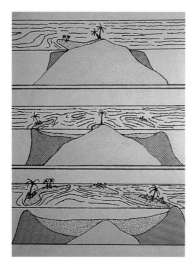

Development of an atoll according to the theory of Charles DARWIN: Around a volcanic island in the ocean a fringing reef develops first (top). Simultaneously the island subsides and corals develop into a rising barrier reef (middle). When the island has subsided and its top is below the water surface, an atoll develops (bottom).

Geographical distribution of coral reefs

The formation of a coral reef and its growth mainly depend on the temperature of the water and the light intensity. The high water temperatures in tropical regions accelerate the metabolic processes of the animals. In conjunction with the low concentration of carbon dioxide they also encourage the fixation of calcium necessary for the development of the skeleton of the corals. The geographical distribution of coral reefs is limited to areas within the 20 degrees Celsius isotherm, i. e. roughly between 30 degrees northern and 30 degrees southern latitude. Within this geographical zone their occurrence is determined by ocean currents that carry water of different temperature, salinity, and oxygen content, containing different nutrients, coral larvae, and types of plankton.

Cold and warm ocean currents are of great importance for the different reefs. Because of diffe-

rences in temperature, for example, there are a lot more genera of corals in the Carribean Sea than in the ocean area west of Central America. A lot of geographical conditions that differ from place to place like river outlets, geological conditions, wind directions, storms, tides, and many other factors also affect the formation of coral reefs.

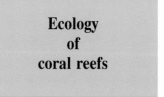

Ecology
of
coral reefs

A coral reef is an ecological system of great diversity. Only the tropical rain forests can compete with coral reefs in terms of variety and complexity. All the organisms of a coral reef are interdependent within a network of highly complex relations. Strictly speaking, however, nobody knows everything about these relationships, though oceanographic research continually provides new insights.

All living organisms consist of organic materials, which are comprised of carbon compounds (inorganic compounds are the opposite). Proteins are one example of organic compounds. They are called organic because in former times people believed these compounds could only be produced by living organisms. Inorganic compounds are chemical elements, e. g. oxygen, hydrogen, sodium or silicon and their compounds (e. g. water and glass).

Photosynthesis

Plants have evolved the extraordinary ability to produce organic compounds from inorganic substances with the help of complex chemical reactions. This process is called *photosynthesis*. The energy needed is supplied by the light. Organisms capable of photosynthesis are called *autotrophic*. They make use of the energy of the light. Organisms incapable of using light energy are called *heterotrophic*. Most prominent among the autotrophic organisms are the plants. Apart from plants there are also autotrophic bacteria. All other organisms on our earth are heterotrophic and thus their ability to live depends on plants.

Photosynthesis cannot take place in the absence of water (H_2O), carbon dioxide (CO_2) and light energy. From these components plants build up sugar compounds, mostly glucose ($C_6H_{12}O_6$) or starch ($C_6H_{10}O_5$)$_n$, at the same time releasing oxygen (O_2). The following formula represents this chemical reaction:

$$\text{light (energy)} + 6\,CO_2 + 6\,H_2O$$
$$\text{results in}$$
$$C_6H_{12}O_6 + 6\,O_2$$

It is worth mentioning that oxygen is a product of photosynthesis and is emitted by the plants. Heterotrophic organisms depend on the oxygen, which makes up 21 % of the atmospheric gases. Oxygen is readily soluble in water. However, its solubility in water is considerably less than in air.

Photosynthesis is the basic chemical reaction of most ecological systems. In a coral reef, where the amount of nutrients available normally is very small, corals have entered into a symbiosis with algae (zooxanthellae), to be able to profit directly from the process of photosynthesis. This symbiotic relationship will be dealt with later on.

Cellular respiration

The process that consumes oxygen is called respiration. It is the opposite of the process of photosynthesis and may be described by the following formula:

$$C_6H_{12}O_6 + 6\,O_2$$
$$\text{results in}$$
$$6\,CO_2 + 6\,H_2O + \text{energy}$$

The process of respiration produces energy in addition to carbon dioxide and water. Organic substances are broken down into inorganic components. The energy released by this process is necessary for all kinds of other physiological processes like movements, maintenance of body temperature, production of sexual cells (gametes), etc. Up to 75 % of the energy, however, is wasted as thermal radiation.

Respiration is mainly associated with heterotrophic organisms. However, autotrophic ones also need oxygen for their cell building processes. As long as the oxygen produced by photosynthesis is completely consumed in the respiration process, no surplus oxygen is emitted. This is the case, at certain light intensity. If the intensity falls below a certain limit, autotrophic organisms consume more oxygen than they produce. This is the case, for example, during the night. Normally, however, the amount of oxygen produced is by far higher than the amount consumed by respiration. The excess oxygen is then available to the heterotrophic organisms.

Producers, consumers and decomposing organisms

The autotrophic organisms are called *primary producers*, because they produce organic substances, that are later (in a secondary stage) used by the heterotrophic organisms. The production of the primary producers is therefore called *primary production*. The total amount of energy (amount of substance) produced

Nature should be the model for our modern reef aquaria. The photo shows a part of a reef in the Red Sea.
Underwater photo: B. Viering

Table 1

Typical concentrations (in μmole/l) of dissolved inorganic nitrogen and phosphorus on coral reefs around the world.　　　　Based on D'ELIA & WIEBE (1990)

A = Offshore or fore-reef, B = back-reef

SITE	NITROGEN A	B	PHOSPHORUS A	B	COMMENTS
Carribbean:					
Discovery Bay, Jamaica	0.59	3.6	0.20	0.20	groundwater inputs of nitrogen
Great Sound, Bermuda	0.50	–	0.025	–	
St. Croix, US Virgin Islands	> 0.283	> 0.512	0.08	0.10	nitrate and nitrite only
Indian Ocean:					
Albrolhos Islands	1.503	–	0.375	–	winter
	0.982	–	0.21	–	summer
Kavaratti Atoll, Lakshadweep Arch.	1.20	–	0.34	–	
Peros Banhos, the Maldives	0.40	0.51	0.43	0.58	
Salomon Atolls, the Maldives	0.98	1.20	0.43	0.67	
Pacific Ocean:					
Canton Atoll, Phoenix Islands	3.8	–	0.56	–	upwelling region
Enewetak Atoll, Marshall Islands	0.349	0.912	0.174	0.169	
GBR (a)	< 0.69	–	0.31	–	
GBR (b)	1.02	1.26	0.26	0.26	
GBR (c)	–	–	0.14	0.14	winter
	–	–	0.07	0.07	summer
Pago Bay, Guam	0.22	< 0.45	0.21	0.16	groundwater inputs
Tuman Bay, Guam	0.86	8.04	0.18	0.55	
Sesoko Isl., Okinawa	< 0.4	< 1.8	< 0.7	< 0.9	groundwater inputs
Tarawa Lagoon, Rep. of Kiribati	3.02	–	0.33	–	upwelling region

by the primary producers is called *gross primary production* (GPp). The *net primary production* (NPp) results from the subtraction of the respiration (Rp) from the gross primary production:

$$GPp - Rp = NPp$$

As long as the relation GPp : Rp is larger than 1, the amount of energy or substance produced by the primary producers exceeds the amount consumed by respiration. We call this an *autotrophic ecosystem*. It is an ecological system that receives its main supply of energy from sunlight.

If the relation GPp : Rp is less than 1, we are dealing with a *heterotrophic system*. This type of system obtains its energy in a different way, by the ingestion of food. The organisms that feed on the primary producers are called *primary consumers*. Moreover there are other heterotrophic organisms that are carnivorous or omnivorous. All these are collectively called *consumers*.

Another group that is essential for all processes of life, are the *decomposing organisms*. They break down dead organic substances into inorganic compounds. Just like the consumers, these organisms feed on organic matter. Most important among the decomposing organisms are the *bacteria*. They are essential for a coral reef aquarium and will be dealt with later in this volume in more detail.

Inorganic nutrients in the coral reefs

Coral reefs, in general, must be regarded as being very poor in nutrients. Nevertheless, they show an extreme richness in diversity of organisms. Scientists have for many years been puzzled by the intriguing question "how is it possible for such a multitude of organisms to exist in what is practically a nutrient desert?". Part of the answer to this question has already been found through intense research, and we will be returning to this matter on several occasions, later in this book series.

From an aquarists point of view, nitrogen and phosphorus are the most interesting nutrient elements (see also chapter 11). They are essential to algae who use them to build organic compounds through photosynthesis. Biochemical processes controlling the accessibility of nitrogen and phosphorus therefore affect the productivity of coral reefs.

The nitrogen cycle, which has been thoroughly studied in coral reef conditions, is primarily mediated by biochemical processes (see drawing below). Nitrogen is found in various oxidation stages from Nitrate (+5) to Ammonia (-3), and can thus serve both as an oxidizing and a reducing agent. In this cycle, the activities of bacteria have been demonstrated to be of indisputable importance. The mechanisms of the phosphorus cycle, unlike those of nitrogen, are rather poorly known for coral reefs. It is, however, likely to be controlled mainly by chemical processes. See chapter 11 for more information on these nutrient cycles.

Nutrients are utilized by the living organisms by being incorporated into the tissues, transformed and used in the metabolism, and subsequently released through decomposition of dead cells. Currents and water motion may transport the nutrients to, across as well as away from the reef. A net accumulation of organic matter in a coral reef (and in any ecosystem) can only occur when nutrient inputs exceed losses.

When the input of nutrients is larger than the loss, the reef will become richer in nutrients and over time we can see a change of the flora and fauna. Frequently this will result in an increase in the growth of algae. If the loss exceeds the input, nutrients are a limiting factor for the ecosystem. The reef can suffer from this.

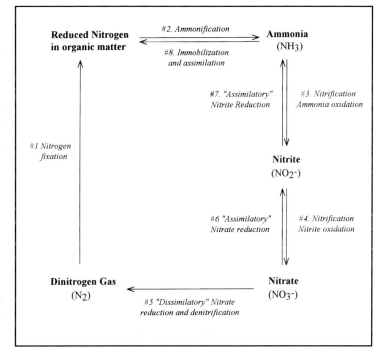

Major nitrogen pools in the coral reef environment and major nitrogen transformation processes affecting the pools. After D'ELIA & WIEBE (1990)

In some areas the coral reefs can be influenced by nutrients imported by upwelling from deeper seas or from runoff of groundwater from coastal areas. In such reefs, usually coastal reefs with variable concentrations of nutrients, even moderately high nutrient levels may result in the blooming of benthic algae that greatly affect the diversity of corals. Most oceanic reefs and many coastal reefs are, however, not influenced by such factors. The level of nutrients is constantly very low. The quantity of plankton and particulate material in the water is minimal, and any changes in the biological activity can be linked to changes in the reef benthos. See D'ELIA & WIEBE (1990).

Direct uptake and utilization of dissolved organic compounds by organisms and the fixation of nitrogen by algae are traditionally considered the most important sources of nutrient input to reef ecosystems. During the last couple of years new theories suggest that the reefs are supplied with nutrient rich water through pores leading to reservoirs deep below the living reef. Through drillings down to 500 meters in the Muroroa Atoll in the Pacific and to 30 meters in the Great Barrier Reef, scientists have found reservoirs containing water 28-30 times richer in nitrate than the water over the reef. This theory is quite new and definitely controversial. See ROUGERIE & WAUTHY (1993) and TRIBBLE et al. (1994).

Summary

As we have seen, organic matter is produced by primary producers, in the sea usually by unicellular or higher marine algae. The primary producers are eaten by the herbivores, these are eaten by the carnivores, which then again serve as food for even larger carnivores, etc. Thus the energy produced by the primary producers is passed on in the *food chain* of the ecosystem. It is important to realize that a considerable loss of energy occurs with each step taken in this food chain.

Algae are the primary producers on the reef. Their importance has often been misjudged. The photo shows *Caulerpa racemosa* growing at a depth of ten metres on the Great Barrier Reef off the coast of Australia.

We have also pointed out that the decomposing organisms break down organic substance produced by the primary producers into inorganic compounds. Thus the food chain, like a wheel, turns full circle for every element in nature.

A lot of what we know about the ecology of a natural coral reef is of great significance for a coral reef in the aquarium. We will therefore have to deal with this aspect repeatedly in this volume.

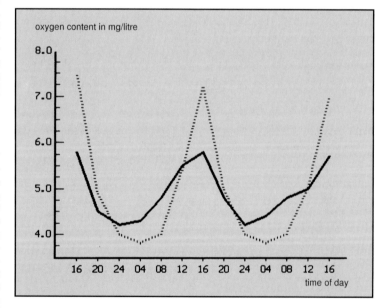

The relative oxygen content in the water on a coral reef at different time of day: the dotted line represents the amount of oxygen produced in the reef itself, the full line represents the amount from the outside.

Primary production in coral reefs

Normally the productivity of a coral reef is determined by measuring the oxygen content of the water that flows from the outside of a reef to its inside. The diagram on page 24 shows the oxygen content of the water in a coral reef depending on the time of day. In the diagram the dotted line represents the amount of oxygen produced in the reef itself, while the full line shows the amount of oxygen that is transferred into the reef from the outside. Both graphs are based on a series of readings, and the difference between them represents the gross primary production of the reef organisms. The increase between the different stages during the day shows the net primary production, the decrease during the night represents the respiration. The graph indicates that a reef is an autotrophic system from 12.00 to 20.00.

FURNAS et al. (1990) have examined the primary production of *planktonic algae* in lagoons of the Great Barrier Reef and have compared this to the situation outside the lagoon. They found that inside the lagoon there are usually more planktonic algae than there are outside. Like all algae, planktonic algae can only thrive if the water they live in contains a certain amount of nutrients. As the water in a coral reef usually does not contain enough nutrients for all the algae, it was most interesting to determine the concentration of the most important nutrients and their effect on the primary production. Only nitrate was considerably higher inside the lagoon with all other essential nutrients remaining unchanged in their concentration. The higher nitrate concentration inside the lagoon, could cause a higher primary productivity. It is remarkable that dur-

ing what is called midsummer there (December to January), an increase of the phytoplankton could be observed inside the lagoon as well as outside (see REVELANTE & GILMARTIN, 1982; RICHARD, 1977).

Comparing the results of the primary production in different coral reefs, we can find significant differences (LEWIS, 1977). One of the reasons for this may be that the productivity has been measured in different types of places. The reading in a lagoon with luxuriant algae growth, for example, reveals a much higher productivity than a reading above a group of corals. In most cases, the production is higher than the respiration, but there are exceptions. Generally the productivity of a coral reef is higher than that of other marine ecosystems, but it is still much de-

bated whether or not the reefs should be regarded as autotrophic systems. For further studies see: ATKINSON (1988 and 1991), ATKINSON & GRIGG (1984), BILGER & ATKINSON (1995), CROSSLAND et al. (1984).

Primary producers in coral reefs

Among the organisms capable of photosynthesis the higher plants are most notable. There are, however, only very few of them in coral reefs. One of them is *Thalassia* spp., marine Hydrocharitaceae,

Large parts of Osprey Reef had been destroyed by a cyclone, but we found red algae of the genus *Galaxaura* and the butterflyfish *Chaetodon trifasciatus* there.

At the base of the corals we often find various algae, so called turf algae, sponges and other tiny organisms.

which are among the most productive plants of a reef. It grows in vast accumulations that look like "marine meadows" in the shallow lagoon waters.

All the other primary producers of a coral reef are algae. Their significance in the net of interrelationships of the organisms on the reef has often been underestimated. They simply were not noticed among the multitude of coral animals that were thought to be the most important factor in the ecology of a coral reef. Scientific research during the last decade, however, has proved the algae to be more numerous and of greater importance than had been assumed earlier on. Their primary production is crucial for the existence of a coral reef. Moreover a lot of the algae are reef-builders or produce sediment. They also ingest nutrients and make them available for other organisms. According to WANDERS (1976), below a 1 m^2 sea surface, on 5.5 m^2 substrate surface the area occupied by algae was 2.9 m^2 (0.8 m^2 fleshy- and 2.1 m^2 coralline species). The area covered by corals was calculated to be 2.1 m^2. The calculation for algae cover does not include the symbiotic zooxanthellae (see chapter 13). Some authors have suggested that the term **coral reefs** should be replaced with **algal reefs** (HILLIS-COLINVAUX, 1986a, b and d; BERNER, 1990). We will return to this and other details regarding algae in chapter 13.

Among the most important primary producers of a coral reef there are a large number of small threadlike algae referred to as "turf algae". They grow on dead corals, on coral rocks between corals, or on coral sand. The genera in this group of algae are quite numerous, with *Bryopsis* and *Ceramium* best known among coral reef aquarists. They are most common on the inner reef slope of a lagoon. The many algae grazing animals keep this algae short, thus the name "turf"-algae. Green calcareous algae, e. g. *Halimeda* species or algae of the genera *Ulva, Cladophora* and *Hypnea* are also essential for the total productivity of a coral reef. Large populations of a brown alga of the genus *Sargassum* may be found on a reef. This alga, which is occasionally kept in marine tanks, is also an important primary producer. It can only grow if the element iodine is available.

The leaf-shaped red coralline algae of the family Corallinaceae cover large areas of the rocky ground of coral reefs. Also in the aquarium they are valuable and much sought after. Their contribution to the total production of the reef still remains to be determined, but they do play an important part in the reef-building process.

The unicellular phytoplankton that flows across the reef with the

The back reef slope of an oceanic reef in the Coral Sea. The surgeon fishes are adults of *Acanthurus olivaceus*.   Underwater photo: E. Svensen

water accounts only for a small part of the primary production. Unicellular algae are of great importance for the marine aquarist in one particular situation only, i. e. if he wants to keep invertebrates successfully in his tank. In this case unicellular endosymbiotic algae that belong to the Dinophyceae are of crucial importance. These algae are called zooxanthellae and live in the tissue of many invertebrate animals of a coral reef, especially the reef-building corals.

The zooxanthellae were discovered in 1930. Since then their significance has always been under discussion. Yet there is agreement on the point that these algae have an essential function for the animals with which they live in a symbiotic relationship. Their oxygen production is usually sufficient or even exceeds the amount needed by their hosts. It has been shown that the hosts not only make use of the oxygen, but also organic products of the zooxanthellae. During the day, these algae also boost the calcium depo-

The reef edge of Harrier Reef, in the mid section of the Great Barrier Reef, was densely covered with table-shaped *Acropora* spp. Never before have we spotted such a dense population of stony corals.

Underwater photo: E. Svensen

sition and thus are an integral part of the reef-building process. It is also probable that these extremely small algae - one million of them may live in 1 cm³ of tissue - are able to make use of the metabolites of their hosts, thus making these available again for the ecological system.

Stony corals at a depth of 3 metres in the Red Sea.   Underwater photo: T. Luther

A fire coral, *Millepora* sp., growing together with a blue sponge.

The most beautiful fire coral *Distichopora violacea* prefers to live in shady zones.

Producers and consumers on a reef:

Microorganisms, algae, sponges, gorgonians, sea squirts, corals and fishes belong to cyclic food chains. The photo shows an area of one square meter of a cave wall in the Male-atoll at a depth of 23 metres.

Probably the largest moray eel: *Gymnothorax javanicus* grows as long as 3 m and gets as heavy as 70 kg.

Colonies of two different species of *Acropora* growing in a shallow lagoon.

The sea urchin *Echinostrephus molaris* lives in holes that it bores itself.

Colourful sponges and sea squirts from the deeper regions of a coral reef.

Producers and consumers on a reef:

Sea urchins, starfish, brittle stars, snails, clams, shrimps and calcareous algae are significant factors that contribute to stable conditions in a reef. They also play an important role in a coral reef aquarium.

A thorny oyster of the genus *Spondylus* is grown over with algae, sponges and sea squirts.

The magnificent giant clam *Tridacna maxima* in its habitat.

Table 2
Number of individuals and biomass of invertebrates and fishes per square metre in the "Porites furcata"-reef.
(After LEWIS, 1977)

Taxonomic unit	Number of individuals	Biomass (in gram dry substance)
Scleractinia (stony corals)	numerous colonies	12,002.3
Zoantharia (colonial anemones)	2 colonies	1.1
Polychaeta (polychaetes)	23,160 individuals	6.7
Sipunculoidea (sipunculids)	20 individuals	0.9
Crustacea (crustaceans)	2,668 individuals	40.3
Mollusca (molluscs)	137 individuals	59.4
Echinodermata (echinoderms)	2,002 individuals	263.3
Pisces (fishes)	15 individuals	6.1

Consumers on coral reefs

There are two basic types of consumers on coral reefs:

– herbivorous organisms (plant eating),
– carnivorous organisms (meat eating).

A lot of animals are also more or less omnivorous, i. e. they feed on plants as well as animals. Among the consuming organisms on a coral reef the corals themselves are most prominent. In addition to the nutrients they obtain from the products of the photosynthesis of their zooxanthellae, most of them also ingest planktonic food. Other consumers are: sea anemones, tube worms, crustaceans, molluscs, echinoderms, and, of course, fish. The table above shows the distribution of the consumers on one square metre of reef. It is quite obvious that the scleractinian stony corals are the group that prevails. Yet, the echinoderms, e. g. starfish, brittle stars, feather stars, sea urchins, and sea cucumbers, are also important.

For the life-cycle of a reef all animals play an important part, though the herbivores are probably most significant. If an area of a reef is blocked off so that no larger animals can enter it, and if one then removes all the herbivores, the result is a convincing proof of their crucial function: within days the green filamentous algae start proliferating. One or two weeks later the blocked-off area may be covered with algae

Part of the outer reef of an atoll in the Maldives viewed from the air. Note how strictly the ring-shaped reef is separated from the deeper water. At the bottom of the picture, inside the lagoon, the depth is about 70 metres maximum, while at the top of the picture, outside of the atoll, the depth can reach some thousand metres. The structure of the reef – with back reef, reef flat, reef edge, and reef slope – can easily be imagined.

and the corals die. This proves that the herbivores have an essential function in the reef, reducing the algae by grazing on them, so that they do not get out of control.

Some marine aquarists like to have filamentous algae in their tanks, believing that they keep the water clean. However, algae should not be allowed to develop in a coral reef aquarium with invertebrates. Nevertheless excessive filamentous algae growing over the corals is a common problem for saltwater aquarists. That is why it is important to add algae-eating animals to the tank community. The most important herbivores are echinoderms, but there are also some fishes, snails, and crustaceans that are important algae grazers.

Apart from the filamentous algae and the herbivores, there are other organisms with a key position in the reef. A well-known example is the starfish *Acanthaster planci*, also called "Crown of thorns starfish". One or more factors that had restricted the populations ceased to apply, and

the number of these starfish increased sharply. As this echinoderm feeds on stony coral tissue, it was inevitable that large reef areas, e. g. in the Great Barrier Reef, were stripped of living coral tissue. Intensive research provides some information on why these starfish invade reef areas in large numbers, at irregular intervals. At the moment their number seems to be back to normal again.

Zones of coral reefs

This seems to be the appropriate point in our considerations to deal with the distribution of the organisms in the different zones of a reef. As the geographical location and the structure of coral reefs vary greatly, it is only natural that fauna and flora are considerably different from one reef to the next.

Every coral reef may be partitioned in different zones. In the following we are attempting a description of the typical flora and fauna within the boundaries of these. This is based on personal observations as well as a large number of literature sources, of which the most important one is MERGNER & SCHUHMACHER (1974). The species examples are typical of the western Indo-Pacific, and may not in all aspects apply for other parts of the world. Still, the general faunal and floral composition of the zones is quite similar in all reefs.

The zone closest to the mainland is referred to as the beach. It lies between the high and the low tideline. During the course of the day it may be twice flooded by the rising tide or drained for several hours respectively by the tide going out. This zone is occupied by a large number of crabs and snails.

Between the low tide line and the level reached at mid-tide there is a zone where the condition of the bottom is quite variable. The hard surface there has been

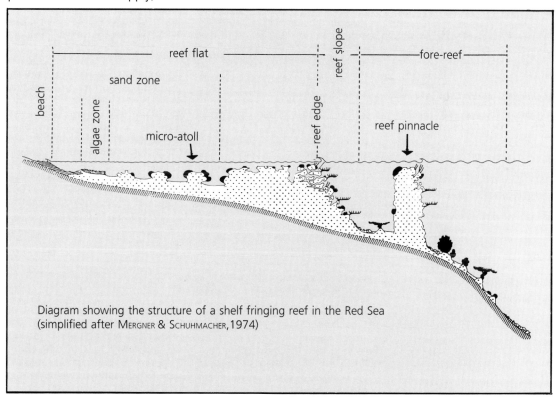

Diagram showing the structure of a shelf fringing reef in the Red Sea (simplified after MERGNER & SCHUHMACHER, 1974)

crushed by the pounding of the waves, is cracked, and the water runs through these cracks and little depressions. The dominant algae are green algae, such as *Enteromorpha* and *Ulva* species, but also some brown algae are found. Snails, e.g. *Nerita* species and chitons like *Acanthopleura* spp., as well as certain small bivalves are frequently numerous. So are many small hermit crabs, *Clibanarius* species among others. The low-tide line is marked by a belt of strongly attached barnacles, Cirripedia.

Underwater we find animals better known in the aquarium hobby. The horizontal part of the reef, the reef flat, has an algae zone on its landward side. Here brown and blue-green algae are most numerous, while further seaward some red algae may be found. There are not many animal species found here, yet sea urchins like *Echinometra mathaei* and *Tripneustes gratilla* can be numerous. Some brittle stars and a few crustaceans are also found here. Among the few fishes that occur frequently here are certain small gobies (Gobiidae) and blennies (Blennidae).

Outside the algae zone, further seaward, the ground becomes less even. There are a lot of uneven patches filled with loose coral sand. The movement of the waves whirls up large clouds of small particles, thus reducing the light intensity at the bottom to half of what it is at the surface. In this zone calcareous red algae are numerous, as are some species of the green calcareous algae *Halimeda*. Several species of brown algae, including *Dictyota*, *Lobophora*, *Padina* and *Sargassum* spp. are frequent as well. Patches of the green algae genus *Cau-*

Sometimes a group of algae grazing surgeonfishes *Acanthurus leucosternon* may appear in the shallow water of a reef flat. They normally lead solitary lives (top). Typical coral growth on a reef flat (below). In the middle of the picture are two octopuses, *Octopus* sp. Both photos were taken in the Maldives.

lerpa occur in certain areas. The shaded surfaces of boulders often support species different from those on more exposed surfaces. The large rounded or pear-shaped *Ventricaria ventricosa*, the "bubble alga", which is so familiar to aquarists, typically occurs here.

The first colonies of soft corals appear in this zone, among them *Cladiella*, *Sinularia* and *Xenia* species, all of which are excellent aquarium animals. Stony corals of the genera *Favia*, *Favites*, *Goniastrea*, *Porites* and *Stylophora*, among others, may be found in scattered colonies. This zone has

which is among those with the highest number of species in the reef. This is caused by favorable hydrographic conditions. The force of the waves that surge over the reef edge is absorbed there and is much less powerful inside the reef. As the water nevertheless moves quite rapidly here, an effective circulation of oxygen, carbon dioxide, nutrients and metabolic waste is guaranteed. The water is deeper here than further landwards, but it is clearer nonetheless. The light intensity at the bottom reaches about 50 to 65% of what it is at the surface.

Young giant clams of the genus *Tridacna* are also found here.

The last ten metres up to the reef edge the water is 40 cm to 1 m deep. This zone never runs dry. Here a considerable number of coral species are found, among them several species of soft corals of all the aforementioned genera. Crowded colonies of stony corals grow between them. Stony corals here include all those mentioned before, as well as *Platygyra* spp. and a scattered few *Acropora* spp. As the reef edge is not far away, breakers cause substantial water circulation. No sand remains

At the reef edge and the upper reef slope the water is quite turbulent. This makes fauna and flora thrive (pictures to the left).

Reef pinnacles may grow in fantastic shapes. Often they are completely grown over with corals. A large group of *Pseudanthias* spp. fairy basslets are playfully swimming around this reef pinnacle in the Red Sea.
Underwater photo: P. G. V. Weckmann

the highest number of species of snails, comprising many genera including well known aquarium animals like the herbivorous *Trochus* and *Turbo*. The proliferating algae and the detritus here are fed on by many sea urchins, including the two species mentioned under the algae zone, but also for instance *Diadema* and *Heterocentrotus* species. In comparison to the more seaward zones, the number of species in the inward part of the reef flat is relatively low. This holds true most of all for the hermatypic corals.

Next we find a transitional zone

Parts of this zone run dry from time to time. As a consequence, densely growing corals may die. Thus by and by small atoll-like structures are formed which are called micro atolls. Typically they are formed by *Porites* spp., but micro atolls are known also from other genera. Red calcareous algae of many species grow over the dead coral structures, which slowly results in a rather uneven surface. The number of animal species in general is much larger here and the first groups of the genera *Capnella*, *Nephthea* and *Sarcophyton* may be found.

lying in the crevices of the bottom. The water forces its way through channels and tunnels where currents are particularly strong. A multitude of animals that are well adapted to these specific conditions live here. Algae, however, are sparse, which is probably why only a few snails can be found.

Typical fishes of the reef flat are first of all wrasses, Labridae, and the very territorial damselfishes, Pomacentridae, e.g. of the genus *Chrysiptera*. Several species of surgeonfishes of the genus *Acanthurus* may be seen in large shooals looking for algae, their main diet.

Parts of the reef flat of Suva Reef, Fiji, jut out from the water surface at low tide. The corals are fully exposed to the blaze of the sun.

The reef edge itself and the reef slope are interesting zones. They are without protection against the breakers of the sea. In the upper region of the reef edge light intensity is 50 to 65% of what it is at the surface, while it amounts to 12% at half the depth of the reef slope, and only 2% at its foot. Stony corals are quite common on the reef edge, in particular several species of the genus *Acropora*. This genus contains a very large number of species, many of which look most impressive. Contrary to commonly accepted theories of only few years ago, a large number of the *Acropora* spp. are also most suitable for aquarium keeping. Also hydrozoans of the genus *Millepora* are found close to the reef edge. Sea anemones thrive where water circulation is strong. Thus a number of the large symbiotic anemones like those of the genera *Heteractis* and *Stichodactyla* grow here, hanging over the reef edge. These anemones are called symbiotic because they normally serve as the hosts of anemone-fishes of the genus *Amphiprion*.

Directly at the reef edge and in the upper zone of the reef slope large numbers of shoaling fishes may be found, e.g. the Blue-Green Chromis, *Chromis viridis*, and the Lyretail Fairy Basslet, *Pseudanthias squamipinnis*. The Regal Angelfish, *Pygoplites diacanthus*, occurs here too and differs from other angelfish by being common in rather shallow waters.

Even in the underwater caves and grottos, where no light enters at all, a multitude of animals are found. In addition to a large number of sponges, one also finds worms, hydrozoans and ahermatypic stony corals, e.g. of the genus *Tubastraea*. These corals have no symbiotic zooxanthellae and are therefore not dependent on light. Many species of fishes enter the caves for purposes of protection or camouflage, e.g. fairy basslets of the genus *Pseudanthias* and soldierfishes of the genus *Myripristis*.

The reef edge itself and the uppermost parts of the reef slope are among the zones of the reef with the highest number of species. The part seaward in front of the reef is called fore-reef. This is where large pinnacles may be found towering towards the surface of the water. The pinnacles are often separated from each other by sandy ground. They are usually densely grown over with corals, whereas the landward parts of the fore-reef, away from the reef face, are inhabited only by a sparse coral fauna. Even secondary organisms growing on dead corals e.g. *Nephthea* and *Capnella* species, are rare here. The reason for this is probably the adverse living conditions caused by coral sand which is whirled up by the turbulence at the reef edge. Hermatypic stony corals living on the less exposed parts of the pinnacles are first and foremost of the genus *Porites*, but also include *Echinopora*, *Favia*, *Favites*, *Goniastrea*, *Lobophyllia*, *Seriatopora*, *Platygyra* as well as *Acropora*. Various species of brown algae, as well as several green and red calcareous algae are often common on pinnacles. Fauna and flora on the leeward side of a pinnacle facing the reef edge differs considerably from what occurs on its windward side.

A copious new growth of corals begins in the deeper areas in front of the pinnacles. Here, at a depth of about 10 metres, the light intensity is only about 10 % of that at the surface. The light spectrum has changed as well: red and orange light are missing almost completely, while green, blue and violet light are still there. This is, however, obviously sufficient for the corals growing there. The number of species and genera of stony corals here is immense, and probably covers most of those familiar to aquarists. Many species of *Acropora, Astreopora, Favia, Favites, Fungia, Galaxea, Goniastrea, Herpolitha, Lobophyllia, Montipora, Platygyra, Plerogyra, Pocillopora, Porites, Seriatopora* and *Stylophora* are among those most frequently encountered. Among the soft corals *Xenia* and *Heteroxenia* are dominant in the shallowest waters, while various non-photosynthetic species of *Chironephthya, Dendronephthya, Scleronephthya* and *Siphonogorgia* become more evident with increasing depth.

One and the same species of coral may vary considerably in shape, depending on the intensity of the light, the exposure to water currents, etc. A good example of this phenomenon are the soft corals of the genus *Sinularia*, as well as stony corals of the genus *Acropora*. Whereas less intense light makes them ramify and branch out, they grow densely and in a lumpy shape under intense light. This reaction may also be observed under aquarium conditions, and frequently leads aquarists to erroneous conclusions about the identity of species.

In the lower part of the reef slope an abundant fish fauna may be found. Typical of this zone are butterflyfishes, angelfishes, groupers and moray eels.

Typical coral fauna of a reef near Bequia in the Caribbean Sea.   **Underwater photo: Dr. D. Brockmann**

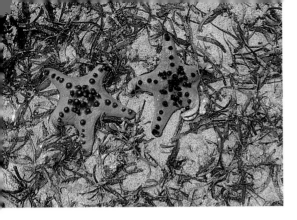

Protoreaster nodusus feed on detritus and various
organisms burrowed in the sand.

The hermit crab *Coenobita* sp. can be seen in
thousands on the beach at night.

Beach and sand zone:

These zones are very
often overlooked by
aquarists. They can
look very different
from location to
location. The picture
(left) shows the island
of Embudu Village,
Maldives. The distance
from the beach to the
beginning of the reef
flat is not very long.

This shrimp of the family Penaeidae lives on sandy
bottoms in the Maldives and the Red Sea.

This beautiful nudibranch *Chelidonura varians* occurs
exclusively on sandy bottoms in the Maldives.

Valencienna sexguttata lives in the sand zone and takes cover in small caves under rocks.

Amblyeleotris spp. are usually found in the deeper sandy habitat.

Beach and sand zone:

In these zones we do, however, find a number of interesting organisms. The picture (right) shows the island of Bunaken, North Sulawesi, Indonesia, where we found a rather muddy zone. The distance to the beginning of the reef flat here is relatively large.

The crab *Ocypode saratan* lives in holes on the beach. The genus inhabits most tropical beaches.

The box crab *Calappa* sp. can bury itself in seconds in the sand.

The sea urchin *Echinometra* sp. is commonly found in and under boulders and corals.

This individual of *Tridacna gigas* lives among seagrass and scattered corals.

Reef flat:

Reef flats can be very wide or rather narrow, depending on location. The outer part of the reef flat of Wheeler Reef, Great Barrier Reef (left; photo: T. Done), has a dense cover of corals.

Soft corals of the genus *Xenia* on the reef flat of Siladen, North Sulawesi, Indonesia.

Acropora gemmifera on the reef flat of Bunaken.

The starfish *Linckia laevigata* is very common in some locations, like here on Suva Reef, Fiji.

Striped Razor Fishes, *Aeoliscus strigatus*, at Bunaken during extreme low tide.

Reef flat:

The reef flat at Bunaken, North Sulawesi, Indonesia, is about 200 metres wide and has a rich and diverse growth of stony corals photographed at low tide (right).

Goniastrea sp. and branched soft corals during low tide at Siladen.

Mixed and beautiful growth of stony corals at Bunaken during extreme low tide.

Heteractis magnifica with the Dusky Anemonefish, *Amphiprion melanopus*, in the Coral Sea.

A shoal of the Bigeye Trevally, *Caranx sexfasciatus*, in the Coral Sea.

Reef edge:

The diversity among the organisms living on the reef edge is highly dependant on the degree of exposure to waves. In exposed areas like here in the Coral Sea (left) only a few coral species can survive.

Underwater view of the reef edge from the reef pictured above.

Acropora sp. living in a very exposed habitat, directly on the reef edge.

A shoal of barracudas, *Sphyraena* sp., at Cabilao, Philippines (photo: O. Gremblewski-Strate).

The Peacock Grouper, *Cephalopholis argus*, is common on most pacific reefs.

Reef edge:

In more protected are, as like here at Bunaken, North Sulawesi, Indonesia, the growth of corals can be very diverse (right). In other locations the exposure to water movement can be so intense that only a few species of calcareous algae can settle and live.

Beautiful and dense growth of stony corals at Bunaken.

Hydrozoans, like *Millepora dichotoma* (here in the Maldives), are often found on the reef edge.

A group of the Indo-Pacific Sergeant, *Abudefduf vaigiensis* and *A. sexfasciatus*, in the Red Sea (photo: T. Luther).

Lionfishes, such as *Pterois miles*, have the dorsal fin stocked with poison.

Reef slope:

The reef slope defines the area where the reef falls from the edge downward to a depth of about 20-30 metres. This zone is highly variable in shape. The slope can be vertical, like here in the Coral Sea (left; photo: E. Svensen).

A bright yellow sponge mixed with corals and various algae in the Coral Sea.

A huge scleraxonian coral – *Subergorgia mollis* – at a depth of 20 metres in the Coral Sea.

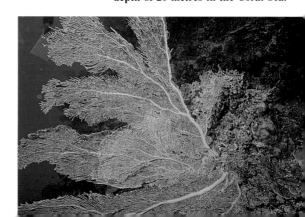

The Regal Angelfish, *Pygoplites diacanthus*, is one of the most beautiful angelfishes.

Giant Morays, *Gymnothorax javanicus*, look dangerous, but they are mostly harmless.

Reef slope:

Here at Sinai, Red Sea (right; photo: T. Luther), the reef slope falls gradually with a most luxuriant growth of corals.

A delicate feather star; unfortunately it usually cannot be kept successfully in a coral reef aquarium.

Tiny photosynthetic sea squirts *Didemnum molle* growing on a larger solitary *Polycarpa* sp.

Fish swim upsidedown along the roof of a big cave in the Maldives.

The Long-Jawed Squirrelfish, *Sargocentron spiniferum*, is very common in these biotopes.

Caves:

Caves are found on many reefs. Huge cathedrals, like this one on Latheef Reef, Maldives (left), are found in deeper regions.

Non-photosynthetic soft corals cover the wall completely (photo: E. Svensen).

A nudibranch – *Chromodoris elizabethae* – searching for suitable food.

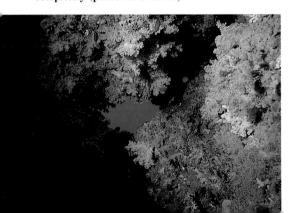

The Spotfin Lionfish, *Pterois antennata*, lives commonly in caves also.

A school of *Myripristis* sp. in a deep cave in the Vadu Channel, Maldives.

Caves:

Small caves, like here in a lower part of a steep reef slope in the Maldives (right), can be found in all depths.

The spiny oyster *Spondylus* sp. in a deep cave in the Maldives.

Cleaner shrimps *Stenopus hispidus* as typically found in small caves in the Maldives.

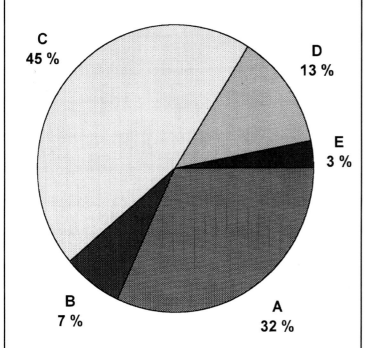

Comparison of Carbon biomass in the plankton over Davis Reef, Australia.
After DUCKLOW (1990)

PLANKTON - % of total biomass

C 45 %

D 13 %

E 3 %

A 32 %

B 7 %

A: Nanophytoplankton; here > 20 μm
B. Bacteria and Bacteriovores
C: Autotrophic Picoplankton; here > 2 μm, mainly blue-green algae
D: Net Phytoplankton, here < 200 μm
E: Ciliates and Zooplankton

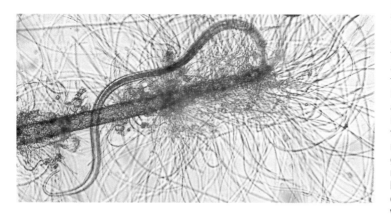

A nematode and bacteria have attacked a green algae in the aquarium (enlargement 300x).

Microorganisms play an important role as decomposers in any ecosystem. By breaking down organic compounds they return valuable nutrients in a form available to the producers. These organisms are collectively called **decomposing organisms**. On the reef this group mainly consists of single celled animals and bacteria. The single celled animals belong to the subkingdom Protozoa of the kingdom Protista. Protozoa contain more than 31,000 species in seven phyla. The bacteria (together with the blue-green algae) are placed in the kingdom Monera, which contain an unknown number of species. In both kingdoms we find both autotrophic and heterotrophic species, and the microorganisms can thus also play roles as producers. Some more complex organisms, like the roundworms (phylum Nematoda) are also important decomposers.

Most decomposers on the coral reef are found in the sediments. However, we also find bacteria in many other locations, such as inside other organisms, inside the porous reef-rocks (live rocks) and dead coral skeletons, as well as in the water column. But the bacteria are by no means equally distributed in these locations. The number of bacteria in the sediments of a coral reef is comparable to that in a eutrophic stretch of fresh water, very rich in nutrients. The average number of bacterial cells per gram dry substance of the sediment has been calculated as high as 1.3×10^9. In this particular search, a lot of the bacteria were autotrophic and their production varied from 1.2 to 11.6 mg carbon per cm^2 per day,

(HANSEN et al., 1987). The number of bacteria in the water column is in generally much lower than in the sediments (Table 3). The Diagram on page 48 (after DUCKLOW, 1990) shows the composition of the microorganisms in the water over Davis Reef, Great Barrier Reef, Australia. As we see, both zooplankton and phytoplankton are represented, as well as ciliates and bacteria.

The **single celled organisms** on the reef are found mostly in and on the substrate, but many autotrophic species can also be found free living in the water column. The phylum Sarcomastigophora contain the flagellates and the foraminiferans. Some flagellates are important primary producers (see chapter 13) while the

Marine nematodes in detritus.   Photo: R. Brons

Table 3
Abundance and biomass of bacteria in waters and surface sediments of some reefs on the Great Barrier Reef, Australia. After DUCKLOW (1990)

LOCATION	ABUNDANCE	BIOMASS
	10^8 cells/liter	μg C/liter
WATER COLUMN:		
Lizard Island		
windward reefs	1-5	24-40
leeward reefs	3-5	24-62
surrounding waters	2-6	17-20
seagrass bed	16-25	24-38
lagoon	10-16	15-24
Davis Reef		
lagoon	0.6-4.3	0.3-2.2
One Tree Island		
whole reef average	1-11	1-16
windward reef	6.8	7.4
lagoon	5.1	5.4
leeward reef	2.5	2.6
SEDIMENT:		
Lizard Island		
reef flat - summer	36-60	72-120
reef flat - winter	72	144
Davis Reef		
lagoon	0.9-20	23-50

foraminiferans play an important role as sediment and sand producers. The substratum known to aquarists as coral sand contains a lot of shells from these tiny and delicate single celled organisms. Other single celled organisms such as many ciliates in the phylum Ciliophora act as food for corals while they in turn eat mostly bacteria themselves. The diagrams page 50 and 51 (after HANSEN et al., 1987) show the difference in the occurrence of ciliates and flagellates at different measuring stations of a reef in Australia.

The **role of bacteria** as decomposers and as contributors to the ecology and flux of nutrients in coral reef ecosystems is very complex. The first studies on this topic were done by the scientist Y. I. SOROKIN in the early seventies, (SOROKIN 1971, 1973a, 1973b and 1978). During the last decade more and more attention has been paid to the role of bacteria. It is now understood that their role is important, but very complex. Still a lot of work remains to be done. DUCKLOW (1990) gives an overview of the present status.

One of the main roles of bacteria is acting as decomposers of organic compounds. They are therefore important agents of the nitrogen and carbon cycling in coral reefs. These bacteria are heterotrophic and depend upon energy from the organic compounds to exist. The *Nitrobacter* and *Nitrosomonas* spp. are well known as participants in the nitrogen cycle (see chapter 11 and this chapter, drawing on page 23). By decomposing organic compounds, the bacteria supply regenerated nutrients for the primary producers. This is one major and essential ecological role of the bacteria. But there is also another aspect which might be just as essential. The large bacteria population of coral reefs – largely found in the sediments – does also act as a food source for single celled animals and other microbial predators.

Many of the bacteria are autotrophic and produce organic compounds through photosynthesis.

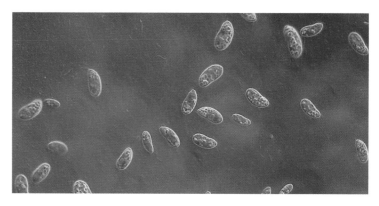

Marine ciliates.   Photo: R. Brons

This is called **bacterial production**, a process that can be compared to the production from other autotrophic organisms like the turf-algae. The bacterial productivity (Table 4) is in general used very inefficiently on the reef (DUCKLOW, 1990).

There is also a tremendous flux of bacteria over the reefs. A fraction of this bacteria flow is captured and utilized, but most of it passes the reef without being captured. However, the bacteria reproduce rapidly, and during low tide the biomass of bacteria on a reef flat can accumulate greatly.

To sum up, one can say that a coral reef is abounding with bacteria and microorganisms. They form a chain of decomposing organisms that work like a giant biological filtration system. Some of these bacteria are capable of photosynthesis, they are thus primary producers. Finally bacteria are an important food for many organisms in the reef. Protista have also been mentioned. Sponges, clams and corals also seem to make use of large amounts of bacteria as food. Detritus eaters, like snails and sea cucumbers, likewise consume bacteria.

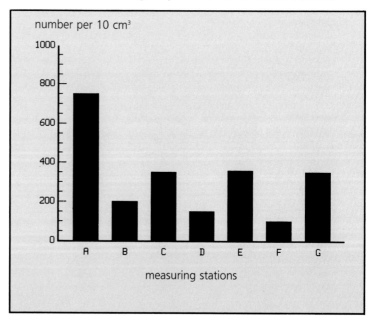

Number of ciliates (left) and flagellates (right, page 51) in the sediment of Davies-Reef (Great Barrier Reef): A - pool at the reef edge . . .

Table 4
Total primary production (PP) and bacterial production (BP) in three Great Barrier Reef lagoons.
After DUCKLOW (1990)

LOCATION	BACTERIAL			PRIM. PROD.	BP/PP
	biomass mgC/m²	production mgC/m²/day	P/B per day	gC/m²/day	
Lizard Island (summer)					
water column	200	180	0.9	100-290	0.6-2.0
sediment	207	120	0.6	200	0.6
total	407	300	0.7	300-490	0.6-1.0
Davis Reef (winter)					
water column	17	6	0.35	250	0.02
sediment *(in vitro)*	1190	150	0.13	210	0.71
sediment *(in vivo)*	–	270	–	270	1.00
total	1208	156-176	0.12-0.26	460-520	0.34-0.53
One Tree Island (summer-fall)					
water column	25	46	1.8	60	0.80

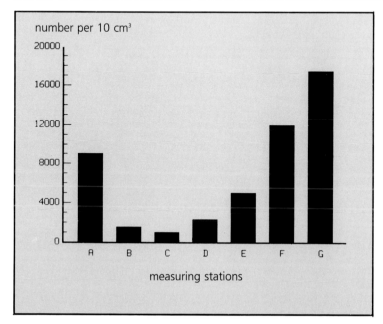

... B, C, and D – sand from the reef flat; E – algal material from the lagoon; F and G – shallow outward part of the lagoon towards the reef edge.

Further reading

The biology and ecology of a coral reef are highly interesting subjects. This brief and simplified survey is intended to encourage the reader to explore further its most important aspects.

General ecology:
BARNES & MANN, 1980; KALUSCHKE, 1982; LONGHURST, 1981

Coral reef, popular science reading:
BENNET, 1971; BERMERT & ORMOND, 1981; CANNON & GOYEN, 1989; HOLLIDAY, 1989; KÜHLMANN, 1984; OCEANUS, 1986; SCHUHMACHER, 1982; TALBOT, 1984

Coral reef, scientific reading:
BURNS, 1985; CHARDY et al., 1989; DINESSEN, 1983; DONE, 1982; DUBINSKY, 1990; EDWARDS & ROSEWELL, 1981; FURNAS et al., 1990; GOREAU et al., 1971; HANSEN et al., 1987; HOBSON, 1974; MEBS, 1989; MERGNER, 1979; MERGNER & SCHUHMACHER, 1974 and 1981; MERGNER & SVOBODA, 1977; POLOVINA et al., 1984; REVELANTE & GILMARTIN, 1982; RICHARD, 1987; SCHILLER & HENDL, 1989; SCHUHMACHER & MERGNER, 1985a and 1985b; TRUSCH & TRUSCH, 1982; VERON, 1986; WELLS et al:, 1988

A lot of marine aquarists also love to observe the world under water as divers. The information they gather helps to improve marine aquaristics.

The tropical seas have a lot to offer for the aquarist and for our aquaria. Over-exploitation of the oceans however, must be avoided at all costs.

Coral reefs also offer most impressive views above the water surface. This photo shows Hastings Reef, a part of the Great Barrier Reef near Cairns, North-Australia (left).

Underwater, the expectations of the diver will even be surpassed. Massive brain corals of the genus *Leptoria* characterize the scene. More delicate soft corals or gorgonians bring some variety into the bulky structure of the reef (to the right).

The photo to the left shows a colony of stony corals with large, fleshy polyps. The coral is probably a species of the genus *Lobophyllia* (family Mussidae).

This bryozoan colony with its beautiful orange colour grows on a stony coral of the genus *Seriatopora*.
Photos: Dr. D. Brockmann

The reefs in the "Pompey/Hardline Complex" in the southern part of the Great Barrier Reef resemble a mosaic with deep water (dark blue) channels and shallow waters (light green). Areas where corals grow show a dark green colour.

Photo: Great Barrier Reef Marine Park Authority (GBRMPA), Townsville, Australia

Chapter 2

Zoogeography

The animals of the coral reefs captivate us with their beauty, complexity and behaviour. Their stunning colours and shapes are a reflection of the complicated interplay and relationships among the organisms on coral reefs. The fishes of the coral reef are no exception here, as they doubtlessly are the most complex and most varied vertebrate fauna we know. We suppose that a short introduction to the basic facts of zoogeography (the science which deals with the question of which animals are to be found where geographically) will help to convey a deeper understanding of this variability.

Water temperature is an important limiting factor in the geographical distribution of marine animals. The isotherms (lines connecting the places where the same temperatures occur) often are fauna boundaries as well. Thus the 20 ° C isotherms are also the geographical limit for the reef-building (hermatypic) stony corals (see the map on page 58). This implies that coral reefs are only found between these isotherms. Other animals that could also exist at lower temperatures, but are bound to coral reefs for other reasons, are thus kept from spreading beyond the 20 ° C isotherms.

The differences in temperature in the oceans of the world are responsible for the fact that most of the organisms living on coral reefs are only found between 30 ° north and 30 ° south latitude. Yet this does not explain why many speci-

Assessor macneilli (the blue fishes in the upper part of the picture) is an endemic species from the Great Barrier Reef and New Caledonia. It belongs to the family of prettyfins, Plesiopidae, which in turn are endemic to the Indo-Pacific. The shark *Eucrossorhinus dasypogon* is shown in the middle of the picture, resting in a cave.   Photo: Scott W. Michael

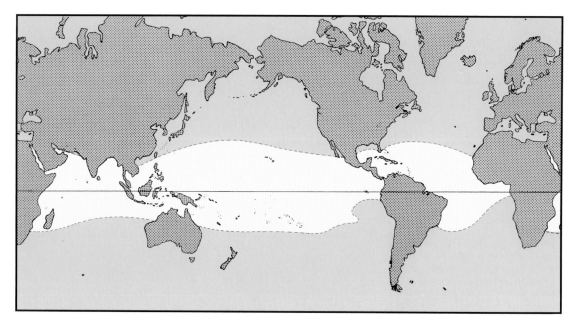

Only between the 20 ° C isotherms (the light blue area between red broken lines) can reef building corals thrive. Thus with few exceptions coral reefs occur only in this area.

es within this area are not found circumtropically (everywhere globally in the tropical region). Apart from a few exceptions coral reef animals are adapted to these surroundings to such a high degree, that they are unable to exist elsewhere. The vast deep sea regions present insuperable barriers to most reef animals. Only a very few of them are able to cross open sea regions of such vast proportions. That is why the animal world of the western region and the eastern region of the Pacific and the Atlantic respectively are fundamentally different.

Continents also constitute effective zoogeographical barriers, e. g. the coastal fauna of the American West Coast has developed distinct differences from that of the East Coast. In very much the same way the coastal fauna of West Africa has little in common with that of the East African Coast. However, if human interference creates gaps in these continental barriers this will allow certain species to spread. Since the opening of the Suez Canal in 1869 about 150 species of what are called "Lessepsian immigrants" (named after Lesseps, who built the Suez Canal) have spread from the Red Sea to the eastern part of the Mediterranean Sea, among them about 40 species of fishes, like rabbit fishes of the genus *Siganus*, for example *S. rivulatus*. Before the opening of the Suez Canal rabbit fishes were endemic to the Indo-Pacific, and could be found only there.

A similar example may be drawn from the subfamily of the lionfishes, Pteroinae, from the family of the scorpionfishes, Scorpaenidae, which were also endemic to the Indo-Pacific. In July 1991, however, a specimen of *Pterois miles* was caught in the Mediterranean Sea near Herzliya, Israel.

The coast of Easter Island is rocky and without any coral reefs. Easter Island is the eastern boundary of the Indo-Pacific, where only a few species of corals can grow and hardly any reef fishes live because of the lower water temperatures.
Photo: Prof. A. Skjølsvold, Kon-Tiki Museum, Oslo.

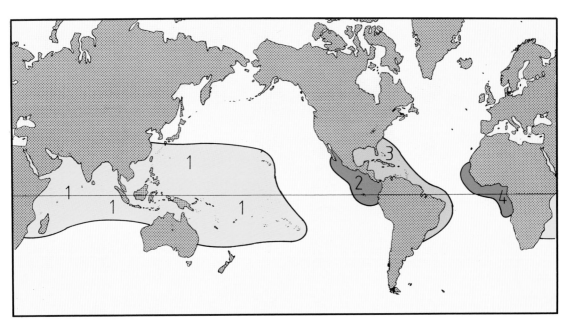

The four zoogeographical main regions:
1 – Indo-Pacific (yellow); 2 – Eastern Pacific (green); 3 – Caribbean (orange); 4 – West Africa (red).

The four zoogeographical main regions

The animal world of the tropical coasts, which to a great extent includes the fauna of the coral reefs, may be subdivided into four zoogeographical main regions. These are:

❶ Indo-Pacific
❷ Eastern Pacific
❸ Caribbean
❹ West Africa

These regions have their own typical faunal elements, that distinguish them from each other. Yet the organisms of these regions are more closely related to one another than they are to those of colder regions in their immediate vicinity to the north and to the south (beyond the 20°C isotherm).

❶ Indo-Pacific

The zoogeographical main region "Indo-Pacific" comprises the the whole tropical area of the Indian Ocean, the Red Sea, the whole oceanic area from southern Japan to Australia (Lord Howe Island at 31° 30' south latitude with the southernmost well-developed coral reef) and eastwards to the Hawaiian Islands and Easter Island. Altogether this zoogeographical main region forms an ocean zone that stretches around more than half of the earth's circumference.

The fauna of the Indo-Pacific is

The typical scenery of the Red Sea: desert hills slope down to the coast and are surrounded by fringing reefs in the crystal clear shallow waters.

Photo: E. Svensen

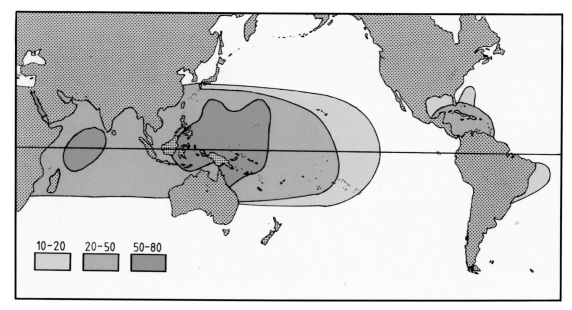

Number of genera of stony corals in relation to their total distribution.

Drawing after SCHUHMACHER, 1982

10-20   20-50   50-80

doubtlessly the one with the greatest biodiversity among the four main regions. It comprises the greatest number of families of coral reef animals as well as a number of species which can also be found in other regions. Calculations have shown that about 500 species of hermatypic corals grow in the Indo-Pacific, a number five times as high as the respective number for the Caribbean Sea, whose richness in animal and plant life is second only to that of the Indo-Pacific. Furthermore,

the greatest number of coastal fish species worldwide can be found in the Indo-Pacific, too. More than 400 species from 179 families have been counted (MYERS 1989). In addition to that a large number of families and genera are endemic to this area. Among these are the giant clams of the family Tridacnidae, the dottybacks of the family Pseudochromidae, the prettyfins of the family Plesiopidae and the rabbit fishes of the family Siganidae (prior to the building of the Suez Canal).

A considerable number of fish species is endemic to the Indo-Pacific, too, yet most of these are found all over that region. Research into the distribution of fishes, crabs and molluscs showed that 50 to 80 % of all species are common to large areas of the Indo-Pacific. Diversity is greatest in the central region, i. e. in the Indo-Australian Archipelago and off the Philippines. The number of species gradually decreases the further away a region is from this central area. The map and the diagram on

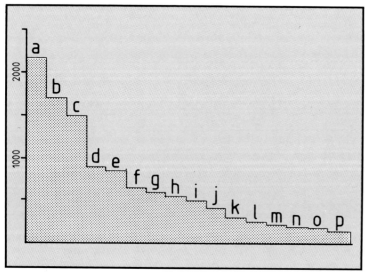

Distribution of fish species:

a: Philippines
b: Papua-New Guinea
c: Great Barrier Reef
d: The Seychelles
e: One Tree Reef in the GBR
f: Marshall Islands and Guam
g: Alligator Reef, Florida
h: Bahamas
i: Venezuela
j: Hawaii
k: Barbados
l: Gulf of California
m: Mafia, East Africa
n: Fanning Island
o: Tampa Bay
p: West Florida

Diagram after SALE, 1980

page 60 present details on these facts concerning stony corals and fishes respectively. This area with its large number of species is generally considered to be the faunistic center from which the animals spread into the other regions of the Indo-Pacific. But it may also be the product of surface ocean currents which tend to concentrate species in the region.

The animal life of some smaller areas is, however, distinctly different from that of most others. This holds true e. g. for the Hawaiian Islands. Though there are only relatively few endemic genera to be found off Hawaii, 30 % of the species are restricted geographically to this group of islands. The fauna of the Red Sea presents a large number of peculiarities as well. Out of the 80 species of corals and the 800 species of fishes, around 20 % are endemic to that region.

From the point of view of marine aquaristics the Indo-Pacific is of utmost importance, as most of the invertebrates and fishes that are on sale in the aquarium shops come from there. The diversity of the oceanic fauna of the Indo-Pacific also becomes obvious by the fact that a considerable number of exporting firms have chosen this area as their place of business. There are regular direct shipments of marine animals from the Red Sea, from Kenya, Sri Lanka, the Maldives and the Philippines, from Australia, Singapore, Indonesia, Taiwan and Hawaii. Less common species of fishes reach Europe via the USA from more remote places like Majuro (Marshall Islands), Guam (the Marianas) and Belau (formerly Palau).

Stations of a voyage through the Indo-Pacific

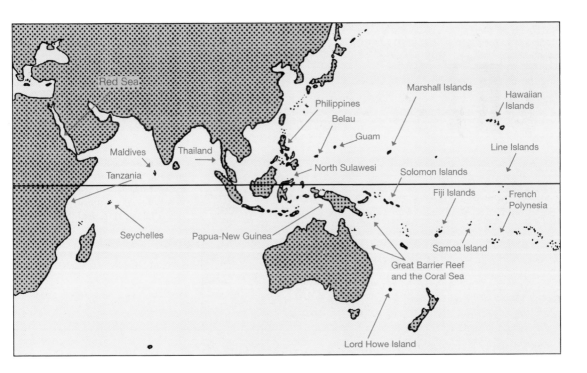

The following picture pages show coral reefs from the zoogeographical main region known as the Indo-Pacific, with the trip starting in the Red Sea and ending in the Hawaiian Islands. The pictures give a good impression of underwater life and of the scenery above the water in the respective regions. The stations visited are named in the map.

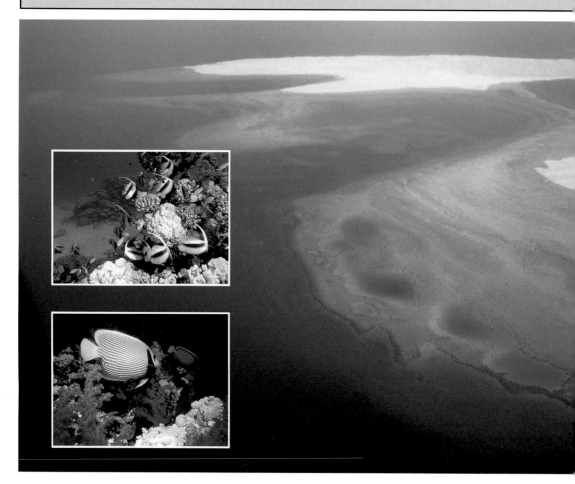

Above: Reefs off Hurghada, Egypt: bannerfishes and basslets at a depth of 15 m (upper inset), a pair of the Emperor Angelfish at a depth of 20 m (lower inset).

Photos: O. Gremblewski-Strate

Left: *Pseudochromis fridmani* is endemic to the Red Sea and belongs to the family Pseudochromidae, which is endemic to the Indo-Pacific.

Underwater photo: Dr. A. Spreinat

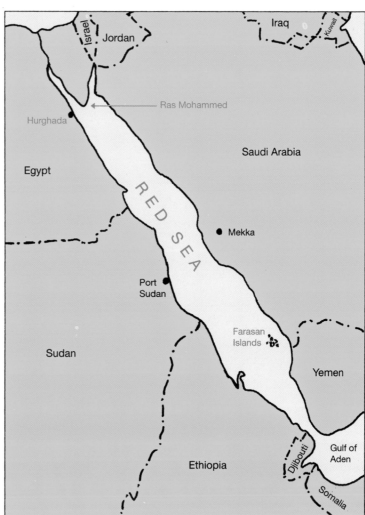

Right: *Dascyllus marginatus*
Underwater photo:
O. Gremblewski-Strate

The Emperor Angelfish *Pomacanthus imperator*, a shoal of hatchet fish *Parapriacanthus* sp., various cardinalfishes of the family Apogonidae and the most beautiful soft corals, *Dendronephthya* spp., make up a typical underwater scene of the Red Sea.   Underwater photo: E. Svensen

Beautiful growth of corals of the suborder Holaxonia at Ras Mohammed at a depth of 10 metres.
Underwater photo: T. Luther

Brown hydrozoa of the genus *Millepora*, gorgonians and soft corals of the genus *Dendronephthya*.

Underwater photo: E. Svensen

The coast and the reef flat during low tide at Tan in Tanzania.
Three photos: H. Franklin

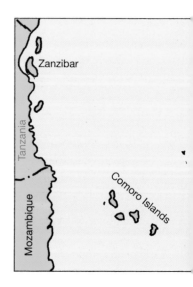

The Seychelles

The Seychelles are mostly volcanic islands (above) north of Madagascar (see map), which have well-developed fringing reefs. In this group of islands there are additional coral islands (below), which have grown on a reef flat. Such coral islands resemble those found in the Maldives.

Photo: R. Lunde

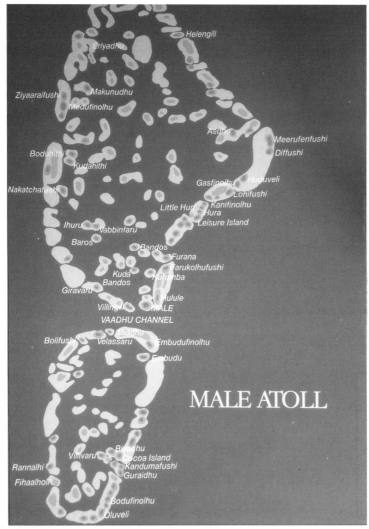

The Isles of the Maldives rise hardly more than a few metres above sea level and are surrounded by very well developed coral reefs. The left picture at the bottom shows a typical Maldive island that developed at the crest of a reef. The island and the reef are formed by the wind and the waves. White coral sand and a growth of coconut palms are typical of the shores of these islands (upper picture in the middle).

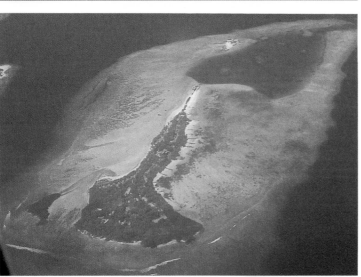

Maldives

The pictures to the right show typical underwater scenes of the Maldives reefs:

In the upper picture a group of Fairy Basslets, *Pseudanthias squamipinnis*, have gathered at a steep reef crest overgrown with a great number of invertebrates.

The picture below shows a thriving profusion of *Acropora*-stony corals.

The Andaman Islands (Thailand)

Hin Mmusang Rock.

Doc Mai Island.

Underwater scenery off Hin Mmusang.

Photos: O. Gremblewski-Strate

The Island of Ko Hi (Thailand)

The coast of Ko Hi.

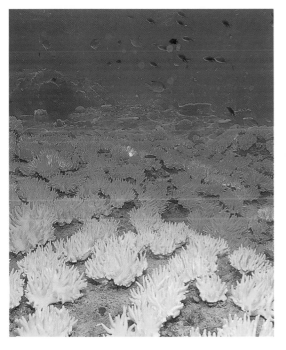

Soft (left) and stony corals (right) at Ko Hi.   Photos: E. Svensen

Indonesia lies in the heart of the Indo-Pacific region and houses as much as 50-80 genera of stony corals. Around some of the many small islands found in the Sulawesi region the growth of corals is spectacular. Often the reefs are very well developed and the typical zonation of a fringing reef can easily be seen. The tide sometimes falls to extremely low levels exposing the reef flats to the burning sun.

View of Garove Island from a hill.   Photo: Dr. Bruce Carlson, Waikiki Aquarium, Honolulu, Hawaii

Reef section with a pair of the Blue-Girdled Angelfish, *Pomacanthus navarchus*.   Photo: Scott W. Michael

The Philippines

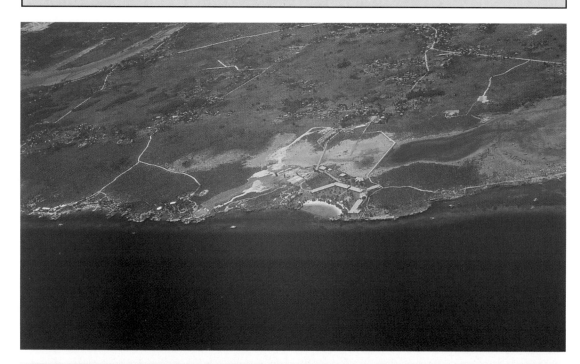

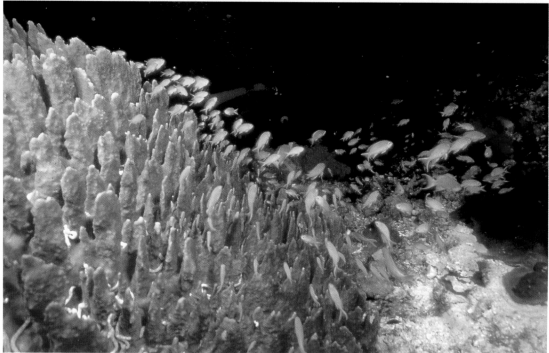

The coast of Cebu (top) and underwater scenery off Cebu (bottom) with a shoal of *Pseudanthias* sp.
Photos: O. Gremblewski-Strate

Amphiprion clarkii at a depth of 20 m off Bohol.

Anemone fishes in the Philippines
Underwater photos: O. Gremblewski-Strate

Amphiprion perideraion (left) at a depth of 15 m off Bohol, *A. ocellaris* (above) and *A. clarkii* (below) at a depth of 15 m off Pescador.

The Great Barrier Reef and the Coral Sea

The Great Barrier Reef (GBR) extends more than 2000 km along the east coast of Australia (see the general map below). It is a young reef system, with its complexity and diversity made up of a number of single reefs. The southernmost part of the reef is not older than two million years, the recent growth of the reef not older than 5000-6000 years.

To the east of the Great Barrier Reef there is the Coral Sea with its most beautiful coral reefs.

Waves and the sun: these two critical factors for the growth of a coral reef are revealed very clearly at ebb tide on Boomerang Reef (Coral Sea). The reef slope is extremely steep (below). The water is crystal clear and nutrient poor.

Great Barrier Reef Marine Park Authority

Alexandra Bay, south of Cooktown at the Daintree Coast in Northern Queensland is one of the few places in the world where rain forests and coral reefs, the two most complex and most sensitive ecological systems meet.

The southernmost coral reefs of the world can be found off Lord Howe Island (31.5 °S.)

Photo: NSW Tourism Commision

Above: Places like Wistari Reef are like a perfect dream for aquarists. Once or twice a month the reefs of the Great Barrier Reef fall dry for several hours at extremely low tides. The corals are then exposed directly to the radiation of the tropical sun and have to protect themselves by mucous secretions and by pigment production.　　Photo: S. Elliot (GBRMPA)

Left: Many beautiful corals grow at a depth of 20 m in the Coral Sea. The dinghy waiting for the diver can be seen at the surface through the crystal clear water.

Underwater photo: E. Svensen

Although the reef flat of Alexandra Reef (GBR) is covered with mud, a large number of corals of the genus *Goniastrea* thrive there (left). Even these magnificent stony corals of the genus *Acropora* (right) grow in this muddy water.

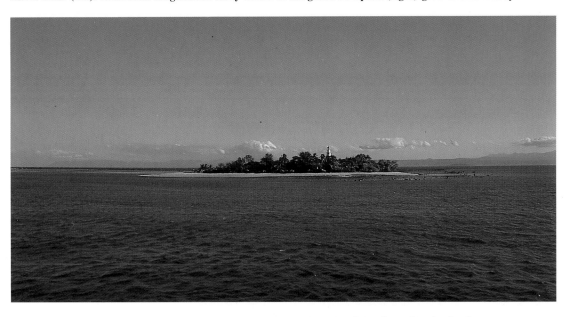

Low Island is one of the typical small coral islands of the Great Barrier Reef.

The Blue Starfish, *Linckia laevigata* (left), in shallow water, and *Porites cylindrica* (right), the most common stony coral on the reef flat of Green Island (GBR).

Belau (formerly Palau)

Above: The "Rock Islands" of Belau are the gems of the central Indo-Pacific.
Photo: Dr. B. Carlson, Waikiki-Aquarium, Honolulu, Hawaii

Left: The reef flat of Belau at ebb tide. Dr. Ken Yates and Dr. Bruce Carlson of the Waikiki Aquarium are busy studying the coral fauna.
Photo: M. Awai, Waikiki Aquarium, Honolulu, Hawaii

Below: The Isles of Belau are covered with rain forest (left photo: M. Awai). Ngemelis Island is a famous diving site (right photo: Dr. B. Carlson).

Guam (The Marianas)

The coastline of Guam. South and east of Guam in the Mariana trench, record depths of 8700 to 11000 m were measured. Shepard's Angelfish, *Centropyge shepardi* is quite common in the waters off Guam. Most of the aquarium specimens of this species are caught here. The geographic distribution of *Centropyge shepardi* is restricted to the Marianas and the Bonin Islands (Japan).

Photo: Dr. B. Carlson

The Marshall Islands

Arno Atoll is situated in the vicinity of Majuro in the Marshall Islands. Majuro is the region where most of the Flame Angelfish, *Centropyge loriculus*, are caught for the aquarium trade.   Photo: M. Awai

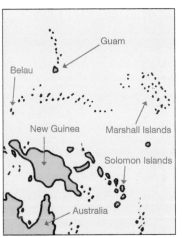

The Solomon Islands

The reefs in this area are really well developed and mostly intact. The picture shows a shallow lagoon with a tropical beach, which is typical of these islands.   Photo: M. Awai

The Fiji Islands

The Fiji Islands in the southeastern part of the Indo-Pacific are surrounded by beautiful fringing reefs, like the "Coral Coast" southwest of Veti Levu shown in this picture.

The underwater scenery is often dominated by colorful soft corals of the genus *Dendronephthya* and red whip-shaped gorgonians.   Photo: Scott W. Michael

The Samoa Islands are located to the east of the Fiji Islands. Well developed fringing reefs can be found in the harbour area of Pago Pago.

Photo: Dr. B. Carlson

French Polynesia

Left: Bird's eye view of Bora Bora showing the typical fringing reefs around the volcanic island. Right: This stony coral of the genus *Pocillipora* photographed in shallow waters off Bora Bora is literally swarming with hundreds of *Chromis* sp.

Photos: Scott W. Michael

The Line Islands

The Line Islands extend on the Fanning Ridge along the eastern border of the Indo-Pacific zone northeast from French Polynesia to Hawaii. Among the Line Islands there are Washington Island (Teraina), Fanning Island (Tabuaeran) and Christmas Island (Kiritimati). Our picture shows Fanning Island.

Photo: Dr. B. Carlson

The Hawaiian Islands

The Hawaiian Islands cover an area 2600 km in length. Along with Niihau, Kauai, Oahu, Molokai, Lanai, Maui and Hawaii they comprise eight larger islands as well as more than a hundred smaller islands and atolls. All of these islands are of volcanic origin and have risen from the sea bed, which is remarkable because the Pacific is extremely deep (5500 m) in the vicinity of this group of islands. The special character of this area developed because of a geothermal anomaly, the "hot spots", which are situated far away from any tectonic platforms. In places like these magma rises in a columnar shape from the centrosphere and penetrates the layer drifting above it.

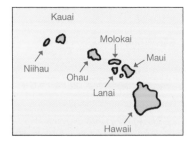

In this peaceful bay near Oahu the reef formations in the shallow waters can be perceived when the sea is calm.   Photo: Scott W. Michael

Bird's eye view of a typical Hawaiian island.

Porites lobata, here at Kailua-Kona, is the most common hermatypic stony coral in the reefs of the Hawaiian islands.
Underwater photo: Dr. D. Brockmann

Above and below: both *Pocillopora meandrina* at Kailua-Kona. The pictures show how the same species varies in colour and shape depending on its location.   Underwater photos: Dr. D. Brockmann

The Reticulated Butterflyfish, *Chaetodon reticulatus*, is a very rare fish in the area of Hawaii and elsewhere. It is here accompanied by two Goldring Bristletooth, *Ctenochaetus strigosus*. Underwater photo: Dr. D. Brockmann

Liopropoma aurora of the family Serranidae is endemic to the islands of Hawaii, living there at great depth. Photo (taken at the Waikiki Aquarium, Honolulu): Scott W. Michael

One of the most beautiful butterflyfishes is *Chaetodon falcifer*. It lives in the region from the California coast to the northern islands of Galápagos and is found at different depths, depending on temperature.

Photo: H. J. Mayland

The Longnose Butterflyfish, *Forcipiger flavissimus*, is one of the few fish species that managed to cross the east pacific deep-sea trench. It is found in the Indo-Pacific as well as in the Eastern Pacific. Photo: F. Nijhuis

"Eastern Pacific" is the zoogeographical term for the tropical sea area outside the Indo-Pacific from the Gulf of California to Peru, including islands like Guadalupe, Revilla Gigedo, Clipperton, Cocos Islands, Galápagos, etc.

The Eastern Pacific is separated from the Indo-Pacific by a deep-sea trench (Eastern Pacific Barrier). The number of coral reefs there is not very high. Its only atoll is Clipperton Island about 1000 km west of Costa Rica. Some rather well developed coastal reefs are found at the entrance of the Gulf of California around the islands of Revilla Gigedo, 500 km west of Mexico, parallel to the Central-American coastline. Some hermatypic stony corals may be found off Galápagos, yet there are no typical reef structures to be found there. This is mainly due to the adverse influence of the Peru Current, which carries cold water from the Antarctic region along the coast of Peru. To the north the spreading of the tropical sea fauna is prevented by the cold ocean currents from Alaska and Canada.

The deep-sea trench is the reason why only a few species have been able to migrate from the Indo-Pacific to the Eastern Pacific. Among them are a number of well-known aquarium fishes, like the Bluestripe pipefish, *Doryrhamphus excisus*, and the Longnose Butterflyfish, *Forcipiger flavissimus*. The fauna, however, has much more in common with that of the Caribbean. There are, for example a number of pairs of sibling species. This term refers to species which are so similar morphologically, physiologically and ethologically that it is difficult to tell them apart. These dificulties may be even greater if the place of origin of these species is unknown. *Ophioblennius steindachneri* in the Eastern Pacific and *Ophioblennius atlanticus* in the Caribbean, and *Chaetodipterus zonatus* in the Eastern Pacific and *Chaetodipterus faber* in the Caribbean are typical examples of

these sibling species. Some ich-
thyologists estimate that there are
about 100 of these sibling species
in these regions (THOMSON et al.,
1979).

This will remain a much debated subject among experts in cases where the features of the species are similar enough to prevent
a proper distinction. This, however, holds true only for a very few
species, e. g. *Paranthias furcifer*, a
basslet which is found on both
sides of the trench. Yet questions
like these are always a matter of

**Central area of the Gulf of California
(Sea of Cortez).**
Photo: Scott W. Michael

opinion and answers depend
largely on the interpretation of the
zoological term "species" on
which they are based.

The number of fish species from
the Eastern Pacific which are suitable for the aquarium is not very
high. This is one of the reas-

**Algae growth is more typical of the
Gulf of California than are coral
reefs, which are found only in the
southernmost parts and which grow
only scantily. Nevertheless this area
is inhabited by interesting aquarium
fishes.**
Underwater photo: Scott W. Michael

ons why imports from there are
sparse. There are, however, a
number of highly interesting fishes coming from there, e. g. the
Bluespotted Jawfish, *Opistognathus rosenblatti*, or those strange
surgeonfishes of the genus *Prionurus*, among them *Prionurus la-
ticlavius*, and the butterflyfish
Johnrandallia nigrirostris. Four
beautiful angelfishes are also native to this region: *Holacanthus clarionensis, H. passer, H. limbaug-
hi,* and *Pomacanthus zonipectus.*

**The Clarion Angelfish, *Holacanthus
clarionensis*, is endemic to the Eastern Pacific.**
Photo: Scott W. Michael

Islands of dreams in the Caribbean: the beautiful hours of the evening on the island of Bonaire.

Photo: O. Gremblewski-Strate

❸ The Caribbean

The term "Caribbean", as we use it, doesn't only cover the Caribbean Sea. The zoogeographical region "Carribean" comprises the Caribbean Sea as well as the West Indies and the area of the Western Atlantic from the Bermudas to Rio de Janeiro. Some smaller islands in the Atlantic, like Penedos de Sao Paolo and Ascension are also considered to be part of the Caribbean. The ocean fauna there, however, is considerably poorer and there are no proper coral reefs. Several species of fishes can be found there, however, which more commonly inhabit coral reefs and which do not occur further north.

The zoogeographical characteristics of the Bermudas are unique. With the exception of the reefs off Southern Japan, nowhere else in the world are coral reefs at such a high latitude (32 ° 15'

Fishes from the Caribbean: *Microspathodon chrysurus* (left) and *Pomacanthus paru* (juvenile; right).

Underwater photos: Dr. A. Spreinat

north), a fact which is closely connected to the influence of the Gulf Stream in this area. Around two thirds of the families of fishes and invertebrates of the Indo-Pacific are found in the Caribbean. The species from these families are, however, different ones apart from a few exceptions. Such exceptions are for example the Sargassumfish, *Histrio histrio*, some bigeyes of the genus *Priacanthus* and most of the suckers of the family Echeneididae. As mentioned before, the Caribbean species have much more in common with those of the Eastern Pacific, and some species and several genera from there occur again in the eastern Atlantic (the zoogeographical region of West Africa), and in the Mediterranean Sea. *Scartella cristata*, the Molly Miller, which is imported quite regularly, is found rather frequently in the Mediterranean and the Canary Islands.

From the aquarist's point of view the Caribbean is a very interesting region. Among the invertebrates, the large number of photosynthetic gorgonians are especially tempting to grow. Formerly this group of cnidarians was believed to be difficult to maintain. However, since many gorgonians have zooxanthellae they thrive in aquaria. Among the fishes from this area are such classic aquarium species as the Yellowhead Jawfish, *Opistognathus aurifrons*, the Royal Gramma, *Gramma loreto*, and the Cherub Angelfish, *Centropyge argi*.

Today fish are caught for aquarium purposes in many regions of the Caribbean. Most of them are imported via Florida. Only very rarely do imports from the more remote areas, like Ascension Island reach us. From this island the beautiful Ascension Angelfish, *Centropyge resplendens*, is imported. On the whole the choice of interesting fishes from the Caribbean for sale in the aquarium trade is constantly on the rise.

Stations of a voyage through the Caribbean

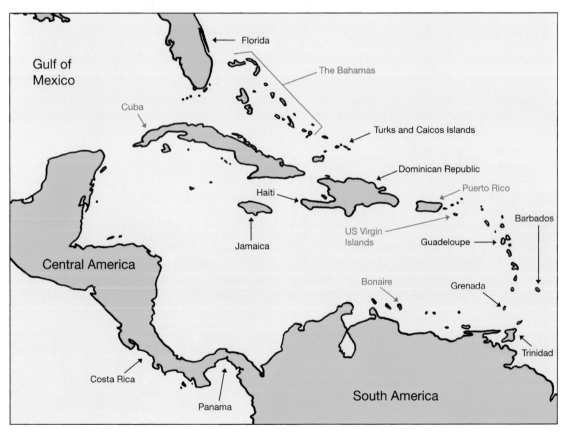

Gulf of Mexico

Florida

The Bahamas

Cuba

Turks and Caicos Islands

Dominican Republic

Haiti

Puerto Rico

Barbados

US Virgin Islands

Guadeloupe

Jamaica

Central America

Bonaire

Grenada

Trinidad

Costa Rica

South America

Panama

The following picture pages show some coastal reef areas in the Caribbean. The map shows the stations that were visited (red letters).

Overview of Caja de Muertos near Puerto Rico.

While the most well-known invertebrates are found below the water levle, a few can also be found higher. The chiton *Acanthopleura grannulata* (left) is common just where the water meets the land. The beautiful hermit crab (right) lives on the beach and even in the forest close to the beach.

Puerto Rico

Right: The beach and coast line of Caja de Muertos near Puerto Rico. The rocks situated about 1 meter above the water level were rich in fossilized corals and shells, and on the beach there were numerous gorgonian skeletons that had been blown on shore during a storm.

Below: Big and colourful sponges are very common in the Caribbean.
Underwater photos: Dr. A. Spreinat

Breakers at a fringing reef.

Photo: Scott W. Michael

The Barred Hamlet, *Hypoplectrus puella*, (left) and the Butter Hamlet, *H. unicolor* (right). Hamlets are small groupers from the Caribbean, reaching about 15 cm in length.
Underwater photos: Dr. A. Spreinat

Cuba

Beach and mangrove (above). Gorgonians dominate the underwater scenery off Cuba (below). Photos: E. Svensen

Left: The Atlantic coast of Bonaire is rather rough.

Below: The Royal Gramma, *Gramma loreto*, at a depth of 30 metres.   Photos: O. Gremblewski-Strate

The Bahamas

On the coral reefs of the Bahamas, east of Florida, the underwater scenery is dominated by gorgonians with symbiotic algae (zooxanthellae). The Angelfish is a natural hybrid of *Holacanthus ciliaris x H. bermudensis*.

Underwater photo: Scott W. Michael

The Longspine Squirrelfish, *Holocentrus rufus*, stony corals, massive gorgonians, and colourful sponges inhabit the coral reefs of the Caribbean.   Photo: Dr. A. Spreinat

Ascension

The Ascension Angelfish, *Centropyge resplendens*, is endemic to the shores of Ascension Island, which is situated in the tropical Atlantic, but nevertheless belongs to the Caribbean zoogeographically.

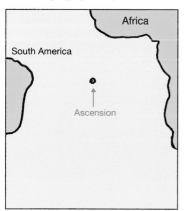

Soft corals off the Islands of Cape Verde.   Photo: H. J. Gruhl

④ West Africa

Among the four zoogeographical main regions dealt with here the "West African" faunal region covers the smallest area. Its fauna has a lot of characteristics in common with that of the Mediterranean and the Caribbean. There are no proper coral reefs found here, however. This may also be the reason why corals and other animals from the West African faunal region are only occasionally exported. Only from the capital of Cape Verde, Praia, is a small number of species of highly interesting fishes imported.

Even though proper coral reefs are missing in the west African region, hermatypic stony corals may be found nevertheless. From the islands of Cape Verde five species of the genera *Madracis*, *Siderastrea*, *Porites* and *Montastrea* are known, and they occur in the Caribbean as well. In the Gulf of Guinea some endemic species have been found, yet other species suggest strong similarities of the fauna to that of the Caribbean Sea. However, the massive sponges and the treelike gorgonians which are so numerous in the Caribbean are quite obviously missing here. As compared to the Caribbean the West African coral fauna on the whole gives a less developed impression. This is partly due to the cold ocean currents, an effect we can also observe at the west coast of South America. In addition this "impoverished" fauna is caused by mud sedimentation from the large estuaries like that of the Niger and the Zaire River.

Sao Tomé belongs to a chain of volcanic islands southwest of Cameroon. The underwater fauna of this former Portuguese colony is most impressive, as shown by the pictures on the following three pages.

Starfish at Sao Tomé.   **Underwater photo: Prof. Dr. P. Wirtz**

Further reading

Briggs, 1974; Springer, 1982

Above: *Muraena melanotis* with a most attractive pattern.
Middle: A West African butterflyfish, *Chaetodon luciae.*
Bottom: The Glasseye, *Heteropriacanthus cruentatus.*

Photos on this page and the two following pages: Prof. Dr. P. Wirtz

Much to our surprise, the underwater scenery of Sao Tomé is magnificent and varied.

Pictures above:
Epinephelus adscensionis, a grouper (left), and a soapfish *Rypticus saponaceus* (right).

Left:
Orange cup coral, *Tubastraea* sp.

Right:
These Blackbar Soldierfishes, *Myripristis jacobus*, are crowded in their hiding-place.

Pictures below: While the moray eel (left) poses most photogenically, the moray eel (right) opens its mouth wide and plays dead.

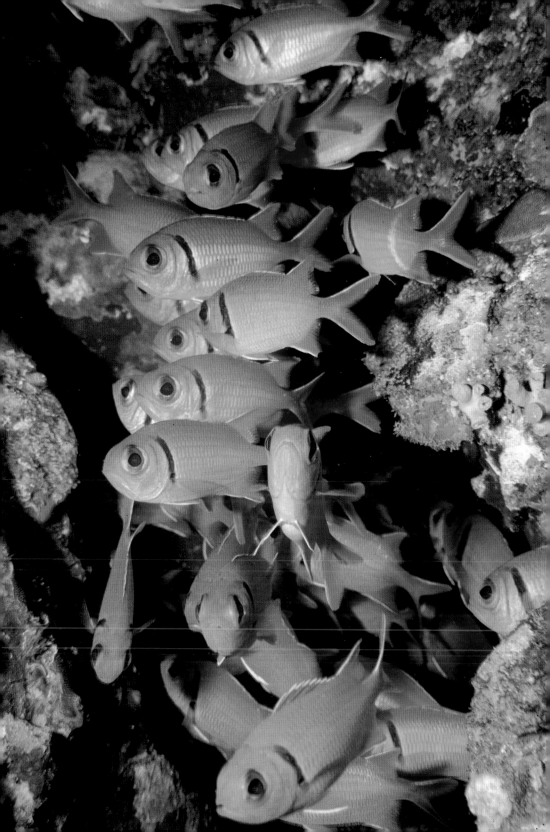

A soft coral Dendronephthya sp. and a pipefish *Corythoichthys nigripectus* in the Red Sea.

Chapter 3

A Coral Reef in the Aquarium

Nearly all tropical marine animals on sale in the aquarium trade come from coral reefs, with South East Asia as the main export region. Invertebrates and fishes from biotopes other than the coral reefs are offered for sale only sporadically. This is also one of the reasons why marine aquarists mainly keep animals from the coral reef.

Some rather popular fishes like most sea horses are not usually found on coral reefs, and should therefore not be kept in a coral reef aquarium. These animals do very well, however, in other types of aquaria especially adapted to their needs, but this is not a subject dealt with in this series of books.

To begin with, a saltwater aquarist is faced with the question of whether he should keep fishes and invertebrates from different geographical regions together in one aquarium. Of course this is usually not a question of great importance for the animals themselves, if for example fish from the Caribbean Sea are introduced into the same tank with fish from the Indo-Pacific region. But with regard to the overall impression an aquarium makes, we are convinced that it is more suitable to choose only animals from one specific geographical region. We

A part of a coral reef aquarium. A miniature *Turbinaria* grows excellently in the close neighbourhood of *Acropora pulchra* and *Pocillopora damicornis*.
Photo: G. Pilling

This coral reef aquarium is 2.5 m deep. It is structured like a reef gorge and gives an impression of endlessness. The sides and part of the back side were made from plywood, coated with polyester and top coat (left). The aquarium, already varnished in this picture, projects into the room for about 40 cm. The aquarium room itself has been fitted with a soundproofing door.

also recommend to select fishes and invertebrates according to the areas in the reef that they come from. Thus the aquarist should make up his mind beforehand whether he wants to keep animals from shallow waters flooded with light, from deep recesses, caves or from steep reef slopes.

It would be ideal, of course, to copy as closely as possible the natural example of the biotope in choosing the animals for an aquarium and in decorating it. This idea, however, is somewhat difficult to realize. Problems would be caused, e. g. by predatory animals that could harm or kill others, animals that outgrow the tank, or animals with very special demands that cannot be met in an aquarium. Keeping fish hardly ever causes difficulties that cannot somehow be overcome, although breeding these fish is mostly very difficult or quite impossible. This does not hold true for invertebrates, however. Until only a few years ago, just a small number of species could successfully be kept in an aquarium. Among these were only some especially hardy sea anemones, tube worms, crustaceans, and snails. Until only recently aquarists had to assume that the most important animals of a coral reef, the stony corals, could not be kept alive in an aquarium for any considerable length of time. But this has changed drastically.

The decoration of live rock is held in its place in the aquarium by plastic straps such as those used to fix electric cables (left). By using a pane of blue plexiglas behind the back side, the three-dimensional effect is enhanced. Lighting is provided by seven HQI-lamps of 250 watts each. Special effects are created by spotlights and a disco sphere-globe lighting up to the background of the aquarium (right).

Three factors seem to be of utmost importance for the maintenance of invertebrates in a coral reef aquarium: **quality and amount of light, quality of the water and algae control.** These parameters are so crucial that we are going to deal with them in more detail in the following chapters. If these factors are under the control of the aquarist, a large number of invertebrate animals, among them also stony corals, can be successfully kept or even propagated in an aquarium. This fact opens totally new horizons for marine aquaristics. Of course we are still left with a number of problems, as the aquarium trade cannot always offer the animals we want in great variety or on a regular basis.

Details about the exact species of the animals, the place where they were caught, etc, are often inadequate or may even not be available at all. We have, for example, seen a King Crab, *Tachypleus gigas*, for sale as a "stingray", a rather grotesque example, of course. However, less obvious mistakes often have more disastrous consequences, because the aquarist then does not even realize that the information is wrong. Thus a harmless frog fish of the genus *Antennarius* was sold as the highly poisonous stonefish, *Synanceia verrucosa*. The other way around this could have had serious consequences.

False identification is much more common with invertebrate animals. With many of them it is the rule rather than the exception. This goes to show that aquarists as well as aquarium dealers still lack adequate taxonomic knowledge of coral animals. For the sake of the animals and of the hobbyists, something should be done about this.

Self-styled "Conservationists" have criticised that damage may be done to coral reefs by commercial catching of aquarium animals on a large scale for the trade. A number of states have already restricted activities of this kind or intend to do so. In certain cases these restrictions are justified and necessary. This applies in particular to the use of cyanide in catching fish which is quite common, for example in the Philippines. We do hope and believe, however, that we will still have access to coral reefs in the future. Even more so, as we aquarists have been able to prove that it is possible to keep and propagate these animals successfully. Yet aquarists should absolutely refrain from buying animals of which experience has shown that they hardly ever survive in an aquarium. This is one way of proving that we are not merely consumers.

This is the right moment to emphasize the importance of the international treaties and the national and international laws dealing with the conservation of nature and of species, such as the CITES. These regulations also apply to certain corals and molluscs. For details you will have to look at the latest versions of these regulations, treaties, and laws.

The removal of corals and live rock from their natural surroundings for aquarium purposes can not possibly be more detrimental to nature than the exploitation of the coral reefs for the extraction of construction materials or for the manufacture of lime burning, which are quite common in many states that have coral reefs at their disposal (see RECK, 1991).

In order to keep alive or propagate the delicate animals of the coral reef in an aquarium we need an aquarium setup that works perfectly. It is not easy to say what such a system should be like, particularly because many aquarists have had quite different experiences with different systems. The range of these includes the so-called "Natural System" as well as near-clinical setups with an exaggerated use of technical equipment. We found out, however, that a biologically based system with a protein skimmer and moderate use of other technical appliances usually brought the best results.

This modern coral reef aquarium was built by Korallenwelt, Rostock, Germany.   **Photo: T. Luther**

A most impressive living room with a window for keeping and displaying flowers and plants and a coral reef aquarium that divides the room. The aquarium setup was built by Royal-Exclusiv-Anlagenbau, Cologne, Germany.

Photo: K. Jansen

On the whole a rather extensive array of technical equipment is needed to set up a coral reef aquarium. The space needed for the lighting appliances and the filtration unit is enormous. Aquaria integrated into walls or pieces of furniture hide the technical equipment most effectively from the view of the observer.

Customary aquaria with an aluminum frame are unsuitable as saltwater tanks. Despite of the surface coating, the aluminum cannot resist the aggressive saltwater in the long run, and the water in the tank is poisoned. Metals should not be used anywhere near a saltwater tank (with the exception of titanium and certain stainless steel perhaps). The same holds true for rubber and plastic materials containing softening agents. These materials may emit toxic substances into the aquarium water.

All-glass aquarium tanks constructed with silicone sealant are the most suitable ones. The aquarium trade offers such mass-produced tanks in standardized sizes. Many marine aquarists prefer dimensions and proportions for their tanks that are not offered in aquarium shops. Therefore they either build their tanks themselves or have them specially made according to their particular requests.

Apart from the all-glass aquarium tanks mentioned above, marine aquaria may be constructed from other saltwater-proof materials: Plexiglas (acrylic glass), polyester and epoxy resin. Glass-fibre reinforced polyester tanks with a topcoat-finish will also do fine. They are not easy to make, however. Such tanks are especially suitable for large aquarium setups. Epoxy varnish may

be used as a surface coating for various materials, e. g. concrete or wood. Meanwhile, we are not absolutely sure how epoxy resin and saltwater react together.

In most cases, the space available will be the decisive factor for the size and the shape of an aquarium. Generally a stable biological environment is achieved more easily in larger tanks than in smaller ones. This is why we always recommend tanks with a capacity of more than 300 litres (75 gallons) for the beginners in the hobby. Tanks should preferably be deep and wide rather than high, as this offers more possibilities of variation in the decoration of the the aquarium.

Unusual aquarium shapes, triangular or round, may be chosen of course, but the large majority of aquarists will prefer the customary rectangular form.

Rectangular aquaria may easily be fit into walls or pieces of furniture, which helps solve the problem of how to hide the technical equipment of the tank. Before you decide where to set up or install the tank, you should make up your mind what kind of technology you are going to use. All devices and appliances should be easily accessible, as it is quite important that filters and protein skimmers can be reached and cleaned without much effort and without much splashing around. We recommend that you draw a little plan of the technical arrangements, before you set up the tank. To avoid salt crusts outside the aquarium, the surface of the water should never reach higher than 5 cm below the top edge of the tank. This is necessary, anyway, in order to fix pumps and other pieces of equipment to its top. Sufficient space for hoses and pipes also has to be provided. A coral reef aquarium should not have any glass cover (we will explain this later). External filters and protein skimmers have to be installed in such a way that the water flowing into them is taken from the surface of the aquarium. This is achieved simply by installing an overflow device. There are various ways to do this. Special surface extractor-devices that serve this purpose are on offer in the aquarium trade.

The aquarium supply industry offers complete marine aquarium setups:

Left: Two panoramic aquaria, built by Royal-Exclusiv-Anlagenbau, Cologne, Germany.
The upper one completely equipped with technical devices produced by aqualine buschke (ab), Melle, Germany.

Right: Complete aquarium setup "Xenia" by Aqua Medic, Melle, Germany.

Below: Aquarium setup completely fitted with technical equipment produced by Dupla, Germany.

Chapter 4:

Setting up and Decorating
the
Modern Coral Reef Aquarium

An aquarium should always be set up and decorated in such a way that whoever looks at it gets an impression of beauty and the idea of looking through a window at underwater scenery. We consider it to be one of the great advantages of a modern coral reef aquarium that here a section of nature may be re-created as closely as possible.

In an aquarium without any decoration whatsoever most animals will feel very uncomfortable. Many of them have special habitat requirements. Some of them need sand to dig in, others need swimming room, hiding places, light or shade. When setting up and decorating an aquarium the aquarist should always try to meet both the biological demands of the organisms he intends to keep and the aesthetic demands of the onlooker. When we try to create an underwater scenery that appeals to the sense of beauty, however, the demands and needs of the organisms living in the modern coral reef aquarium should always have priority over the aesthetic sensitivity of the aquarist.

The underwater scenery we try to design should be based upon the characteristics of the reef zone we try to re-create. Underwater photos of this reef zone are most helpful in conceiving the right ideas. A sand zone, a cave, a reef wall or any other part of the reef may be

Above: In Agincourt Reef, a section of the Great Barrier Reef, we found this large piece of living rock sized 1.5 x 1 m at a depth of 15 m. It was settled by 21 different species of corals (nine soft corals and twelve stony corals). A sight like this can give us a good idea of what a coral reef aquarium should look like.

Left: Diverse growth including the hydrozoan *Millepora* sp. as well as scleraxonians and gorgonians in the Coral Sea, where the water is crystal clear and nutrient poor. **Underwater photo: E. Svensen**

Corals growing on living rocks in their natural surroundings may provide suggestions for the decoration of a modern coral reef aquarium.

A reef section off the Maldives, left, and the reef face of Agincourt Reef, right, are examples on which the decorations shown on pages 114 and 115 could have been modelled.
Below: This reef section may serve as a model for the decoration of a tank in which rocks and sand are combined.

observed to model our aquarium. In many cases, however, a combination of various zone types will prove to give the most pleasant impression. Many of the aquarium photos contained in this volume reproduce the beauty of the coral reef true to life.

Decoration materials

The largest share of the aquarium decoration consists of the material that is used to re-create a reef structure. No materials should be used for decorating a modern coral reef aquarium that are not chemically safe and could poison the aquarium water. Moreover the decoration should be positioned in such a way that the technical equipment in the tank is hidden. It is important, however, to ensure that the appliances can work properly and are easily accessible. Several different materials could be used. Here we discuss the ones most commonly encountered.

Live rock

Most of the sessile organisms in a coral reef grow on what we call live rock. This material consists of dead stony corals that are more or less eroded and have turned into interesting and sometimes very strange forms and structures. It is a matter of course that for the decoration of a modern coral reef aquarium these living rocks should be preferred over any other material. Apart from the fact that they convey a very natural impression they have a positive influence on the biological milieu of the aquarium.

These living rocks have two considerable disadvantages, however. On the one hand this material is sold at a high price and decorating a larger aquarium with these rocks may turn out to be prohibitively expensive. On the other hand these living rocks are communities of live organisms and have to be treated accordingly. They can only be introduced into an aquarium which has been fully set up before. Thus it is impossible to create larger constructions by glueing or cementing them together. Smaller formations could, however, be constructed by using an underwater epoxy resin

Construction of a column which forms part of an overhang on one side of the aquarium. In order to join living rocks together they must be worked on to give them the proper shape and to make the most of them: with a percussion drill a 16 mm hole is drilled into a living rock (left), another rock is sawed in half (middle). To remove the muddy limestone remains and the metal chips and particles produced by drilling and sawing, the rocks have to be rinsed at once very thoroughly with running water (right). After rinsing the living rocks you must put them back into salt water immediately to avoid damage by osmotic influences.

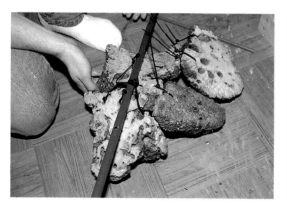

The rocks are tied together with cable ties and fixed to a 16 mm PVC-tube. The picture on the left side shows the rear view of the column-shaped construction. The front view as it will be presented in the aquarium looks totally different. As seen in the picture on the right the plastic parts are completely hidden.

Two column-shaped constructions fixed to PVC-tubes in the tank: the picture on the left shows an overhanging construction which is supposed to give an impression of bulkiness. The view is from the backside of the aquarium. The picture on the right shows how the PVC-tubes are attached to a crossbeam on the top of the tank. The upper part of the rock overhang is positioned as little as 10 cm under the water surface.

The rock overhang after its completion: even though the decoration looks quite strange when seen from above and behind, you get a very natural effect when you look at it through the front glass of the aquarium.

In the left part of the aquarium a lower and more massive formation sloping down to a sand zone was created. To get a rather loose construction using as little live rock as possible at the same time, a 90 mm PVC-tube is used as a basis of the structure. Holes are drilled into the tube to avoid stagnation of the water; at the same time more hiding-places are created for the animals in the tank. The tube is supported by triangular pieces of glass which are fixed to the bottom of the tank with silicone. The living rocks are bound to the tube and tied together with cable ties.

The complete decoration as viewed through the front glass of the aquarium: to the left the lower formation, sloping down to the sand zone, to the right the columnar construction with the overhanging rocks. This doubtlessly is a setup that resembles very closely the natural structure of a reef. The pictures on this page show the aquarium a short while after the conditioning process has been completed.

as glue (see page 120). It may, however, turn out to be difficult to join live rock to form larger decorative structures which are robust and will not collapse. The series of photos on pages 114 to 115 shows how live rocks should be treated to fit them together to make imaginative and true to life structures (further information on this subject is to be found in chapter 7).

We believe there is a need to reconsider the ways coral reef aquaria are decorated. Far too many tank decorations resemble a pile of stones rather than a reef structure, mostly lacking the illusion of depth. A little more imagination and creativity should go a long way towards solving this problem.

Some aquarists use dead mate-

taken as it increases the pH of the aquarium water considerably. Therefore the resulting cement seams have to be treated with a

> **Attention! Always use goggles and gloves when handling hydrochloric acid.**

10 % solution of hydrochloric acid and rinsed with clean water in between.
After this treatment the construction has to be soaked and rinsed thoroughly. It is necessary to change the water repeatedly until the pH remains stable, i.e. identical with the pH of the water used for rinsing. Dental cement as used

also be produced from styrofoam, which is then coated with concrete surfacer and epoxy varnish. We have, however, never used this material ourselves. Lacking personal experience in this respect, we cannot say if it is completely safe to use.

It is also possible to use polyurethane foam as a basis on which decorations may be fixed. This foam can be shaped into any form the aquarist wishes. After it has been sealed with epoxy varnish it seems to be seawater-proof. It has been used successfully in public aquarium exhibitions (see pictures to the right and on pages 156/157).

There is a large selection of artificial decorations on sale in aquarium shops. These materials may easily be worked on and have been tested for safety in the marine

Porous limestone is excellent material for decorating a modern coral reef aquarium.

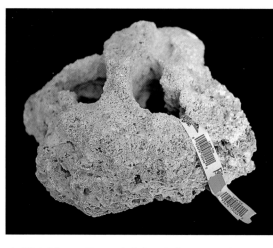

Artificial decoration material made from ceramics as produced by Korallenwelt, Rostock, Germany.

rials – natural or artificial – to build the basic structure of their aquarium decoration.

Dead rocks

We always try to dissuade aquarists from using lava. It is impossible to know which other materials it includes. Most often it contains harmful metallic compounds. The most suitable material is limestone, especially the variety with large holes, that may easily be linked together with glue or cement. Normal cement may be used for this purpose, yet care should be

by dentists would be more appropriate, yet it is much more expensive. Rocks should never be placed directly on the bottom of the aquarium, but on a 1 or 2 cm layer of styrofoam or a similar material.

After a while, when calcareous algae have started to grow these limestone structure look remarkably like living rocks. In fact, many porous types of limestone are remains of coral reefs of past geological eras.

Artificial material

Very impressive decorations can

aquarium. Most artificial materials have one considerable disadvantage: they lack the porous surface which is important in order to provide substratum for settlement of bacteria and other microorganisms.

Coral skeletons

Even though some time ago it was quite common to use coral skeletons to decorate marine aquaria and they are still on offer nowadays, they are not a natural decoration for such an aquarium at all. Unfortunately it still happens to-

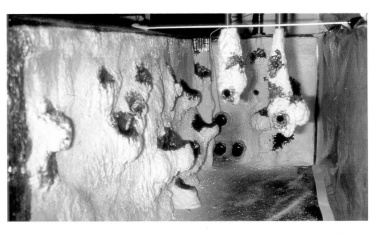

A large aquarium exhibit lined with polyurethane under construction in Hagenbeck's Zoo, Hamburg, Germany. Photo: U. Richter

day that in the setting up of a marine aquarium colorful fishes and a few sea anemones are presented against a background of bleached coral skeletons shining chalky and white. In some aquarium books it is recommended to dye these coral skeletons to make them look more natural. We have come upon gruesome and shocking sights in marine aquaria: coral skeletons in all sorts of shades from pink to dark lilac or sky blue. It goes without saying that these

coral graveyards have nothing in common with nature and do not make sense against the background of modern aquaristics which stresses the idea that tank setups should emulate natural surroundings.

It may be justifiable to use coral skeletons in marine aquaria if only small amounts are used, if they are combined with living rocks and if they are covered by calcareous algae. If coral skeletons are used at all they should not be set

up in the aquarium ground, but rather placed on a footing of living rocks or a similar material. All coral skeletons have to be cleaned carefully, before they are introduced into the aquarium. There are special cleaning agents available for this purpose (the instructions for the use of these chemical substances must be followed most carefully).

In spite of all this **we want to reject the use of coral skeletons** firmly. We also have to do this, because marine aquarists often have to face allegations that the export of fishes and other animals collected for aquarium purposes is harmful to the biotopes they come from (see chapter 14).

These accusations are also made because coral skeletons are being quarried in many countries. It is regrettable that as a consequence some authors of aquarium books only discourage the purchase of live stony corals. We think that the trade in live corals for aquaristic purposes is insignificant compared to the enormous turnover in the trade with coral skeletons. The high costs of the transport and the enormous freight expenses thus incurred already set a limit to the trade in live corals. At the same time huge amounts of large, magnificent coral structures are quarried worldwide, bleached in chlorine and exported to Europe and North America by shiploads, where they are bought by collectors for ornamental purposes (bric-à-brac to decorate living-rooms, bathrooms and even lavatories). Unfortunately they are also bought by aquarists.

Keeping live corals in coral reef aquaria is a chance to arouse interest in biological processes and to make people aware of the necessity of the conservation of nature. Dead corals are neither natural, nor beautiful or interesting. We do not want them in our modern coral reef aquaria!

Moreover, perfect copies of coral skeletons hardly different from the originals may be produced by casting them in plastic material. In the USA such copies have been on sale for a number of years al-

The old-fashioned way of decorating the marine aquarium does not provide the natural look of underwater scenery at all.

ready. By now they are also being sold worldwide. So if an aquarist thinks he cannot do without coral skeletons to decorate his tank, he should at least use these artificial ones.

Bivalve and snail shells

Large bivalve and snail shells are often used for the decoration of coral reef aquaria. We think that aquarists should refrain from using them. Smaller shells may be integrated into the decoration as hiding-places for certain animals that prefer them. Yet we do not encourage this because the same effect can be achieved in a better and more natural way by using limestone or living rocks. In order to keep hermit crabs however, it is necessary to provide a range of empty snail shells for the crabs to choose from when the time comes for them to "move house".

Aquarium ground

In coral reefs large sandy areas can only be found in certain zones. Elsewhere living rocks and coral formations are the substrate on which animals can settle. Thus, except in an aquarium emulating the conditions in the sand zone of a coral reef, it is quite natural not to introduce a large amount of material as aquarium bottom. Only small spaces between the decoration objects are filled with coral sand, ground limestone, living rocks, crushed shells or special artificial aquarium ground. Aquarium gravel, as used in freshwater aquaria, or fine sand from a beach may **not** be used.

If animals that like to dig are kept in the aquarium, for example jawfishes of the genus *Opistognathus*, wrasses of the genus *Coris*, pistol shrimps or seapens, the aquarium ground should be considerably deeper in several places. Normally the layer of gravel should be rather thin having a maximum thickness of about 1 or 2 cm. In special operated systems like the "Jaubert System" (see chapter 12) the bottom has a thick layer of gravel. The bottom sub-

A modern coral reef aquarium inhabited by a careful choice of fishes and invertebrates and decorated by someone with a sense of harmony gives the impression of looking through a window on a real underwater scene.

strate fills a decorative as well as a biological effect and so we do not recommend a bare bottom.

Decoration of the aquarium background

The limited space available in an aquarium poses the greatest problem in the creation of an impressive scenery. The distance between the front and the rear glass is usually quite small, which results in an unnatural impression that lacks the illusion of depth. As a modern coral reef aquarium is normally decorated with constructions that reach to the surface of the water, this adverse effect may be reduced. Much more impressive effects may be achieved, however, if the decoration of the aquarium is planned and laid out with the goal

effects; the aquarist will have to experiment to determine what works best.

Live organisms

The organisms living in an aquarium are its most characteristic detail. In a freshwater aquarium usually plants are the dominating element of the decoration. What impresses us most in a coral reef aquarium are the animals, i.e. different groups of sessile invertebrates, and also the algae. Corals, anemones, sponges, fanworms all may be dominant elements of the decoration. Their size and form and the decorative effect that they create must be taken into account when the rock formation on which they will be placed is set up. All the animals have to be positioned in such a way that their main characteristics are shown to advantage. At the same time their physical requirements have to be met, e. g. their hydrodynamic adaptability and their demand for light must be taken into consideration. Stony corals, giant clams or other large and heavy animals can only be positioned to their advantage if their needs are not neglected when the aquarium is set up and decorated.

① Invertebrates

Usually corals are placed on living rocks where they find sufficient support. In most cases this method works well, but it may be difficult to place them in a position which reflects their natural way of growing. Moreover this method might cause the impression that the decoration of the tank is just a "pile of stones"; an impression that we want to avoid, of course. Corals only supported by loose pieces of rock may tilt as well, which will keep them from growing onto the decoration firmly. Some types of corals will even die if they are not positioned and fixed on the decoration in exactly the right way. Thus the magnificent orange *Tubastraea* species have to be placed upside down (their

In a modern coral reef aquarium the sessile invertebrates dominate the overall impression of the decoration. It is important to make colours and shapes harmonize in a natural way. The demands of the animals kept in the tank, however, are of prime importance.

of creating an illusion of great depth.

To do this many aquarists place a compartment against the back glass of the tank, a diorama. This compartment appears to be a continuation of the aquarium scenery and creates the impression of an underwater seascape fading away into the distance by degrees. The form of this box, square, triangular or semicircular, can be adapted to the space that is available. It should, however, always be as deep as possible. It is important to use the same materials in the diorama as in the tank. In order to create a greater illusion of depth and of a large quantity of water, an opaque sheet of plexiglass may be inserted into this construction. Different lighting installations above the diorama (see page 105) will create different

Sessile invertebrates can be attached to rocks and other pieces of decoration with plastic cable ties.

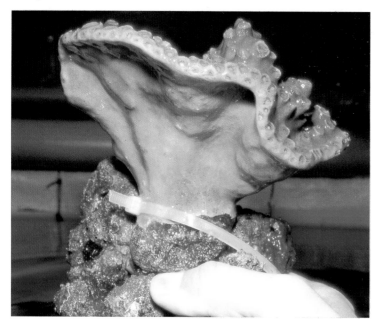

c) Even though reef aquascapes can be arranged using cable ties and PVC-tubes, the very best material for cementing corals to the rocks are the so-called "underwater epoxys". Dentist wax or dental cement have previously been used, but these materials cannot compete with underwater epoxys in applicability. In our experience these epoxys are the best material so far for attaching cuttings as well as smaller or larger colonies to rocks. Epoxys are useful even for rock to rock attachment. By using epoxys we have the very best possibility to make a highly natural decoration. It is important, though, to first build a basis of living rocks, which lay steady.

A typical underwater epoxy is the American product AquaStik™ (see the pictures on page 121). It consists of two components which react when kneaded, and it hardens under water in 20 minutes. Full strength occurs after 24 hours. It has the natural pink colour of calcareous algae, and thereby blends well with the surroundings.

The use is most simple: Twist or cut off the required amount and mix the epoxy between your fingers for about one minute until it has uniform colour. The mixed epoxy must be used within two minutes, which makes it important to know where the object will be placed before starting the mixing.

As the freshly mixed epoxy does not exhibit bond strength at the beginning, it is important to support large colonies or rocks, in order to prevent them from loosening before the epoxy has cured. Such support can be accomplished with rubber bands, cable ties or monofilament lines etc. The epoxy can even be used to mount small pieces of corals and rocks straight on a glass wall, but the glass must be cleaned first with a razor blade. A good idea is to support the pieces being attached to glass by means of algae cleaning magnets until the epoxy cures.

We have found the underwater epoxy to be especially suitable for mounting small cuttings of stony corals to living rocks. Tiny cuttings

tops hanging downwards) if they are to thrive.

We would like to describe some methods of attaching corals to the tank decoration that might help to solve even some of the more difficult problems:

a) To fasten coral to larger pieces of live rock (which for their part have to be fixed firmly to the rest of the decoration) we use plastic cable ties (as used by electricians to bind cable harnesses together). These cable ties are soon grown over by calcareous algae or the corals themselves, thus they become hidden.

b) In order to fix corals to vertical reef walls or overhanging rocks, holes have to be drilled into the rock and into the bottom side of the coral itself. Always take care not to drill too deep to avoid damage to live tissue. A plastic screw of just the right length and diameter is driven into the hole in the bottom of the coral and the screw head is pressed into the hole in the rock. Thus the coral may be fixed in a most natural position.

Above: A hole is drilled into a brain coral (left). A plastic screw is driven into this hole and the screw head is then inserted into a hole in a live rock. Epoxy could be used in combination to secure the screw in the holes.

Below: The pictures show the underwater epoxy AquaStik™ and how to use it (further explanations see text on pages 120 through 122).

The stony coral *Tubastraea coccinea* is not easy to keep. It may be placed "upside down" in the aquarium with the help of a plastic screw used to hang it under a ledge. Epoxy cement can also be used to attach it to rock or to the aquarium wall.

of for instance *Acropora* spp. (see the left picture at the bottom of page 121), are easily rocked by currents, and therby hindered from attaching firmly and starting to grow. Although epoxy does not attach to live tissue, it will form a good, steady foundation that prevents cuttings from moving. The tissue will soon grow over the epoxy, and cover the material completely (see the right picture at the bottom of page 121).

Most sponges, sea squirts and some corals need a location in the shade. Therefore they must be placed under an overhanging piece of rock or in a cave and still be within sight of the viewer.

Invertebrates with symbiotic zooxanthellae need a higher amount of light. The needs of those demanding the most light can only be satisfied by placing them as high in the tank as possible, i.e. as close as possible to the source of light, right beneath the surface of the water.

A lot of animals, especially soft corals, mushroom and colonial anemones grow quickly, sometimes reaching twice their size within a few months. This growing demand for space must be taken into consideration when their positions are chosen.

Stony corals also grow fast in the modern coral reef aquarium. We highly recommend to build an aquarium where stony corals are the dominant group of corals. Such an aquarium is best started from the use of small stony coral off-springs. Several cuttings can be cemented with underwater epoxy where their potential size and growth shape are taken into consideration. Given good conditions combined with the aquarist being a bit patient, the result is a small reef slowly rising from the rocks. To watch this happening is

In the following series of pictures (on this and the next pages) we show a method of preparing small and delicate corals with a pair of tweezers and plastic needles or plastic hooks in such a way that they can be fixed on the decoration.

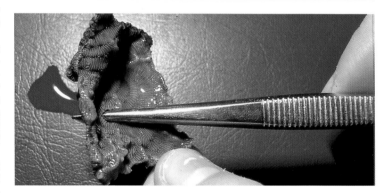

Above: A small hole is pierced into the coral with a tweezers. This has to be done cautiously to avoid breaking the coral. Below: A hole is pierced into a live rock if there is no suitable natural opening into wich the plastic pin would fit.

 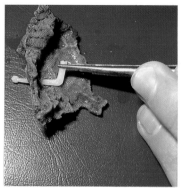

Before the coral is put into position the aquarist has to make sure that the plastic pin fits tightly into the holes in the coral and the live rock.

The coral is fixed to the stone (above) which is then placed in a still zone of the decoration (below). The coral will soon start growing and will grow onto the substrate, anchoring its tissue on the rock surface. We should be aware of the fact that excessive algae growth may impede this process.

interesting and exciting, and in the process one learns a lot about the different stony corals themselves, how they are influenced by light and current and how they all have different growth speeds and growth shapes.

② Algae

Algae are a part of every coral reef aquarium. This holds true particularly for the red calcareous algae which dominate most coral reefs. Most living rocks are covered completely by the lichen-like growth of these algae in all shades of red and violet. There are also several decorative green calcareous algae as well as red and brown algae.

Several species of the genus *Caulerpa*, which are green algae, are extremely common in coral reef aquaria. As these algae like to grow rampant we have to make sure they are not allowed to dominate the overall impression of a modern coral reef aquarium. Apart from calcareous algae an excessive growth of algae does not look natural in a coral reef aquarium which is in good order.

Résumé

When you set up and decorate a new coral reef aquarium there is a host of important points to be heeded. An experienced aquarium dealer, knowledgeable marine aquarists as friends and good books pertaining to this subject are of great help. It is always worthwhile planning this task thoroughly before it is begun, and "Think first, act later" is the best motto to act upon.

Colourful sponges, tunicates, and soldierfish commonly inhabit shady regions.
Underwater photos: R. Heselhaus (above and below) and Dr. H. Moosleitner (right)

Chapter 5

Modern Coral Reef Aquaria

In many tropical countries reef animals are collected for aquaria. Aquarium shops display and sell fishes and invertebrates from areas which are far apart geographically. Most of the animals on sale in our shops come from the Asiatic area and are imported via Singapore, Indonesia and the Philippines. Fishes from the Red Sea, East Africa, the Maldives, Sri Lanka, Australia, Hawaii and the Caribbean are on offer on a regular basis as well. These animals not only come from different reefs, they also come from different zones within these reefs.

Dendronephthya spp. can grow in full sunlight, and they do so in the Red Sea, Fiji, and elsewhere - though usually they prefer shade.

Nocturnal fishes, like soldierfishes of the genus *Myripristis* are not suited for a well-lighted aquarium with a low water level and without any caves or other appropriate hiding places. Batfishes, *Platax* spp., would hardly be able to move around in an aquarium with densely growing corals, whereas the same surroundings will create a feeling of well-being in damsel-

Nature can give us inspiration for ways to decorate a modern coral reef aquarium. The pictures to the left and above show underwater scenes from the Red Sea at a depth of 18 metres.

Underwater photos: O. Gremblewski-Strate

A magnificent pair of *Pomacanthus maculosus* in their natural surrounding in the Red Sea.

Underwater photo: D. Heimig

fishes of the genus *Chromis* and basslets of the genus *Pseudanthias*. Many of the animals cannot be kept together because they may harm or even kill each other. There are at least several species of fishes that should not be kept together in a small aquarium with corals or other delicate invertebrates. For certain angel- and butterflyfishes coral polyps are a staple food. Fish also often feed on polychaete worms and small shrimps. For the same reason large predatory fishes like moray eels, scorpion- or anglerfishes may not be kept together with smaller fish and crustaceans. Moreover the excretions of large fish, especially predators, pollute the aquarium water so heavily that they should most certainly not be introduced into a small coral reef aquarium with its sensitive invertebrates.

Tube anemones of the genus *Cerianthus* are one example of invertebrates that have to be treated with utmost care. The poison in their nematocysts is so strong that other sessile animals have to be placed at a safe distance to avoid damage to them.

It is no problem at all to set up aquaria which are especially adjusted to the needs of certain groups of animals: for example special aquaria for batfishes, small sharks and predatory hermit crabs, or an aquarium which meets the necessary requirements of animals living in a symbiotic relationship, like certain anemones and their partners in symbiosis. It is also highly interesting to set up an aquarium in such a way that the chances for fishes or invertebrates to reproduce are increased considerably. Last, but not least there are also aquarists who would like to have a community tank only for marine fishes, probably also because they want to dodge all the problems which are inevitably caused by an aquarium with invertebrates.

We hold the opinion, however, that in many respects the attempt to keep fishes and invertebrates successfully together in a community tank is one of the most interesting ways to set up a modern coral reef aquarium. The conditions in such a tank resemble natural conditions most closely. There is a wide range of choices in the design of aquaria and their decoration and, as we all know, there is no accounting for taste.

The most popular type of a coral reef aquarium is a community tank in which fishes and invertebrates have been brought together more or less arbitrarily, availability being the only guiding principle in their selection. Such an aquarium can be very beautiful, as a number of pictures in this book prove. Therefore it is a matter of course that in this chapter we will also give some guidelines for the creation of a community tank. After gaining considerable practical experience in the hobby an aquarist may feel inclined to try out some new ideas. We would therefore also like to deal at length with coral reef aquaria that are laid out especially for animals with particular demands on their surroundings. Such aquarium systems provide the aquarist with new challenges and tasks.

Fish aquarium

Many of the most beautiful and most conspicuous fishes of the coral reef are difficult to combine with invertebrates in a regular coral reef aquarium. This is partly due to their eating habits (for example many coral feeding butterfly- and angelfishes), and partly a result of a large adult size, which frequently entails a large degree of water pollution (for example large scorpionfishes, groupers and sharks). This is most unfortunate, because the spectacular beauty and colouration of such fishes, often are the main incentives for many people to start with a marine aquarium.

The consequence frequently is that new aquarists end up with a highly artificial looking aquarium, which bears very little resemblance to the natural reef biotope. Although the fish aquarium hardly can become a typical coral reef aquarium in the common comprehension of the term, we still think it is achievable to make even such aquaria much more decorative, natural appearing, and interesting than what traditionally has been the case. You can make a fish aquarium without having to rely on artificial decorations and coral skeletons alone.

Size and shape

There are no general requirements as to the shape and size of this type of aquarium. It will, of course, depend fully on the requirements of the actual species one wants to keep. In most cases, the box shaped aquaria commonly on sale are perfectly appropriate. As the majority of the fish species normally taken into consideration grow to a very large size, the aquarium chosen for them should be as large as possible.

Technical equipment

We often find that marine aquaria with a lot of large fish are grown over with "slime" or "smear" algae (blue-green algae). This is certainly due to the very high organic pollution of the aquarium water. Very effective protein skimming is needed to reduce this pollution. A powerful mechanical filter will remove suspended particles which would otherwise cloud the water. If there are only a few live rocks in the aquarium, it is recommended to install a biological filter, for example a trickle filter.

When many and/or large fishes are present, nitrates often tend to build up. In such cases the inclusion of a denitrification filter can prove useful. An aquarium exclusively for fish does not require any special lighting installations. If one includes any sessile invertebrates, their light requirements must, however, be taken into account.

Setting up and decoration

We can style the aquarium scenery mainly to our own taste. We have to take care, however, that we provide enough hiding-places, as otherwise the fish will become jumpy and easily startled. Large open swimming space is also of prime importance. We always re-

The Orangespotted Filefish, *Oxymonacanthus longirostris*, is a highly specialized coral polyp feeder. It prefers *Acropora* spp., but also feeds on other corals such as *Pocillopora* sp., as seen in this photo taken in an exhibit in the Waikiki Aquarium, Honolulu, Hawaii. In order to maintain both the fish and the coral, there must be sufficient quantity of corals. In time the fish can adapt to other foods, but we do not consider it a good choice for the novice.

The Orbiculate Batfish, Platax orbicularis, attains a length of 50 cm.

The Blackbacked Butterflyfish, *Chaetodon melanotus*, feeds on soft and stony corals.

commend the use of live rocks even if the organisms on their surface to some extent are eaten off by the fish.

Stocking the aquarium

❶ Algae

Whether algae are able to thrive in an aquarium depends mainly on the fish species that are kept with them. A number of species do not touch the algae whereas others will feed on them and often consume all of them. Frequently, several of the *Caulerpa* spp. are an excellent choice.

❷ Invertebrates

Often the chances of successful introduction of selected invertebrates into a fish aquarium are quite good. The actual selection will have to depend on the predatory habits of the fishes, and on the achievable water quality.

Many of the best known coral predators are highly specialized on eating particular species of stony corals. Soft corals, however, typically contain high concentrations of terpenes, which are highly toxic to most fish species and thereby act as a protection against predation (this will be further discussed in volume 2). The more robust and fast-growing soft coral species, particularly of the genera *Capnella*, *Nephthea* and *Sinularia*, could thus be a good choice, even for combination with many butterfly- and angelfishes.

In addition it will frequently be possible to add some photosynthetic gorgonians (which also contain toxic terpenes), sea anemones and mushroom anemones, as well as echinoderms and a variety of crustaceans, including cleaner shrimps and hermit crabs.

As for aquaria where the level of water pollution is the limiting factor, one will have to select species which can adapt to high nutrient levels. Several coral species are found in nutrient rich habitats. These include stony corals like *Catalaphyllia jardinei* and *Galaxea fascicularis*. We have to refer to volume 2 for further specifics.

Note that the most important condition for correct selection of animals to combine in the aquarium is a careful study of their biology, eating habits etc.

❸ Fishes

As a fish aquarium is intended for species which are difficult to keep in the typical coral reef aquarium, we will refrain from enumerating fish species that could just as well be introduced into one of the types of coral reef aquaria that we describe on the following pages.

Our suggestions of fish species for the fish aquarium are as follows:

– most (angelfishes) of the family Pomacanthidae;
– butterflyfishes of the family Chaetodontidae (stay away, however, from food specialists which are impossible to keep alive in an aquarium for long, like for example *Chaetodon trifasciatus*);
– parrotfishes of the family Scaridae;
– most triggerfishes, filefishes, boxfishes and pufferfishes of the order Tetraodontiformes;
– most large growing fish species, which are big eaters and tend to pollute the water to such an extent that they cannot be kept in a traditional reef tank. These include batfishes of the genus *Platax*, lionfishes of the genus *Pterois*, several groupers of the family Serranidae, as well as rays and sharks. Bear in mind that some of these also demand extremely large aquaria.

Sharks are one example of fishes which, due to their size and appetite, are difficult to combine with invertebrates unless special precautions are taken. In its 80,000 litre shark aquarium, the Aquaria Vattenmuseum in Stockholm, Sweden, has nevertheless managed to combine five sharks and some hundred smaller fishes with a selection of soft corals and anemones, thereby creating a much more pleasing and natural looking exhibit. In this particular exhibit protein skimming and a large denitrification filter manage to keep the water quality reasonably good, despite the high load on the system. The nitrate concentration is kept at a maximum of 25 mg/litre.

Photo: Akvaria Vattenmuseum

Community aquarium

When we set up a community aquarium there is no need to pay any special attention to the geographical origin or the original biotope that the animals come from. The aquarist usually buys the fish or the other organisms that he finds interesting and available. The basic idea of such an aquarium is to associate many different species without disregarding their natural way of life and their well-being.

Size and shape

Concerning the shape of this type of aquarium there are no special rules. The common box shaped aquarium, triangular, polygonal or semicircular form will do fine. Its capacity should not be less than 150 litres, as many of the corals that are usually kept in there will grow to enormous sizes.

Technical equipment

The technical equipment used usually depends on the financial means that are available. Restrictions to the choice of equipment, however, may result in limitations to the range of species that may be associated. The basic principle is that the technical equipment used must be appropriate to the species that are kept. The plans for the aquarium setup should follow the rules described in this volume.

Setting up and decorating

When we set up a community tank we should do it with the aesthetic impression in mind that it should later have on the people who look at it. It is worthwhile giving the underwater scenery as much variety as possible. If the lighting and the flow pattern in the water

In a community aquarium the peaceableness of the animals and their wellbeing are the only principles which are of greater importance than the ...

column are favourable we will be able to keep together even animals that demand different living conditions.

Stocking the aquarium

❶ Algae

There are a lot of different species of algae that may be introduced into a community tank. We have to take care, however, that algae should never be allowed to overgrow and suppress sessile organisms.

❷ Invertebrates

The range of invertebrates available is enormous. We would like to recommend some fast growing and relatively hardy species for the beginner. It is dependent on the setup of the decoration whether species that prefer a lot of light and those that like less can be kept in one and the same aquarium.

The obvious choices among the abundant number of corals are the soft corals of the genera *Alcyonium, Cladiella, Lemnalia,*

... aquarist's wishes to set up the aquarium in such a way that it appeals to the viewer's sense of beauty.

The choice of the fishes for a community aquarium is much more of a problem than the choice of the invertebrates. This is so because we do not know very much about the feeding habits of most of the fishes. But even if we know the most important facts about these, it is still difficult enough to compose a suitable community for an aquarium of this type. A number of fish species do go together well with corals, yet like to feed on smaller fishes, shrimps or other small crustaceans. This holds true for example for the Comet, *Calloplesiops altivelis*, for most of the hawkfishes of the family Cirrhitidae, the Ribbon Eel, *Rhinomuraena quaesita*, and scorpionfishes from the family Scorpaenidae. Fortunately there are lots of fishes that can be mixed successfully with invertebrates as well as smaller fish species. The following list contains the most important and the most easily available species and genera:

– tangs of the genus *Zebrasoma*;
– anemonefishes of the genera *Amphiprion* and *Premnas*;
– damselfishes of the genera *Chromis*, *Chrysiptera*, *Dascyllus*;
– cardinalfishes of the genus *Sphaeramia*;
– algae-eating blennies from the family Blenniidae;
– gobies from the genera *Ambly-eleotris*, *Amblygobius*, *Cryptocentrus*, *Gobiosoma*, *Nemateleotris*, *Ptereleotris*, *Valenciennea*;
– dragonets of the genus *Synchiropus*.

If we are ready to accept that now and then one of the shrimps may get eaten, the very colourful *Pseudochromis* spp. and *Gramma loreto*, the Royal Gramma, are good company in such an aquarium as well. Pygmy angelfishes of the genus *Centropyge* are just as well worth a try. You should always keep in mind that some of the corals in the tank may come to harm because of these fishes.

Sarcophyton and *Sinularia*, the mushroom anemones of the genus *Discosoma* and colonial anemones, Zoanthiniaria. The species from the family Xeniidae, genus *Xenia* are especially interesting, and they are imported quite regularly. Some stony corals, e. g. from the genera *Trachyphyllia* and *Heliofungia*, which can often be found in imports from South-east-Asia, are also very well suited for a community tank if it has a stable biological milieu.

Large symbiotic anemones are less suitable as they are able to move around considerably and may damage other animals with their poisonous sting. Small sand anemones, however, are much more appropriate. Many species of shrimps and other peaceful crustaceans make good tank mates for a coral reef community aquarium. Still, it is advisable not to associate too many different species. Particularly if a great number of different soft corals are kept together the underwater scenery may soon bear witness of the collecting mania of the aquarist rather than the beauty of a coral reef.

12,000 litre community aquarium in a separate aquarium room.

 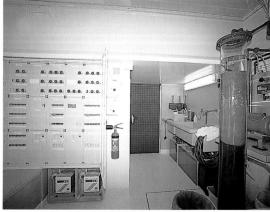

Room for the technical equipment of the aquarium pictured above.

Community aquarium in the home of L. Moritz, Siegburg, Germany.

5,000 litre community aquarium in a living room.

Top: This mangrove/seagrass zone aquarium designed by Exotic Aquaria, Inc. of Miami, Florida, and aquascaped by Julian Sprung is located on a balcony where it receives natural sunlight. It has tidal fluctuation and is connected to a chiller outside and the coral reef aquarium inside, in the adjacent living room.

Left: In the Waikiki Aquarium, Honolulu, Hawaii, we have seen some very interesting aquaria in which stony corals were kept. The material from which these aquaria are made is PVC, and they are placed outside the building, where they are flooded with sunlight. There is a continual flow of natural seawater through these tanks. The colouration (pigmentation) of the stony corals is remarkable. Bruce Carlson, director of the aquarium, admires the view from above in natural sunlight

Right: This reef pinnacle in a community tank displays a marvellous combination and great variety of reef organisms.

Below: Friends are looking at the wonderful coral reef aquarium of Enrico Enzmann, Geretsried, Germany. A multitude of invertebrates thrive and reproduce in this tank.

Photo: E. Enzmann

Sand zone aquarium

The sand zone is the natural habitat of a number of species that are commonly for sale in our aquarium shops. They are not really well suited for the community tank that we just described. For these animals we suggest a coral reef aquarium with a wide sand zone. This is also the correct biotope for keeping the interesting seagrasses, true angiosperm flowering plants.

Size and shape

The ground space of the aquarium should be as large as possible with the front and back glass far apart. The height is only of secondary importance. An attractive decoration with an appealing impression on the viewer may be much more easily designed in a larger aquarium with at least 400 to 500 litres capacity. It is certainly true that you can do with less, but it is much more difficult to create a pleasing sight and the diversity of the animals that may be kept in a small tank is considerably restricted.

Furthermore it could be highly interesting to design the aquarium such that it can be looked into from above as well as from the front. A front glass pane placed at a 45 ° angle could be one possible solution for achieving this.

Technical equipment

For this type of aquarium we mostly use the technical equipment generally used in a coral reef aquarium. Such equipment has been described in other chapters of this volume. As the sand zones we try to copy are areas with little water turbulence, there should only be a slight water movement in such an aquarium, at least in the sand zones.

Above: This reef wall in the Coral Sea borders a sand zone at a depth of 25 metres. The scenery offers quite a number of interesting new suggestions for the planning and layout of a modern coral reef aquarium with a sand zone.

Below: A huge stock of *Goniopora* sp. grows in a sand zone of a reef in the Red Sea at a depth of 20 metres.

Underwater photo: O. Gremblewski-Strate

Above: The Little Tree Anemone, *Actinodendron arboreum*, we found on the sandy ground of a shallow lagoon. It has especially venemous nematocysts. This specimen lived in a deep sand hole of about 5 cm diameter. When disturbed, it withdrew immediately into the hole. The tentacles were inhabited by a pair of a *Periclimenes brevicarpalis*.

Above: A school of young Bluelined Snappers, *Lutjanus kasmira*, above sandy ground in a shallow lagoon.

Above: This sponge from the class Demospongiae lives on the sandy ground of a reef flat, where the light intensity reaches 60,000 lux. Such organisms might be very well suited for a sand zone aquarium with a high light intensity.

Below: Magnus' Prawngoby, *Amblyeleotris sungami* (left), and the Spotted Gardeneel, *Heteroconger hassi* (right), at a depth of 3 m in the Red Sea.   Underwater photos: T. Luther

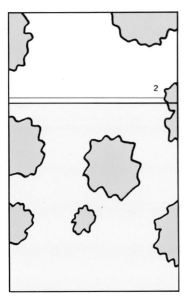

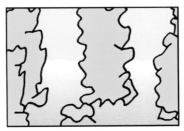

The biotope that we model the sand zone aquarium on is a shallow lagoon, so the light intensity has to be kept at a very high level. As a sand zone aquarium definitely must have a thick layer of bottom substrate, it is highly advisable to make use of the Jaubert-system (as described in chapter 12), or an adaptation thereof. Otherwise there will be a much higher risk of reductive processes within the substrate causing disturbances in the aquarium system.

Setting up and decorating

The aquarium scenery should be designed in such a way that the sand zone gives the impression of dwindling away towards the rear, towards the "horizon". This impression can be intensified by reducing the lighting of the areas at the back of the aquarium. To avoid monotony in the sand scenery some pillars, for example live rock, limestone constructions, or artificial decoration material with some live rock added to it may be placed in suitable positions. A blue acrylic pane placed behind the aquarium will create the impression of a natural transition towards "infinity". A diorama, a dry compartment behind the aquarium in which the decoration is continued, will further intensify the depth effect.

The bottom substrate in this type of aquarium should be coral sand, finely crushed limestone or a substrate mix as it is produced by the aquarium industry. Whatever you choose, you should make sure that the material used has such a fine grain that the sand zone animals will have no problems and cannot hurt themselves when digging in it. Most of the animals that can be taken into consideration for a sand zone aquarium need a 10 to 15 cm layer of bottom substrate.

Stocking the aquarium

❶ Algae and true plants

The sand zone is the true home of the fascinating seagrasses. In many sandy and silty shallows they are extremely abundant, forming extensive beds. Such seagrass fields are important breeding grounds for numerous fishes and invertebrates, and even home to some species of coral.

Some seagrass species have been shown to grow very well, although frequently slowly, in aquaria. Species worth trying are *Cymodocea serrulata, Enhalus acoroides, Halodule beaudettei, H. pinifolia, Syringodium filiforme, S. isoetifolium, Thalassia testudinum,* and *T. hemprichii.*

Mangrove trees, particularly *Rhizophora* spp., have also been shown to grow well in marine aquaria, and are highly appropriate as borderline vegetation in a sand zone aquarium.

Among algae species, it could be particularly worthwhile to intro-

This coral reef aquarium by R. Latka, Rastatt, Germany, displays a successful combination of a sand zone with reef walls, reef pinnacles, and reef crevices. In such an aquarium a multitude of reef organisms from different microhabitats can be associated and kept successfully.　　　　Photo: R. Latka

Sand zone with seagrass at low tide off Bunaken, North Sulawesi, Indonesia.

Searching for animals in the sand zone of an Indonesian reef.

Mangrove trees, *Rhizophora* sp., bordering a sandy flat in the Florida Keys.

duce certain species of *Caulerpa, Halimeda, Penicillus,* and *Udotea.* See chapter 13 for further details. In addition there is a wealth of other algae which will attach and grow on rock substratum present in the biotope.

❷ Invertebrates

Starting with anemones, the beautiful *Stichodactyla gigantea,* which is host to many anemone fishes, is a frequent inhabitant of sandy zones. The small sand an-

emones of the genus *Phymanthus* also occur in the sand substrate. They are quite often available in aquarium shops, are inexpensive and easy to keep, but very decorative. They go very well with anemone crabs of the genus

Left: A healthy specimen of the Wonder Coral, *Catalaphyllia jardinei,* growing on sand with *Thalassia*-seagrass. Right: Interior from a sand zone aquarium with *Thalassia hemprichii* and the stony coral *Montipora digitata* (both photos taken at the Waikiki Aquarium, Honolulu, Hawaii).

Petrolisthes and symbiotic or partner shrimps of the genus *Pericli-menes*.

Other crustaceans suitable for these surroundings are pistol shrimps of the genera *Alpheus* and *Synalpheus*. They are imported primarely from Indonesia and the Caribbean and are the most common prawns in reef lagoons. They live in a symbiotic relationship with certain gobies (see below). This relationship between crustaceans and prawn-gobies or the symbiosis of anemones and crustaceans may very well be the focal point of this type of coral reef aquarium.

A single reef lobster, *Enoplo-metopus* sp., is a superb eye-catcher in a sand zone aquarium. A group of tube-building polychaet worms may also create a very impressive effect. *Sabellastarte indica*, the featherduster worm, which is regularly on sale, will do very nicely. Digging sea cucumbers, holothurians, and brittle stars also do very well on a sandy ground. As they feed on detritus, they are useful for cleaning the bottom substrate.

Three species of stony corals which are imported frequently, the Mushroom Coral, *Heliofungia actiniformis*, the Wonder Coral, *Catalaphyllia jardinei*, and the Open Brain Coral, *Trachyphyllia geoffroyi*, are found in biotopes with sandy ground and therefore thrive in a sand zone aquarium. So will the less frequently seen *Montipora digitata*, which is very abundant in some sandy areas of Indo-Pacific reefs.

The excellent aquarium species *Pocillopora damicornis* is, in nature, often found growing on the roots of mangrove trees, and could possibly be used similarly in the aquarium.

One or several species of fast growing soft corals, for example several of the beautiful and hardy *Sinularia* spp., are the most suitable coral animals to be placed on the pillars described above. They grow profusely and are not very demanding. Alternative corals that will do well in this position are *Sarcophyton*, *Lobophytum*, *Alcyonium*, and *Cladiella* spp.

❸ Fishes

In an aquarium with pistol shrimps symbiotic prawn-gobies of the genera *Cryptocentrus* or *Amblyeleotris* are an absolute must. Jawfishes of the genus *Opistognathus* are also first choice for a sand zone aquarium. As an alternative to these smaller fish species it could also seem like a good idea to include a Blue Spotted Ray, *Taeniura lymma*, yet that means elimi-

Anemones of the genus *Phymanthus* are well suited for modern coral reef aquaria, especially for a sand zone aquarium. They make excellent hosts for anemone shrimps, like *Periclimenes brevicarpalis* in this case, or for anemone crabs.

The beautiful Lyretail Hoogfish, *Bodianus anthioides*, lives in an area where reef slope and sand zone coincide. Though it is a little bit aggressive against other fishes and feeds on invertebrates like crustaceans, brittle stars, and star fishes, it is well suited for a larger sand zone aquarium.   Underwater photo: T. Luther

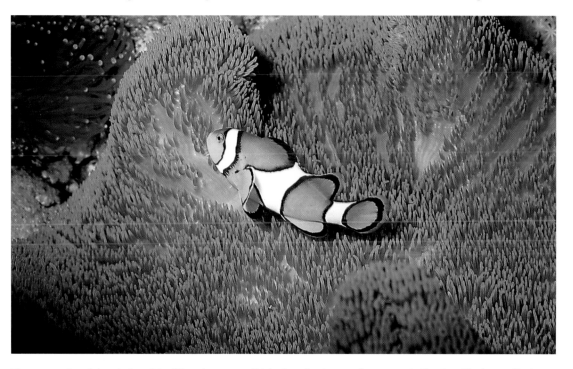

The many colourful varieties of the Giant Anemone, *Stichodactyla gigantea*, here occupied by *Amphiprion ocellaris*, are eye-catchers in any sand zone aquarium (photo taken at Löbbecke Museum and Aquazoo, Düsseldorf, Germany).

The Bluespotted Ray, *Taeniura lymma*, is a common fish in sand zones, but due to its size it is not suited for a "normal" private coral reef aquarium.   Underwater photo: O. Gremblewski-Strate

nating all crustaceans. In addition the sheer size of this fish will entail possible water quality problems. Moreover most people will not know what to do with such a ray when it starts to outgrow its aquarium. An adamant NO is the only good answer if we find fish species on sale for which the space available in our aquarium is not sufficient.

Flounders or soles, for example *Bothus* spp. or others, are only rarely imported, yet they would make up an excellent completion of the fish community of a sand zone aquarium. This is also true for the frogfishes of the genus *Anten-* *narius*. They are often found in the vicinity of sand zones.

Groups of damselfishes of the genus *Chromis* or of the colourful basslets of the genus *Pseudanthias* are the most suitable species to populate the water column around the pillars.

Nemateleotris magnifica is imported quite regularly. We found it off the Maldives at a depth of 10 m or more, always in pairs or in small groups and always over sandy ground. It digs small caves there in which it can hide. Aquarists should try to emulate these living conditions in the aquarium.

This view of a sand zone in a lagoon at a depth of 10 m may give valuable hints as to the way a sand zone aquarium should be decorated. Some live rocks, corals, crustaceans, and fishes brought together may result in an interesting sand zone scenery, even in a smaller tank.

Reef gorge aquarium

In coral reefs we find numerous rock crevices, gorges and channels with strong water currents. The conditions in these places result in a very special fauna and flora that especially inspire us to duplicate this environment in a coral reef aquarium.

Size and shape

To provide the space which is necessary to carry out the idea of such an aquarium the distance between its front and rear pane should be extraordinarily large (if possible as much as four or five times its width). It should preferably have a trapezoid form and become narrower towards the back. Aquaria in the standard form as they are sold in aquarium shops have to be placed in such a way that what usually are the side panes become the front and the rear pane.

Technical equipment

The main characteristic of a reef gorge aquarium is the water current that flows through the gorge. It should be strong enough to be clearly perceived. The power heads necessary to provide this current can be bought in every aquarium shop. The water at the bottom of the aquarium should flow in the opposite direction to that at the top. It is recommended to create alternating currents, for example by using pulse or interval switching devices, which are on sale in aquarium stores as well.

Setting up and decorating

The decoration objects for this kind of tank are constructed from limestone or styrofoam covered with a layer of epoxy resin or similar materials. The construction

A diver entering a reef gorge at Myrmidion Reef, Great Barrier Reef. This view can suggest a lot of details for the creation of a reef gorge aquarium.
Photo: E. Svensen

should provide hollows in which live rocks can be placed. On each side a massive reef wall should extend from the front to the back of the aquarium (see diagrams on page 146). The walls should be high enough to reach the surface of the water. Care should be taken that a sufficient number of places are supplied where invertebrates can be positioned. Corals and live rocks are fixed to the decoration in the way described in chapter 4 of this volume. Also the ground of a reef gorge aquarium may consist of massive rather than finely ground materials.

A diorama placed behind the tank, which creates (for example by an opaque acrylic pane) the illusion of a view into the endless

distance and depth of the sea, is essential for the fascinating effect which comes from a reef gorge aquarium.

Stocking the aquarium

❶ Algae

The shaded areas of a reef gorge aquarium and its hydrodynamic characteristics provide ideal conditions for seaweeds and coralline algae.

❷ Invertebrates

If the lighting system provides the reef gorge aquarium with a high light intensity, e. g. when metal halide lamps are used, fast growing

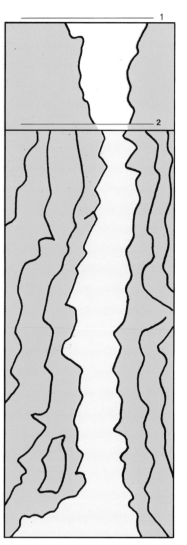

1

2

Left: Ground plan of a reef gorge aquarium. If enough space is available and one really wants something exceptional one should try to model the aquarium scenery on a reef gorge with a strong water current going through it. The gorge extends from the front to the back of the aquarium. This type of aquarium has to be much deeper than it is wide. A diorama with a blue plexiglas pane at its backside (1) and a blue plastic film on the back pane of the aquarium (2) result in a very impressive depth effect.

Below: Front view of the reef gorge aquarium.

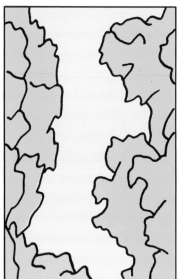

animals which need a great amount of light may be placed in the upper regions of the gorge walls. The general character of this type of aquarium results in shaded areas in the lower regions, which are very well suited for animals that do not require much light or even prefer these conditions.

Animals needing a lot of light that can be used for the reef gorge aquarium are again the soft corals that we recommended for the sand zone aquarium. They are regularly on offer, they grow fast and are not very demanding; moreover most species reproduce easily by budding. For this type of aquarium we recommend to buy only a few species and to arrange them extensively in larger numbers. Too many different species crowded together in the limited space of a reef gorge will look unnatural.

In the half shadow and the completely shaded regions of the reef gorge sponges find very favourable conditions to live and thrive. The strong current there also makes the gorge a good place for them. Before we introduce sponges into our aquarium we should always make sure that they are in good condition. Dead or dying colonies emit a foul smell and will probably exude their pigments in the aquarium water, which has an adverse effect on many cnidarians, particularly mushroom ane-

Even in a smaller aquarium a reef gorge may be emulated.

Right: This aquarium at Biotop Aquaristik, St. Augustin-Hangelar, Germany, was modelled on a reef gorge.

mones and soft corals. Substances released in the water by dying sponges are also toxic to fish.

Together with sponges you may try to keep soft corals which prefer shaded conditions, like *Alcyonium* and *Dendronephthya* spp., as well as various gorgonians, for example *Swiftia exserta*. To keep all these species successfully, frequent feedings with fine-grain foods are essential.

Mushroom anemones of the genera *Discosoma* and *Rhodactis* are very well suited to be placed on the ground substrate of a reef gorge aquarium. A suitable stony coral which requires only little light and is rather undemanding, is the Bubble Coral, *Plerogyra sinuosa*.

A pair of cleaner shrimps *Stenopus hispidus* or a group of anemone shrimps *Thor amboinensis* are also good company as long as there are no large fishes in the tank that might feed on these crustaceans. Problems may also arise, however, if shrimps are kept together with large *Rhodactis* mushroom anemones, as these anemones lead rather predatory lives at times.

❸ Fishes

There are lots of suitable fish species for a reef gorge aquarium. We suggest some surgeonfishes, *Zebrasoma* spp., a school of the Pajama Cardinalfish, *Sphaeramia nematoptera*, dartfishes of the genus *Nemateleotris*, and perhaps some pygmy angelfishes of the genus *Centropyge*. You should always keep in mind that angelfishes may do harm to corals or other invertebrates, yet there will be considerable differences in this

Right: In a reef gorge aquarium moray eels that do not grow too large, like the Ribbon Eel, *Rhinomuraena quaesita*, are good company; however they eat small crustaceans and smaller fishes.   Photo: H. Hansen

Above: Angelfishes of the genus *Centropyge*, here the Flame Angel, *C. loriculus*, may be kept together with invertebrates, even if they sometimes feed on them.

Right: The Pajama Cardinalfish, *Sphaeramia nematoptera*, is a peaceful little fish and good company for invertebrates in any aquarium.

respect between one individual and the next. If there are no crustaceans in the aquarium for them to eat, the Comet, *Calloplesiops altivelis*, the Panther Grouper, *Chromileptes altivelis*, and the smaller moray eels are also suitable inhabitants of a reef gorge aquarium. The *Assessor* spp. from the Great Barrier Reef which are closely related to the comets are also highly recommended. The guideline in choosing the fish for a reef gorge aquarium should always be the question if the fish selected will behave peaceably towards its tankmates, fish or others.

The Decorated Dartfish, *Nemateleotris decora*, is one of the most beautiful fish species that can be kept together with invertebrates.

The Yellow Prawngoby, *Cryptocentrus cinctus*, and its partner pistol shrimps are highly interesting animals for the sand zone in any aquarium.

Cave aquarium

In most modern coral reef aquaria shallow biotopes with a high light intensity are copied, a milieu which is quite suitable for the majority of the marine organisms on sale in aquarium shops. Yet divers in a reef realize before long that even in the shallow waters of a reef flat numerous caves and overhangs with a highly interesting fauna and flora are found. Several of the organisms which prefer shaded conditions are also on sale in our shops. We suggest the creation of a special cave aquarium for these animals, where they will find the best possible living conditions.

Size and shape

The surface area of the cave aquarium may be square or rectangular with a greater depth than width. The dimensions of the reef cave should be large enough to create a wide cave mouth and a sufficiently spacious interior.

Technical equipment

The two main characteristics of the cave are the water current and shadow. The animals that live here are dependent on these factors. A circulating pump with a flow rate of up to twenty times the aquarium volume, operated by a timer or a pulse control device, will create most natural conditions.

Right: Soft corals of the family Nephtheidae do not live in a symbiotic relationship with zooxanthellae. They mostly grow upsidedown in the shaded area under the overhanging rock of a cave, like here off the Maldives at a depth of 15 metres. These corals are very difficult to keep in an aquarium. A strong water current and special food are essential to keep them alive.

In a large cave in Latheef Reef off the Maldives we found numerous sponges, soft corals, stony corals, gorgonians, and fishes. It is next to impossible to recreate the composition of biological components in this cave in an aquarium, but its shape may very well serve as a model for the design of a cave aquarium.

In this cave near Arch Rock, Flinders Reef in the Coral Sea, magnificent gorgonians grow at a depth of 30 metres.

Caves sometimes offer most beautiful sights. With enough care the aquarist can design a magnificent "hole-in-the-wall-scenery".

The lighting of the cave should not be intense, and blue should be the dominating colour in its spectrum. This effect can be achieved by using blue fluorescent bulbs combined with daylight tubes (also see chapter 8). To illuminate the interior of the cave one or more fluorescent tubes can be placed outside the aquarium pane on end and hidden behind the side wall of the cave. Another way of illuminating a cave aquarium is through openings in the cave roof, which will let in "sun rays" produced by spotlights above. The light will thus reach only certain areas in the cave, a method of lighting which will produce especially decorative effects.

For animals that need more light we can create a shallow water zone (see drawings to the right), a kind of platform, on top of the cave. The light intensity should not be too high, however, because this would impede the view into the cave (the human eye adapts automatically to the brighter

area). The best way of finding the ideal amount of light for the illumination of the cave and the platform above it is by trial and error.

As we keep animals in this cave that have to be fed regularly, an effective protein skimming device is an absolute must! Moreover you should have a high-performance mechanical filtration system ready to remove surplus food from the water. This filter should be cleaned every time it has been used and should not be kept running

continually as a biological filter.

An automatic feeding device for live food (for example brine shrimps), which introduces food into the aquarium drop by drop, may be especially useful for the maintenance of a cave aquarium.

Setting up and decorating

The cave should be as spacious and as deep as possible, on the one hand to offer enough room to the animals, on the other hand to

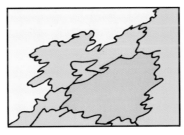

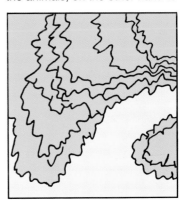

Above: View into a cave from the front of the aquarium.
Right: Cross-section of a cave aquarium from above.

Under a large piece of rubble at a depth of 3 m on the sandy ground of a lagoon off the Maldives we found a small cave. It was inhabited by the moray eel *Gymnothorax favagineus* and its "companions", two cleaner shrimps *Stenopus hispidus*. It is quite easy to replicate such an underwater scene in the aquarium.

The holaxonian coral *Swiftia exserta* has turned out to be the least demanding among those without zooxanthellae. It is ideal for a cave aquarium, but it has to be placed in a strong water current.

create a true-to-life impression of a cave biotope. There are different ways of putting up a steady construction, by fixing living rocks, limestone or other decoration objects to a framework of PVC tubes or similar materials (see chapters 4 and 7).

To provide a sight that also satisfies the viewer's aesthetic sense, it is important to create an impression of unity, i. e. the decoration materials should be put together in such a way that there are not too many openings. In the cave we provide a number of ledges and platforms on which the animals can be placed. The bottom of the cave can be decorated with live rocks or with coral sand and live rocks together.

Stocking the Aquarium

 Algae

In a cave aquarium red calcareous algae will be dominating because of the low light intensity they prefer. Red algae with leaf-like structures will also thrive because they can also do with little light. They are, however, extremely dependant on the nutrient content of the aquarium water (see chapter 13).

❷ Invertebrates

Cnidarians without zooxanthellae are generally difficult to keep. A lot of them, however, do quite well if they are fed regularly. We may recommend gorgonians such as *Swiftia exserta* and *Diodogorgia nodulifera*. These Gorgonians are frequently imported from the Caribbean and have proved to keep well. Other Gorgonians without zooxanthellae are on offer now and then and are certainly well worth a try.

Among the other corals that demand less light, the strange soft corals *Studeriotes* spp. are imported occasionally and are very well suited for the cave aquarium. The colourful *Dendronephthya* spp. are much more difficult to keep, yet they are extraordinarily decorative. In the coral reef these soft

A holaxonian coral in a blue grotto at a depth of about 22 m (above) and a soft coral of the genus *Dendronephthya* under a rock overhang at Blue Corner, Belau, at a depth of 10 metres (below).   Underwater photos: Dr. D. Brockmann

corals usually hang down from the cave roof right in front of the cave mouth – sometimes some of them are even found in the more intense light on the reef flat. We may place some hard corals with zooxanthellae like the Bubble Coral, *Plerogyra sinuosa*, in front of the cave. Sea pens, Pennatulacea, are also cnidarians very well suited for the cave aquarium.

Most sponges thrive when exposed to a reduced or even small amount of lighting. Thus remarkable sponge colonies may be grown in a cave aquarium. A number of non-sessile invertebrates may also be kept there, yet their choice is restricted to those that do not feed on sponges, like some starfish, sea urchins or snails. Among the starfishes *Linckia, Fromia*, and *Nardoa* spp. are welcome to the community of a cave aquarium. Brittle stars are completely harmless and may be kept in larger numbers. Detritus-eating sea cucumbers, like the colourful and undemanding *Holothuria* spp. are very useful as "cleaners".

Among the crustaceans there are several suitable species, for example dancing shrimps of the genus *Rhynchocinetes*, cleaner shrimps of the genera *Stenopus* and *Lysmata*, rock lobsters of the genus *Panulirus*, and reef lobsters of the genus *Enoplometopus*. There are also a number of mussels that may be considered for a cave aquarium, especially the thorny oysters of the genus *Spondylus*.

❸ Fishes

Again there is a large number of possible choices, yet we would like to restrict ourselves to **typical** cave dwellers. Unfortunately most of the fishes that live in caves feed on crustaceans, which leads to problems when we try to keep them together with shrimps. One of the typical problems of reef aquarists is that they are spoilt for choice.

The Comet, *Calloplesiops altivelis*, is a fish that was made to live in a cave aquarium, especially if you are lucky enough to find a pair on offer. A small group of Royal Gramma, *Gramma loreto*, or of the less common Blackcap Basslet, *Gramma melacara*, would also convey a beautiful impression. A lot of *Apogon* spp. are cave dwellers and schooling fish that are very suitable for this type of aquarium.

Even in a regular coral reef aquarium it often can be worthwhile to include a small cave in order to create variation and the possibility to keep particular organisms.

Tiny tubeworms of the family Sabellidae hanging from an aquarium cave roof.

The Comet, *Calloplesiops altivelis*, is among the most suitable fishes for the cave aquarium. If possible, one should buy a pair, as it is possible for them to spawn in the aquarium.

Not only the soldierfishes, but also the squirrelfishes, here the Rosset Squirrelfish, *Sargocentron rubrum*, are "friends of the night". They are hardy and undemanding species.   Underwater photo: Dr. H. Moosleitner

Reef profile aquarium

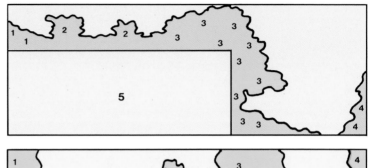

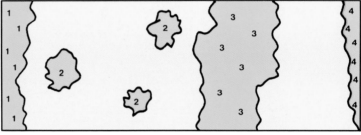

In this type of coral reef aquarium we try to replicate several reef zones: reef flat, reef edge, reef slope and fore reef (compare the diagram on page 31). The reef profile aquarium may rightly be called the "Haute êcole" of reef aquaristics. In most cases it will probably be left to only a few well-to-do specialists who can afford it. Nevertheless we would like to present it here, as it offers extraordinary possibilities for the association of a great number of organisms. A project of such a high standard requires careful planning, a lot of time and a lot of money.

Size and shape

Only extremely large tanks especially built for this purpose can be used for setting up a reef profile aquarium. Its length should be at least 3 m, width and depth should not be less than 1 m. This results in a minimum of 3000 litres gross volume. For an aquarium of that size it is necessary that it be accessible from all sides. The technical equipment takes up a lot of space and should be easily accessible.

Technical equipment

It is only a question of the money available to decide which technology and which special effects and how much of them are installed. Strong and alternating water currents, the simulation of the movement of the waves and the turn of the tides are interesting effects that may be recreated in an aquarium. Metal halide lamps with a high wattage are necessary to illuminate the water surface intensively and evenly enough. Below the surface there are always areas where the light is more intense and others where it lacks intensity, because the depth of the water is different from one place to the next.

Sketches of a reef profile aquarium:

The upper diagram shows a view from the side and the diagram below the view from above into the aquarium. The numbers indicate: 1 – shore and sand zone, 2 – reef flat with micro atolls, 3 – reef edge and reef slope, 4 – fore reef, and 5 – cavity that serves as water reservoir.

Setting up and decorating

The idea on which the design and the decoration of this type of aquarium is based is the profile of an imaginary coral reef (see drawings). The reef flat with its shallow water zone is placed above a cavity, which at the same time serves as a water reservoir. For the construction of the rock formation limestone can be used or other kinds of porous materials which are connected with cement. Thus a steep reef slope can be built up. Living rocks should be placed between the artificial material.

Stocking the aquarium

This kind of design and decoration offer extraordinary opportunities to keep various algae, invertebrates and fishes together. In such an aquarium it is possible to associate organisms with different

This reef profile aquarium which is 6 m long and holds 3000 l of water is on display in Stockholm, Sweden. The basic structure of the reef formation was made from polyurethane. In such an aquarium we have enormous possibilities ...

Trachyphyllia geoffroyi **is an undemanding stony coral which may very well be kept in a modern coral reef aquarium.**
Photo: Dr. D. Brockmann

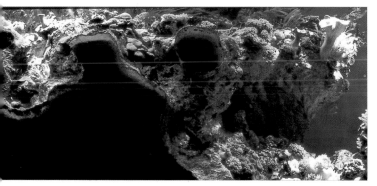

... to create different reef zones with respect to lighting and current. The options to combine various invertebrates with fishes are also great.
Photo: Aquaria Vattenmuseum

demands concerning water turbulence, illumination and ground substrate. As the reef edge nearly reaches the water surface, larger fish are kept away from the reef flat.

It is impossible to go into the details of stocking such an aquarium. As only experienced reef aquarists will set up a reef profile aquarium, we will take it for granted that they will know which fish, invertebrates and algae to choose. We would like to point out, however, that the choice of the organisms for this type of aquarium needs careful planning as well.

A soft coral probably of the genus *Sinularia* in a modern coral reef aquarium.
Photo: T. Luther

Further reading

Basics and technology:
ADEY & LOVELAND (1991); DELBEEK & SPRUNG (1994); MOE (1993); SPOTTE (1979)

Invertebrates:
ALLEN & STEENE (1994); ANDERSON (1990); BAENSCH & DEBELIUS (1992); COLIN (1978); DANCE (1977); DELBEEK & SPRUNG (1994); DITLEV (1980); FAUTIN & ALLEN (1992); GEORGE & GEORGE (1979); HUMANN (1992 and 1993a); KERSTITCH (1989); KNOP (1994); SCHMIDT & PASCHKE (1987); VERON (1986); VINE (1986); WILKENS & BIRKHOLZ (1986); WILKENS (1987); WOOD (1983)

Fishes:
ALLEN (1980 and 1991); BAENSCH & DEBELIUS (1992); BURGESS et al. (1988); DEBELIUS (1986); HUMANN (1993b and 1994); LIESKE & MYERS (1994); MYERS (1989); RANDALL et al. (1990); SMITH & HEEMSTRA (1986); STEENE (1979); THRESHER (1980)

Upper part near the surface of a modern coral reef aquarium.

Photo K. Jansen

Dendronephthya sp. at night at a depth of 20 m in the Red Sea.

Two underwater photos: O. Gremblewski-Strate

Goniopora sp. at a depth of 18 m in the Red Sea.

Chapter 6:

The Break in Period

As soon as the installation of a coral reef aquarium has been completed and it has been filled with water most aquarists crave to see it become populated with some live creatures. Some people just cannot resist the beautiful sight of colourful fish and invertebrates, which often induces them to buy animals too early. This often results in the death of the fish and in disappointment on the side of the aquarist. The reason for this is that the coral reef aquarium needs a "break in period" first; its water has to be conditioned. This period certainly tests the aquarist's patience, yet it is an absolute must.

In order to achieve results like these it is important to be patient during the first year after the set up.

It is important to know that great chemical changes take place in the water if artificially prepared saltwater is used, which is most common (see also chapter 10). The concentration of many trace elements is much higher at the beginning than in natural seawater. The elements in the aquarium water at first have an aggressive effect on live tissue.

In an aquarium newly set up **without** live rock microbial life may be so scarce that the biological milieu may be regarded as virtually sterile. In this case it will be beneficial to introduce microorganisms from a well-conditioned aquarium into the new tank.

If the new aquarium has been set up **with** live rock, the conditions are quite different. In this case vast quantities of microorganisms of different kinds are present in the aquarium from the beginning. As many of them die at first and large amounts of organic substances are released, a considerable increase in the concentration of ammonia, ammonium and nitrite is induced. At this stage it is not at all unusual to get readings of 6 or more mg per litre for the concentration of nitrite and at the same time considerable amounts of nitrate. These facts indicate quite clearly that the decomposition processes have not yet become fully established and that the biological milieu has not yet been stabilized. This accumulation of toxic substances may however be restricted by a powerful protein skimming device.

During the initial stage the biological conditions in a coral reef aquarium are virtually lethal to many organisms. Even vigorous and very robust animals are weakened to such a degree that they obviously become more susceptible to parasitic and bacterial diseases. It may take **four** to **twelve** weeks until stable populations of nitrifying bacteria (*Nitrosomonas*, *Nitrobacter*) have developed. Even if the concentrations of nitrite and nitrate have been reduced to almost zero level, higher orga-

This is a dull decoration made from non-living material. The picture does, however, clearly show the typical first spotting growth of brown diatoms most often seen during the first 2-3 weeks after the setup. Please refer to the diagram on page 164.
Photo: J. Frische

nisms must never be introduced into the aquarium before the end of four or five weeks.

During the break in period, which will take weeks, it may be interesting and helpful to monitor the concentrations of nitrate and nitrite carefully. pH readings should also be taken regularly as well as readings of the carbonate hardness (buffering capacity) and perhaps also the redox potential. The test kits necessary for these checks are on offer at aquarium shops (see also chapter 10).

Within the first few months considerable changes in the growth of the algae can be observed (see the diagram on page 164). The

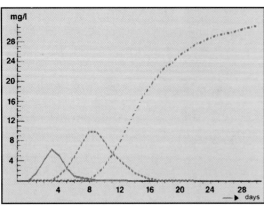

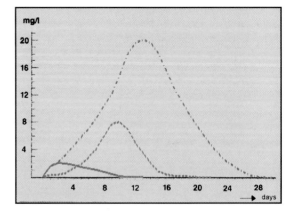

The two diagrams show the typical development of the nitrate, nitrite and ammonia in a newly set up coral reef aquarium without live rock (left) and with live rock (right) during the first days of the break in period. Red graph = ammonia; blue graph = nitrite; green graph = nitrate.

It may be hard to believe, but this picture shows the aquarium from the series of photos on pages 114 and 115 about six months after 120 kg of live rock had been introduced into it. The rocks are covered completely with filamentous algae, mostly *Derbesia* sp. and *Bryopsis* sp. One year (!) later these algae had disappeared completely and calcareous red algae were dominating. It is of utmost importance to be patient at the beginning and to refrain from taking rash steps that disturb or disrupt the process of biological stabilization.

normal course of events will be that at first diatoms will grow considerably, a development which is reduced by the decrease of the silicate concentration of the aquarium water. Soon afterwards blue-green algae will grow for a short while before green filamentous algae and perhaps leafy algae of the genus *Caulerpa* take over. This sequence, however, is not always the same, but may differ from one aquarium to another. For more information about this see chapter 13.

Among the factors that influence algae growth are filtration technology, quality of the source water (freshwater) and the materials that are used to construct the decoration of the tank. If live rock is used and a powerful protein skimming device is installed it is sometimes possible to avoid the filamentous algae, which are a nuisance, before they start growing after one or two months. If these algae do not appear the break in period will be reduced considerably. The growth of filamentous algae may also be inhibited by the competitive growth of large colonies of *Caulerpa*-algae introduced into the aquarium. This method is not absolutely safe; large amounts of *Caulerpa* spp. are not welcome in a coral reef aquarium.

Our most important objective is to avoid the growth of filamentous algae completely and to make sure that the aquarium decoration is grown over as quickly as possible with calcareous algae. This is why animals that will eat filamentous algae, e.g. surgeonfishes of the genus *Zebrasoma* or algae-eating blennies (Blenniidae) should be the first to be introduced into the aquarium. We are also satisfied with detritus-eating animals like brittle stars or sea cucumbers as pioneers. Detritus stimulates algae growth and pollutes the aquarium water at the same time. If the amount of detritus is reduced from the start, conditions are much better to get the growth of the algae under control.

During the break in period, unsightly red slime algae may also start to grow. These algae are very difficult to fight. As long as they are in the aquarium, no corals should be introduced into it (for more details see chapter 13). We keep getting inquiries from aquarists full of despair who cannot cope with the algae growth in their tanks. In most of these cases the animals have been introduced in-

One of the best algae-eaters in the coral reef aquarium is the jeweled blenny, *Salarias fasciatus*.

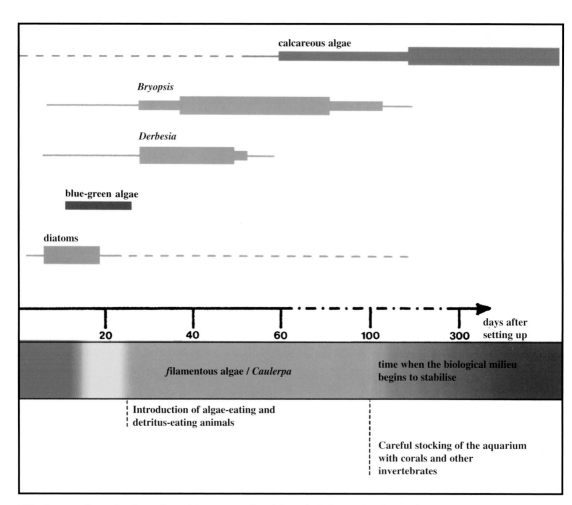

calcareous algae

Bryopsis

Derbesia

blue-green algae

diatoms

| 20 | 40 | 60 | 100 | 300 | days after setting up |

filamentous algae / Caulerpa

time when the biological milieu begins to stabilise

Introduction of algae-eating and detritus-eating animals

Careful stocking of the aquarium with corals and other invertebrates

This diagram shows the chronology of the common break in period of a coral reef aquarium. It may serve as a model, but not as a universal rule, as every aquarium follows its own rules. The break in period may take considerably longer and depends on the source water that is used, the lighting installations, the protein skimming device and the filtration and flow regulation technology used. Moreover it is important whether the aquarium was set up with or without live rock.

A section of the reef gorge aquarium (pictures on pages 104 and 105) during the break in period. Algae and detritus eating animals have already been introduced, as the biological milieu is getting stabilised.

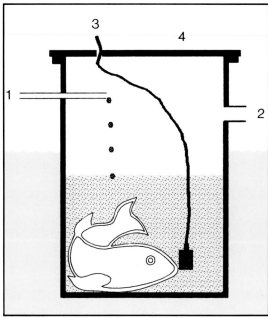

Container for the acclimatisation of aquarium animals: the container is fixed in the aquarium in such a way that the surface of the aquarium water is just below outlet 2 (this also guarantees that the temperature is kept at the right level during the acclimatisation). Now aquarium water is pumped through a thin tube (1) into the container and mixed with the water that the animal was transported in. At the same time the water is aerated weakly (3). When the water level in the container reaches the outlet, the surplus water flows into the aquarium. It is important to put a cover (4) on the container during the acclimatisation. It is best if the container is blacked out completely, as the darkness seems to reduce the stress for the animals.

to the aquarium too early. Especially if the number of fish brought into the tank during the break in period is too high, algae problems will result. Patience, patience and again patience is the prime necessity at this stage.

Experience has shown that it is very useful to keep a record of the break in period. Notes should be taken daily of the various readings (pH, KH, density, etc.), also of observations concerning the growth of the algae and of life forms appearing on the live rock. Such records will at any stage provide valuable information on the state of affairs and the development in the aquarium.

Acclimatisation of fishes and invertebrates

In chapter 10 we emphasize that an organism that is introduced into new surroundings has to be

acclimatised (adapted, adjusted) **gradually**. Some groups of animals, among others crustaceans and and a lot of fish species are very sensitive to a sudden change in the quality of the water or to other changes in their surroundings. Crustaceans that are introduced directly, i.e. without a gradual acclimatisation, into the new coral reef aquarium or into one

Håvard Nilsen prepares a large *Acropora* sp. for its acclimatisation.

set up a long time before, often die within a few days. A slow adaptation with the help of what is called "drip method" is an absolute necessity.

The simplest way of acclimatising an animal is to place it in a bucket together with the water in which it was transported and to allow the aquarium water to trickle into the bucket through a thin plastic tube drop by drop (the flow of the water can be varied by a locking screw). This process should take a few hours and the amount of the aquarium water added should be greater than the amount of water in which the animal was transported. Care should be taken that the temperature of the water in the bucket always remains the same as that in the aquarium.

The acclimatisation of echinoderms also has to take place very slowly and it is extremely important that the animals must never be lifted out of the water. Otherwise their system of water canals may get filled with air, which would kill them. The same holds true for sponges.

The first animals in a coral reef aquarium should be algae and detritus eaters. In this picture a group of yellow tangs, *Zebrasoma flavescens*, is released into the aquarium after a proper period of acclimatisation.

Most fishes, corals and other cnidarians may be acclimatised slightly faster. Nevertheless we recommend to keep the equipment necessary for the acclimatisation of new animals at hand.

It is always best to be on the safe side by acclimatising the animals slowly and carefully. There simply is no excuse for losing animals by carelessness in their acclimatisation.

duced. This problem has discredited marine aquaristics with many people. Reliable aquarium dealers by now have a watchful eye on this problem and boycott the exporters of fish caught with cyanide. Even so, there is always a chance that now and then an animal poisoned with cyanide may be on offer in a shop. Thus the sudden death of newly bought fish may be due to cyanide poisoning. If this happens, tell your aquarium dealer about it, he will certainly want to check up on this matter.

The damages cyanide catching does to nature are worse by far compared to these aquaristic pro-

blems. Not only the animals caught are harmed by the poison, but also all the other organisms that remain there. ROBINSON (personal information) reports that in certain areas of the Philippines less than 25% of the original coral colonies are left. This grave destruction of nature is partly due to the use of cyanide in the capture not only of aquarium fish but also food fish. Food fish are even collected with dynamite! The authorities in the Philippines recognize the problem but change is slow, and the problem has spread to new regions (also see chapter 14).

Résumé

To sum up the essential idea we would like to emphasize again that patience is most important in the break in period of a new aquarium. All the changes that occur should be recorded and analysed later. Every aquarium follows its own rules and not always exactly those we have pointed out.

Animals impaired by cyanide

Though we will deal with this subject extensively in chapter 14, it seems important enough to touch on it also here briefly.

In many places, especially in the Philippines, fish are still caught with poison, e.g. cyanide. The fish caught with cyanide usually survive long enough to be exported and sold in aquarium shops, but their life expectancy in the aquarium is considerably re-

This is the way our aquarium fish should be caught: a diver drives a fish into the net.   Underwater photo: K. Kvalvågnæs

Algae grazing fish are musts for a newly established reef aquarium. Here are *Zebrasoma veliferum* and *Z. xanthurum.*

Snails have a special modified radula to scrape minute algae from the substratum.

Brittle stars should be kept in numbers. They are excellent detritus feeders.

Chapter 7

Live Rock in the Modern Coral Reef Aquarium

Live rock is so important for the coral reef aquarium that we would like to deal with the subject in a chapter by itself. We have already stated that by the term "live rock" we mean the more or less eroded skeletons of stony corals on which other organisms have settled and larvae and spores have been deposited. Live rock is normally covered with plenty of calcareous and other algae as well. It is important to realize that some authors have used the term "live rock" erroneously, referring to colonies of live *Porites* spp. stony corals on which Christmas Tree Worms of the genus *Spirobranchus* have settled. We regard this as a misunderstanding.

Live rock is very porous, with thousands of holes of different sizes – from the size of a pinhead to a few centimeters in diameter – scattered throughout the whole structure. The degree of porosity depends on the age of the rock. Thus the surface available for the colonization by bacteria is normally very large. The amount of oxygen available decreases continually from the outside towards the interior of a rock. Accordingly

Above: For the most part live rock consists of dead stony corals. If you cut such a rock in two, the coral skeleton which has remained intact can be seen, as well as the fact that boring organisms have started to perforate the stone. In the course of the years the perforation will grow. Finally the rock will disintegrate and become fine sand.

Left: This aquarium was decorated with live rock only. A nice flora and fauna developed from the rocks. In 1995 the aquarium was eight years old and still "new" organisms show up from the rocks.

Live rock has a very porous surface and is colonized by a large variety of organisms.

Before we start decorating the aquarium it is best to spread out the pieces of live rock on the floor. This gives us a general idea of their forms and structures and of the life they house.

Decaying organisms, like this dead sponge, should be removed from the live rock.

there is a changing bacterial flora, which means that different decomposition processes take place in the different zones of a piece of live rock. Therefore the build up of nitrate is often prevented by these processes in aquaria decorated with live rock. This is probably the most important quality of live rocks.

In addition to this favorable biological effect live rock is also of an aesthetic interest, because it is perfect for creating a most natural scenery in the coral reef aquarium. After some time much of the rocks will cement themselves together by the help of calcareous algae, to form a decoration that will look most natural. New species of algae and animals will continue to appear even after several years. It is really justified to use the term "live" rock with respect to this material.

How to treat live rock

There are various ways of using live rock in a coral reef aquarium. The aquarium may be decorated with nothing but live rock. This can, however, turn out to be exorbitantly expensive for larger aquaria. An aquarium that exceeds 200 to 300 litres will definitely cost the aquarist a great deal of money if live rocks are the only material used, but it might very well be worth the expense. Live rock can also be combined with other decoration materials, e.g. "dead" calcareous rocks from fossilized reefs etc., or certain artificial decoration materials. In the beginning this may lead to some problems concerning the colour combination, yet it results in a considerable reduction of cost. Moreover it is possible to build some kind of an artificial foundation plate first, into which the rocks can be inserted. After the break in period, when chemically and biologically stable conditions have been established, calcareous algae will gradually grow over most of the decoration and will effect a uni-

Pieces of live rock have two different sides: the side that originally faced the sunlight is covered with light-loving, photophilous animals and algae. (In very shallow waters with an extremely high intensity of light this may, however, hold true for the side that faces away from the light.) The dark side will be colonized by shade-loving, photophobic organisms.

form colouration. Whatever you do, it is always very important to plan the decoration in advance. What type of rock formation do you intend to imitate? How will the pieces of rock be cemented together to form a natural and stable decoration? These and similar questions must be answered in advance. Finally alternative ways of decorating should be considered in case the rocks available do not fit in with the plans for the decoration.

When the rocks have been bought, time is limited! The rocks must be treated as living material and cannot be stored dry without access to oxygenated water. Otherwise much of the valuable macro- and microlife on and inside the rocks dies!

Start by inspecting the rocks closely and carefully. It is best to spread the pieces on the floor to get a general idea of what sizes and shapes you have and what kind of larger organisms they house. Larger colonies of algae, sponges and other organisms that look dead or unhealthy or damaged should be removed. Otherwise they might decompose and decay in the aquarium. This could poison the aquarium water. With few exceptions organisms that look healthy and alive should, however, never be removed! After this preliminary cleaning we can set out to start the decorating work. In smaller aquaria the pieces of rock may

be arranged without taking further precautions. Usually we place the larger rocks at the bottom and put the smaller ones on top. The result must be stable and as natural looking as possible (do study chapter 4 and 5). It certainly takes a lot of skill and experience to place the pieces in such a way that they are locked in a fixed

position and cannot slip or slide away. When you are finished the decoration should give the impression of a small, natural reef section. Under no circumstances must the decoration look like "a pile of rocks", as it so often does. Live rocks are the product of the natural growth processes of corals and should be arranged in

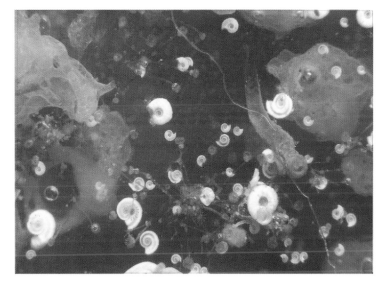

The potential for development and growth of micro- and macroorganisms in a coral reef aquarium decorated with live rock is enormous. We can easily follow the growth by placing a small glass pane (5 x 2 cm) in such a position in a filter chamber (or in the aquarium itself) that it is exposed to a continuous water flow and to moderate or weak light. The glass will soon be colonized by tiny, delicate organisms. If you examine the glass regularly you can keep a record of some of the meiofaunal organisms that are present or prevalent in your aquarium. The piece of glass shown above had been placed in a filter chamber for six months. Sponges, hydrozoans, worms, and entoprocts have developed remarkable colonies (enlargement: 20x).

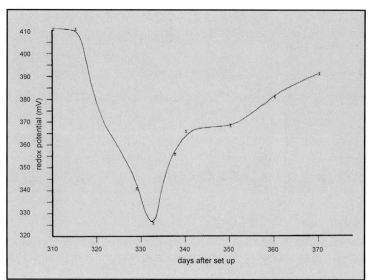

The diagram shows how the redox potential was reduced abruptly in an 800 litre aquarium on day 315 after it had been stocked with 25 kg live rock on day 310. The potential reached a minimum at about day 333 and only went back to a normal value very slowly.

formations that replicate nature. We cannot stress enough the need for studying the underwater- and aquarium pictures in this and the following volumes, and to use them as models and plans for further decorating work.

In larger aquaria it is usually best to start by installing the various materials and foundations that are necessary to support the heavy live rock decoration. These may be PVC tubes or glass props or supports that are fixed to the sides or to the bottom of the aquarium (see page 115). If PVC tubes are installed for filtration or circulation purposes, they may as well be useful as a foundation for the rocks.

Some tools should be at hand. The rocks are trimmed with a compass saw, a hammer and a chisel, so that they fit together. The holes which are needed are drilled with a percussion drill. You should have a supply of cable ties of different lengths ready to tie up and fix the pieces of rock. You should also have access to underwater

epoxy such as AquaStik™ (see page 121). To create freestanding pillars you need large rocks into which you can drill holes as thick as a thumb. Solid PVC tubes can be run through these holes. These tubes have to be attached firmly to the aquarium bottom (for details see the series of pictures on pages 114 and 115).

Whatever you decide to do, whether you pile up the rocks loosely, tie them together with cable ties or mount them together in other ways, you must content yourself with what you have built and leave the decoration as it is. A lot of damage can be done if you redecorate the aquarium repeatedly. Therefore it is most important to build a decoration that you are pleased with when the rocks are fresh. This once more underscores the need for careful planning. An aquarium where the rocks are moved around at intervals will never settle and look good. The organisms will be severly stressed and may die if the aquarist always has a hand in the aquarium. If one must rearrange the rocks, keep in mind which side faced the light and which was in the dark. The rocks must be put back in a similar position. A lot of sponges and other photophobic organisms grow on the dark side, while algae and cnidarians grow on the side facing the light.

Live rocks that are fresh have an adverse effect on the biological stability. When a coral reef aquarium is set up this is of minor importance, as the "maturation process" of the live rock coincides with the break in period of the aquarium. If this period is over, however, and the growth of the algae is under control, one should be very cautious and never introduce larger amounts of "fresh" live rock all at once. This could disturb the biological balance severely and induce the algae to start growing heavily again. The diagram to the left shows the changes of the redox potential in an aquarium after it was decorated with a considerable amount of live rock.

Live rock may also be used as a filter medium in biological filters. The filter may be charged partly or completely with this material. Usually the live rocks in the filter will not be exposed to light, and little or no algae will therefore colonize them. Instead sponges and other photophobic organisms will develop and flourish in the dark filter environment. At the moment when this text is being prepared our filter chamber houses a few small pieces of live rock densely covered with vermetid snails (see page 189). Experience also shows that live rocks that are exposed to strong water movement will develop better than those placed in calmer water.

Organisms living on live rock

It is always fascinating to watch live rocks and to inspect them for "new" organisms. Very often the aquarist discovers tiny creatures that he has never seen before, or observes that a tiny spot of the decoration is developing an interesting and most beautiful growth of algae. Even after years this can happen – the life on the rocks never seems to stop developing.

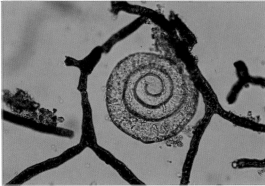

Ciliates are often found on rocks; left: probably a *Euplotes* sp. (enlargement: 800 x). Most forams are "large" compared to other unicellular animals. There are considerable differences between the species; right: a very small species that lives in association with algae (enlargement: 400 x).

The most common foraminiferan is *Homotrema rubrum*. It can develop to large populations in the reef aquarium. The colour is bright red and they are easily recognized, but they prefer shady areas. With a magnifying glass the thin, filamentous pseudopodia can be perceived (right; enlargement: 12 x).

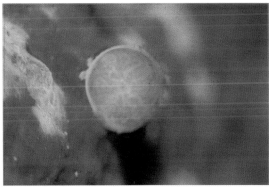

Another foram, which is quite similar to *Homotrema rubrum*, is found very frequently (left: enlargement: 12 x). It grows bushy and can reach a few centimetres in size. In the darker areas of the aquarium it may develop large colonies. A foram that does not live a sessile life (right; enlargement: 20 x). The chambers inside the shell in which the animal lives can be seen quite clearly.

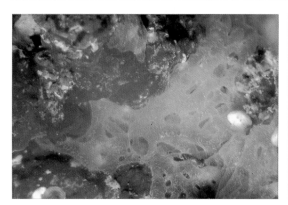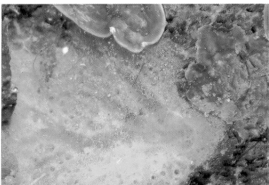

On the dark side of live rocks we commonly find sponges that often show many different colours (left; enlargement: 15x). A lot of small sponges develop in the company of calcareous algae (right: enlargement: 12x).

In one aquarium we found a sponge that was "moving". It clinged to the substrate with its pseudopods and crept slowly (left: enlargement: 2x). During the course of four years large populations of this red sponge grew in some shady areas of the aquarium (right; enlargement: 12 x).

This is surely another of the most interesting aspects with this fascinating material, and it is also an aspect that can teach the aquarists a lot of biology!

In the next part of this chapter we would like to present some of those organisms that are most commonly introduced to the coral reef aquarium with live rocks.

❶ Unicellular animals (Protozoa)

Apart from bacteria (which we will avoid in this chapter, but deal with in chapter 11) unicellular animals are among the most numerous organisms associated with live rocks. Most of them cannot be seen with the naked eye. Looking through a microscope at samples from the sediments or at a tiny piece of algae scraped off of live rock will reveal a fascinating world of microorganisms. There are plenty of ciliates, a few amoebas and some flagellates – all moving rapidly through the field of view, and all contributing to the important decomposing processes that keep up the biological stability of the aquarium (see chapter 11).

From the aquarist's point of view the forams, (order Foraminifera), may be the most interesting group of single celled animals as they can be observed with the naked eye without using a microscope. Still they are single celled ani-

mals. Many draw calcium carbonate from the water and build rather large and conspicuous shells. Much of the coral gravel in some reefs consists of foram shells, giving the layer an extremely porous structure.

Most forams are free living, yet *Homotrema rubrum*, a very common species in coral reefs all over the world, lives a sessile life on the shady sides of corals and live rocks. As the name *rubrum* indicates, its colour is between bright pink and red. These foram shells are the very reason why the Bermuda beaches are famous for their pink hue. In most coral reef aquaria we also find large jagged-looking colonies of *Homotrema rubrum* on the dark sides of the rocks. Normally they are 2 to 3 mm large, only rarely up to 5 mm. Their reproduction rate is very high, and large colonies can develop from a few specimens within a short period of time.

Another foram, which also occurs in large numbers on the shady side of live rock, branches out and is mostly light-beige to white in colour (see page 173). Neither the species nor the genus to which this foram belongs have been identified.

❷ Sponges (Porifera)

Among the organisms most often found on live rock are sponges, phylum Porifera. When you unpack fresh live rocks you will always notice numerous sponges, both inside the rocks as well as on their surface. Although the rocks are wet during transportation they are usually packed without much water, which is the reason why most of the large, conspicuous sponge colonies are unable to survive. A submerged packing would, however, be impossible both from an economical and a biological point of view – at least in the majority of cases where the transportation time exceeds a few

hours. In most cases it is therefore better to remove the dead sponges, before the rock is placed in the aquarium. Problems caused by the decay of the sponge and the increase of the nitrate concentration following it may thus be avoided.

Smaller sponges have a much greater chance of survival, and a few species can recover rather rapidly and start growing again in the aquarium. Under favorable conditions these sponges can develop large colonies and thus contribute considerably to the natural balance of the biological milieu in the coral reef aquarium.

To thrive most sponges need strong water movement and dim light. Some species are phototrophic and can tolerate high or moderate amounts of light. For these it is a precondition that there are no uncontrolled growths of filamentous algae in the aquarium. If these conditions are met, you will sooner or later discover sponges in your aquarium. And when or if a coral reef aquarium is emptied after a number of years, you will certainly find large sponge colonies in the shady areas. The species *Acanthodendrilla* is a common example. The variety of the phylum is enormous and not only does an

unknown number of species exist, many of the species show different shapes in different conditions. Sponges are so difficult to identify for the aquarist that we think it is out of the record to touch the classification and identification of sponges in this volume. We will, however, return to the subject in volume 3. The pictures on page 174 show sponges that have grown well in coral reef aquaria.

❸ Cnidarians (Cnidaria)

Cnidarians are no doubt the most conspicuous organisms of a coral reef. Thus it is not surprising to find them as "stowaways" on live rocks quite regularly. The hydroids (class Hydrozoa) are often found in several species and in large numbers. *Myrionema* sp. (see the left picture at the bottom), which is a small, colonial animal with a bad habit of stinging other animals, is rather common and grows profusely in moderate to heavy light. The animal itself does not ingest food, but is dependent on the products of its zooxanthellae. If the light is not intense enough for the zooxanthellae, *Myrionema* dies.

Some Hydroidea, and especially *Myrionema* sp. can reproduce at an incredibly fast rate and

Below: Colony of a hydroid polyp of the genus *Myrionema*: this hydroid grows fast under strong light, but it rapidly vanishes if the light is too dim (photo: Dr. D. Brockmann). To the right: a drawing of the polyp stage of the jellyfish *Nausithoe* sp. which grows to about 1,5 cm in height (drawing after a photo in BRONS, 1982).

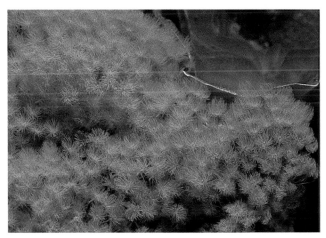
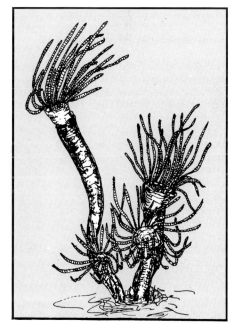

spread almost all over the aquarium. This is why some aquarists regard this species as a pest. In such cases it might be necessary to remove parts of the colonies at regular intervals. We hold the opinion, however, that hydroids in general are beautiful and that they liven up an aquarium.

The fire-corals, which are hydrozoans from the genus *Millepora*, are also occasionally introduced to the aquarium with live rocks. Although their growth might be very slow, they have an intense sting that can harm other cnidarians severely, and certainly hurt also the aquarist himself.

Another cnidarian, shown above to the right, is often misidentified as a Hydrozoan. The tiny polyps are frequently seen on fresh live rocks, but disappear during the first year after decoration. This is not unusual as this is not a hydrozoan at all, but the sessile polyp-stage of a jellyfish (class Scyphozoa) from the genus *Nausithoe*. Scyphozoans, like many hydrozoans, alter in life-cycle between a freeliving medusa stage and a sessile polyp stage (a fact we will return to in volume 2). The freeliving medusa stage of *Nausithoe* is small and does not reach more than 2-3 cm in diameter. The medusae have occasionally been seen in the reef aquarium, but never lived to undergo the complete life-cycle of the species. Jellyfish are in general very difficult to keep in captivity and require special tanks and care.

Among the other cnidarians that are found more or less regularly on live rock are sea anemones (order Actiniaria), clove polyps (suborder Stolonifera) and colonial anemones (order Zoanthiniaria).

The reef aquarist will often focus his attention on stony corals, however. Until a few years ago the opinion that it was difficult, if not impossible to keep stony corals alive over a longer period of time was still dominating. To get them to grow or even to reproduce was considered utopian. Thus it is not difficult to understand that reef aquaristics began to boom since

Below: Anemones of the species *Anemonia* cf. *majano* are often introduced to the coral reef aquarium. It can reproduce so heavily that it can overgrow large areas of the rocks. Be careful with this anemone!

Above: The polyp stage of the jellyfish *Nausithoe* sp. is often mistaken for a hydrozoan. It is commonly seen on fresh live rocks (enlargement: 2 x).

Soft corals such as this *Briareum* sp. from Indonesia can be found on most live rocks and can develop to really beautiful stands in the coral reef aquarium. This picture shows an unknown species that is very common on live rocks.

A primary polyp of the stony coral *Euphyllia glabrescens* grows out of a live rock (left). Within a year a magnificent colony of *Euphyllia glabrescens* in the coral reef aquarium of N. Nesje and J. Enger, Oslo, grew to a height of 8 cm (right). This stony coral is mostly imported on live rocks from Southeast Asia.

reports of stony corals growing out of live rock started coming in. And these reports keep on coming in! We have observed ourselves a number of times that primary polyps or very young colonies of stony corals on live rocks developed into magnificent colonies within a rather short time.

One of the most common species to develop on live rocks is *Euphyllia glabrescens* from the family Caryophylliidae. This beautiful stony coral is among the species most frequently imported from Southeast Asia. It can easily be recognized by its branched gray-brown tentacles with their white tips. It is one of the hardiest corals for aquarium-keeping, but unfortunately the colony fragments imported with rocks are often severely damaged. If the skeleton is infected with calcium-"boring" green algae, which is a common problem, it may turn out to be very difficult to save the coral. Accordingly it is all the more interesting to observe the development of *Euphyllia glabrescens* in the aquarium from its first appearance as a small primary polyp on a piece of live rock to its final stage as a fully developed colony with its skeleton white as chalk and without the undesirable green algae, which in the coral reef infest so many colonies.

A genus of corals which is seldom seen in the aquarium trade but nevertheless quite topical among reef aquarists is *Psammocora*. We know of a number of cases where *Psammocora contigua* started growing out of live rocks. In all these cases its growth was very fast. *P. contigua* seems to be very hardy. Under bright light it develops a fluorescent green colour, which makes it look very attractive.

The largest families of reef-building corals, Acroporidae and Pocilloporidae contain a number of

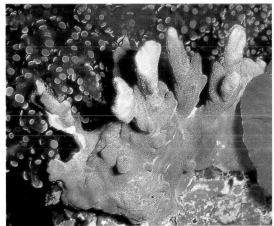

A small colony of the stony coral *Psammocora contigua* with a diameter of about 3 cm has grown out of a live rock (left). In the aquarium of K. Olsen, Oslo, *Psammocora contigua* grew to a height of more than 10 cm (right). *P. contigua* is often found on live rock, is hardy and also quite attractive.

genera and species that are among the fastest growing stony corals in the modern coral reef aquarium. Occasionally fragments are imported with live rocks and colonies develop. This happened in Berlin, Germany, in the early eighties where a branching *Acropora* sp. grew out of live rock and formed the very first (?) *Acropora* kept in a closed aquarium system. This event, which now is well known by European aquarists, can stand as a breaking point in the history of reef aquaristics. It also underscores once more the need for introducing live rocks to the reef aquarium. The rocks imported for use in the aquarium are often collected in areas situated far from the true reefs and do therefore rarely contain fragments or polyps from reef building corals, but occasionally *Acropora* spp., *Montipora* spp. and *Pocillopora* spp. are discovered on live rocks.

Apart from hermatypic (reefbuilding) stony corals we have also found small, orange-coloured ahermatypic (not reefbuilding) corals of the genus *Tubastraea* on the shady side of live rocks. This is probably something that does not happen very often, but it shows what incredible growth potential corals have in a well-kept coral reef aquarium that has been decorated with live rock. The small colonies of *Tubastraea* spp. are on the contrary well known to form after the brooding of the mother colony when asexual planula larvae are produced and released. Asexual planula larvae are also known from a few other stony corals such as from *Pocillopora damicornis* of the family Pocilloporidae.

Furthermore we would like to mention a coral which is regarded by most aquarists as a stony coral because of its hard, calcareous skeleton. However, it belongs to the same class as the leather corals and the order Helioporacea. It is the Blue Coral, *Heliopora coerulea*, which has received its specific name (coeruleus, Lat. for blue) because of the colour of its inner skeleton, which has its blue from iron salts. Veteran aquarists

This photo shows the original "Berlin-*Acropora*" *Acropora* sp. that grew from live rock in the aquarium of D. Stüber, Berlin, and which probably was the first *Acropora* sp. to be grown in a closed aquarium system in Europe. The identity of this species has been much debated and the problem still remains unsolved.

Photo: D. Stüber

This small polyp of an ahermatypic stony coral, probably a *Tubastraea* sp., has a diameter of about 4 mm. This particularly beautiful species was found on the back side of a live rock which had lain in the same position for five years.

know this coral quite well as in former times its dead skeletons were imported as decoration material for aquaria. Its importation is usually only allowed with CITES documents (compare WA, appendix 2). We know of several instances, however, where *Heliopora coerulea* arrived in the aquarium on pieces of live rock. From what seemed to be dead skeletons magnificent colonies developed.

Among the other (true) stony corals which we know from live

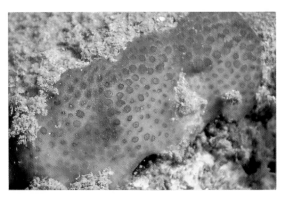

Small colonies of stony corals of the genus *Porites* are found on most live rocks. Unfortunately they usually do not survive the transport, but if they do they have proven to be very hardy and grow well in the reef aquarium (enlargement: 2 x).

Also stony corals of the genus *Goniastrea* are often imported on live rock. This genus belongs to the family Faviidae which contains some beautiful and hardy species for the coral reef aquarium.

rock we would also like to mention the genera *Goniastrea, Favia, Favites* in the family Faviidae and *Porites* in the family Poritidae as those most commonly seen. The latter genus seems to do especially well in the reef aquarium when grown from live rocks.

❹ Flatworms (Platyhelminthes)

Flatworms (class Turbellaria in phylum Platyhelminthes) are usually regarded as parasites, and best known from the reef aquarium as parasites or comensals on various cnidarians, such as mushroom anemones and soft corals. These flatworms belong to the or-

The Blue Coral, *Heliopora coerulea*, is not a stony coral, but an octocoral belonging to the order Helioporacea and, thus, related to the soft corals. The picture shows a colony three years after its first appearance on a live rock. It had tripled its original size in that time.

When a small reef-aquarium was emptied this delicate flatworm showed up. It belongs to the genus *Pericelis* in the order Polycladida (class Turbellaria). The flatworm must have been introduced with live rocks about three years earlier and was transferred to another aquarium. This demonstrates what delicate life rocks can house.

der Acoela and are surely introduced to the reef aquarium by live rocks and corals. Acoels often contain symbiotic algae and feed from detritus and algae and therefore easily find plenty to eat in the aquarium. Occasionally the populations can explode and really become a plague. We will return to this problem in volume 3.

The best known flatworms from the reefs are the most beautiful coloured species in the genera *Pseudoceros* and *Pseudobiceros* (order Polycladida). Unfortunately most of these are nutrient specialists feeding from colonial sea squirts and thus they are very diffi-

cult to keep in captivity. They are not commonly imported with live rocks though. One polyclad genus, *Pericelis* sp. has, however, occasionally been found in the reef aquarium (see left). The genus does probably contain mainly carnivorous species (but little is known about the diet of *Pericelis* spp.), and since specimens positively have survived for a long time in the reef aquarium, they must be able to find food there. Unfortunately these flatworms hide during the day living mainly in holes and cavities in the rocks, and are thus seldom if ever observed unless the aquarium is emptied.

⑤ Threadworms (Nematoda)

Threadworms are among the most common organisms world-wide. They can be found in nearly all kinds of biotopes and also as parasites in other organisms. To this coral reefs are no exception, where threadworms are the most common organisms in the interstitial meiofauna. Somebody has put forward the interesting question what the world would look like if all organic materials and all live organisms were to disappear all of a sudden – except for the threadworms. The result might be a ghastly world, made of writhing threadworms.

The most common worms in the world – and of course in the coral reef aquarium as well – are threadworms (nematodes). The species found in aquaria are small and usually harmless. They play an important role in the decomposition of detritus (enlargement: 150 x).

Even if we usually do not notice the threadworms in our coral reef aquaria, they are nevertheless there, thousands of them, on and in the pores of the live rocks, especially in places where algae grow. It is no problem to locate and study them if you use a microscope. Most of the threadworms feed on detritus. Some of them also feed on diatoms, small invertebrates, single celled animals and other nematodes. Nematodes have a high metabolic rate and are therefore by no doubt of great importance for the decomposition processes in the coral reef aquarium.

⑥ Ringed worms, annelids (Annelida)

Polychaetes or bristle worms (class Polychaeta) are the largest class in the phylum Annelida (Ringed worms) which contains some 11,500 species. Of the larger animals that live associated with live rocks the marine polychaetes are probably the most common. The class can roughly be divided into two groups – the freeliving species and the tube dwelling species, both groups having a body clearly divided into segments and carrying bristles and cirri. Without a close examination many of the polychaetes look rather similar and it is difficult to identify them to a distinct species. Usually we will have to be satisfied if we can identify the worms to the correct family.

When you work with live rock for the first time, you may be alarmed when you find the first worms. Sometimes they are as long as 15 cm and come crawling out of the holes of the rocks. In most cases these are freeliving bristle worms, usually belonging to the families Syllidae, Nereidae or Eunicidae. Like all polychaetes they have bristles and other appendages on each body segment. This may give them a dangerous look, yet on the whole they are in most cases totally harmless. Only some species are able to bite so that it can be felt. Other species may sting

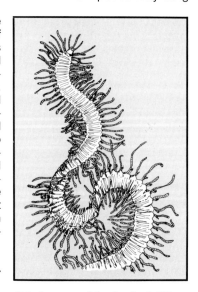

Bristle worm of the family Syllidae. (Drawing after BARNES, 1980)

the aquarist, which, however, is the only harm they can do. In the aquarium they have a high reproduction rate and they may slowly become a plague (WILKENS, 1983). Nevertheless they are fascinating creatures.

On one single occasion the hi-

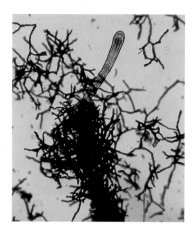

This small and rare worm that lives in a "house of algae" belongs to the phylum Gnatostomulida, and was not described until 1956 (enlargement: 70 x).

Bristle worms of the family Nereidae look wild, but they are completely harmless (actual size).

This small bristle worm (above) can often be found swimming rapidly in the reef aquarium. This is the reproductive stage (Epitoke) of freeliving polychaetes of the family Nereidae.

story of a bristle worm in a reef aquarium has turned to the extreme. In Germany in early 1995 Mr. Günther Gross of Speyer discovered that his soft corals were severely damaged. It looked as if something was feeding on the tissue. When he examined the aquarium at night using a flashlight, he discovered a monster of a bristle worm. He emptied the tank and found an almost 2 metre long and 2-3 cm thick Polychaete which later was identified as *Palola siciliensis* – the famous "Palola Worm", well known from the Central Pacific. In nature this species can reach more than 3 metres in length.

Other bristle worms with completely different shapes are also

This huge specimen of the Palola Worm, *Palola siciliensis*, was introduced to the aquarium of Mr. G. Gross, Germany, with live rocks.

found in coral reef aquaria. The family Cirratulidae is one of the most common ones and they are generally harmless detritivores. They can be identified by the fact that the bristles they bear on each segment are only very small. The long, reddish filaments that grow out of the forward segments is another characteristic of the group. These filaments mainly have the function of gills, as the Cirratulidae usually bury themselves in fine-grained sand or in mud. Only the

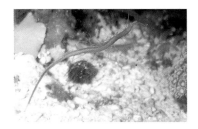

Bristle worms of the family Cirratulidae are occasionally introduced with live rocks. They can be identified by the modified long bristles at the forward part of their body. This photo was taken during the night.

"gill filaments" project into the water to draw oxygen from it. So look for cirratulids in the gravel, although the worms occasionally can be seen moving around freely in the aquarium.

Another rather strange group of bristle worms are the scaleworms, suborder Aphroditiformia. The best-known species from the family Aphroditidae is the Sea Mouse, *Aphrodita aculeata*, which is found in the Atlantic, in the North Sea and in the Mediterranean Sea. The species that regularly reach the aquarium with live rocks are usually from the family Polynoidae with the species *Lepidonotus carinulatus* being one of the most common ones imported with Indo-Pacific live rocks (see above). The scaleworms are not spectacular, but they provide for variety in the aquarium. Their name hints at the clearly visible sca-

The segmented scale-worms of the family Polynoidae are commonly imported on live rocks. They are usually not very long, have a broad body and strong bristles. The photo shows *Lepidonotus carinulatus*.

les that cover the back of these worms.

Among the second group of bristle worms – the tube dwelling worms – several species are found living on live rocks. The most remarkable ones are in the family Chaetopteridae. These bristle worms live in u-shaped, wide tubes in the sand. At both ends of the tube there are narrow openings facing out from the sandy ground. The worm spends its whole life in this tube and feeds on microorganisms that it filters from the water with a slime net. Even though the Chaetopteridae are rare in our aquaria, they may occur and should be looked for because they are interesting — not because of any danger.

Calcareous tube-worms of the family Serpulidae build tubes from calcium carbonate, while worms of the family Sabellidae build their

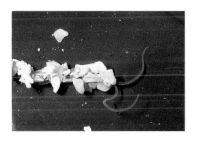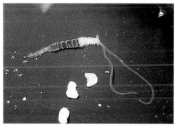

The gravel of a reef aquarium does often contain a variety of interesting organisms, among them a number of worms. This worm, which measures the size of about 4 cm including the two palps, belongs to the family Chaetopteridae, genus *Phyllochaetopterus*. In our aquarium this worm formed a huge population in the coral gravel asexually by budding or fission. It builds parchment like tubes decorated with coral fragments and coral sand and only the two palps project above the sand.

tubes from soft materials with a high content of polysaccharides. Both families contain a number of genera (which we will return to in volume 3) and are commonly found on live rocks. The array of tentacles in Sabellidae is often very large, yet not so colourful as that of the Serpulidae. Sabellids on live rock can multiply greatly which can result in large, magnificent colonies. One small, but unfortunately yet unknown species is very common on live rocks and capable of building magnificent populations. Please note that the butterfly-fish *Chelmon rostratus* will rapidly destroy a population of these delicate worms. *Sabellastarte indica*, the species best known to marine aquarists can also be found on live rocks.

There are also many species from the family Terebellidae that can be found within live rock. These bristle worms bore themselves into the substrate with their tentacles wriggling over the surface searching for food. Most of the species found in our aquaria are small with hair thin tentacles, but on the reef itself a few really big species with pencil lead thick tentacles are common. *Terebella*, *Amphitrite* and *Polymnia* are the most common genera of this family.

Species of the family Spionidae are among the most common bristle worms on live rocks. Some-

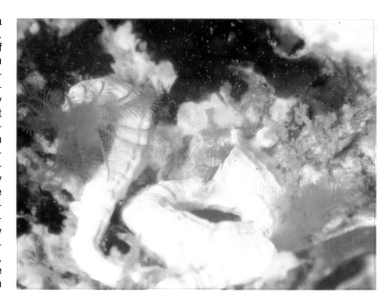

Small calcareous tube-dwelling worms of the family Serpulidae, with their colourful tentacles can grow to magnificent colonies. The worm shown in the picture is about 1 cm long (enlargement: 18 x).

times they can multiply to form large populations and really be the dominant group of polychaetes in the aquarium. Compared to the other families earlier mentioned these are, however, less noticeable bristle worms. The spionids live in short tubes which are often overgrown with calcareous algae. Only two thin tentacles jut out from the opening. Some species bury in the sand and build tubes

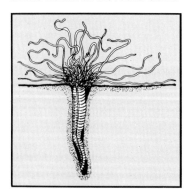

Above: an *Amphitrite* sp. from the family Terebellidae.
  (Drawing after BARNES, 1980)

Right: *Sabellastarte indica* grew from a live rock in the aquarium of K. O. Dahl, Bergen.

The small worms of the family Spionidae bore themselves into rocks. Only the two tiny palps project out from the holes they drill. These worms may appear in large numbers in coral reef aquaria (enlargement: 40 x).

from gravel particles and resemble small Chaetopteridae. These worms are very common in the reef aquarium and make the bottom really living.

❼ Peanut-worms (Sipunculida)

Peanut-worms, which belong to the separate phylum Sipunculida and are thus *not* a part of Annelida, are sausage-shaped animals that differ from the bristle worms by not being segmented. Some species occupy tiny holes and live buried in the rocks themselves. They are, however, seldom seen during the day-time and therefore

This small Peanut-worm was taken out from a piece of rock and observed through a binocular magnifying glass.

Peanut-worms of the order Sipunculida often live hidden in live rocks and play an important role in the decomposition process in the reef. They feed on detritus and algae which they catch with their small tentacles around their mouth. Other Peanut-worms live buried in the sand.

aquarists normally overlook them. The Peanut-worms are nevertheless among the most common animals associated with live rocks. With their strong chitinous body they can widen cracks in the rock and bore themselves new passages deep in the limestone. We have found Peanut-worms many times in our own aquaria, and have observed cleaner shrimps eating them. In nature we can also find many sand-dwelling Peanut-worms as a part of the interstitial fauna of the reef. This group does not seem to be as common in reef aquaria as the rock-burrowing ones.

❽ Crustaceans (Crustacea)

Crustaceans are well known and it is not surprising that this phylum is common and diverse on live rocks. The small copepods (class Copepoda) and amphipods (order Amphipoda in the class Malacostraca) are particularly numerous. Although the two groups are systematically wide apart, they both belong to the meiofauna and

must be regarded as very common in the reef aquarium as well as on the reef itself. Most aquarists know these animals as live food for freshwater fishes. These microscopic animals are also very common along northern and southern seashores and are an essential part of the food chain of most marine ecosystems. This might very well also be the case of many closed reef aquarium systems. The majority of the copepods and amphipods belong to the zooplankton, yet there are also several species which are found on the surfaces of live rocks, in the detritus on the bottom or between algae filaments. There are also a lot of species that live a

If you look at detritus or algae through a microscope you very often find small crustaceans, usually from the orders Amphipoda, Tanaidacea (above; enlargement: 50 x) and the class Copepoda (below; enlargement: 30 x). Often they reproduce in small openings of live rocks or between algae. They play an important part in the ecology of the reef.

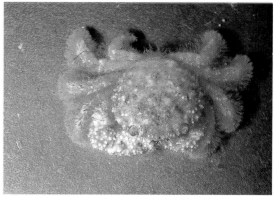

Many of the most beautiful and most colourful crustaceans belong to the family of the coral crabs, Xanthidae. The two crabs to the left were introduced into the aquarium with stony corals of the family Pocilloporidae. Many coral crabs have specialized on feeding on coral slime. We have not found these to be harmful to their host at all, and we recommend them to be left in the corals. Some other species are harmful to stony corals. The crab on the picture to the right, probably a *Pilumnus* sp., did feed on coral polyps in our aquarium.

parasitic life, especially associated with fishes. If you search the decoration with a flash-light in the middle of the night, you will always find a lot of small crustaceans.

Thus it is quite natural that copepods and amphipods are an essential part of the food for those fishes that feed off the surface of live rocks, e.g. dragonets of the genus *Synchiropus*, pipefishes of the family Syngnathidae and angelfishes of the genus *Centropyge*. Like the nematodes the copepods digest a lot of plant material and detritus. They are in this respect an indispensable part of the fauna of the coral reef aquarium.

Other meiofaunal crustaceans like isopods (order Isopoda), cumaceans (order Cumacea) as well as tanaidaceans (order Tanaidacea) are associated with live rocks.

Together with live rocks we can occasionally discover barnacles (class Cirripedia). The shelled barnacles give the impression that they have an array of tentacles like the tube-dwelling bristle worms. But the fan like cirripeds that stand out from the opening of the shell to catch plankton are really highly modified feet.

Larger decapods (order Decapoda, class Malacostraca) like shrimps and crabs are common

on live rock. Hairy coral crabs of the family Xanthidae are found very often and have surprized many aquarists. Like many of the other animals that are associated with live rocks, coral crabs hide during the day. Their nocturnal activities may be observed quite well, however, by flashlight. Some species of coral crabs are predatory and can be a danger to other aquarium animals. Most species are harmless, and in nature many of them even live in a comensal relationship with stony corals of the families Acroporidae and Pocilloporidae. Many other crabs, most of which are hard to identify, arrive

Hairy coral crabs of the family Xanthidae often arrive in the aquarium with live rocks. These crabs do sometimes, but not always harm other organisms. We have had good as well as bad experiences with them. Personally we like these "hairy monsters" (left). In a piece of live rock we found this predatory crab (right), probably belonging to the family Palicidae. Such crabs may also harm other animals, yet they can also be harmless. We keep rather large specimens of crabs in our coral reef aquaria, yet we have seldom seen them behave predaciously.

Mantis shrimps, stomatopods, are interesting crustaceans, but very predatory. To the right *Odontodactylus scyllaris* (Photo: F. Nijhuis). Now and then they are brought into our aquaria with live rocks and have to be removed and kept in a special aquarium (drawing after BARNES, 1980).

in our aquaria with live rocks. The pictures on page 184 show some examples. We should pay special attention to one group of crustaceans: the mantis shrimps (order Stomatopoda). The genera *Squilla*, *Gonodactylus* and *Odontodactylus* are the most common ones which can be found in live rocks. They have predatory habits and they can easily "rid" an aquarium of shrimps and smaller fishes. With their very sharp claws – which actually are their second thoracic appendages folded under the thorax – combined with an exceptionally rapid movement, they can murder bypassing organisms and even hurt the aquarist if he does not take care. Luckily the large mantis shrimps are only brought in rarely with live rocks. Usually we find smaller specimens, which are not too predatory yet, but they do grow, even if slowly. Fortunately they can easily be removed if the rock which they use does not support the whole decoration. In most cases the mantis shrimps have a place to which they retreat regularly, e.g. a cavity in a rock. This rock can then be taken out of the aquarium together with the mantis shrimp. It is then placed in a container and left there until the animal leaves its hiding-place. Mantis shrimp are nevertheless such in-

teresting animals that it is always worthwhile to set up a separate tank for them, even a small one.

⑨ Sea Spiders (Pycnogonida)

Arachnids and their relatives are not animals we usually associate with the sea – and certainly not with the aquarium. Yet even representatives for this group have been found in the modern coral reef

Again and again small harmless crabs like this one arrive in our aquaria as "stowaways" on live rock.

aquarium. The best-known marine arachnids are the rather large horseshoe crabs of the genera *Limulus*, *Trachypleus*, and others, which are, however, hardly ever imported for the aquarium.

A little known group are the sea spiders (class Pycnogonida in the subphylum Chelicerata), which are interesting for the coral reef aquarium, although they are not common. We do mention them here because they are a rather special and highly fascinating group of organisms. About 600 species of sea spiders have been described and they are found in all ocean regions, in sizes from a few millimeters to half a meter. In colder oceans they are especially abundant and live there at depths of up to 600 m. But many species are also found in coral reefs, where they can show a variety of beautiful colours. Their diet varies, but most of them seem to feed on hydroids and bryozoans.

In a few cases we have found sea spiders in aquaria, obviously introduced with corals or live rocks, and in one case as a parasite on stony corals of the genus *Acropora* (see photos on page 186). In the last case the animals were very small, only 8-10 mm in size. They ate from the tissue of the coral and if we had not removed eve-

Sea spiders are sometimes introduced to the reef aquarium through live rocks or corals. In this case we can see how a parasitic sea spider from the genus *Callipallene* fed from the tissue of a stony coral, *Acropora* sp. The greenish part of the colony shows where the tissue was eaten. Below left we can see the tiny spider crawling on the coral while below right the animal is shown against a dark background.

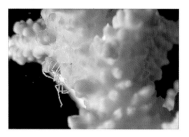

ry single animal, the colony would have died. This parasitic sea spider has been identified as *Callipallene* sp. Freeliving sea spiders move slowly across the rocks in our aquarium and then "disappear". As they appear several months after the rocks are introduced into the aquarium, we draw the conclusion that these interesting animals can survive in the aquarium.

⑩ Molluscs (Mollusca)

Molluscs belong to the phylum Mollusca which is a giant phylum of animals covering well known groups such as bivalves and gastropods. Both are of course numerous with live rocks. But the phylum also contains the class Cephalopoda – nautili, cuttlefish, squids and octopus – that hopefully never will be introduced to our aquaria with live rocks.

Of the bivalves found with live rocks the boring clams and piddocks of the genera *Lithophaga* (lithos, Greek = stone and phagein = eat, thus "stone-eaters"), *Arca* and *Pholas* are relatively frequent. They bore themselves so deep into the rock that only part of their siphon can be seen. The shells of the *Pholas* spp. are often coloured deep red. This is just one example of bivalves typically found in the rocks. All in all we have found a large number of bivalves of different families. For their identifications please consult the suggested readings given on page 191, (e.g. DANCE (1977), WELLS & BRYCE, (1988) and WILSON (1993)).

Tube-dwelling snails of the family Vermetidae are quite frequent and can in some cases be the dominant molluscs in the reef aquarium. For unknown reasons it seems that these snails thrive ex-

traordinarily in captivity. Perhaps this has to do with their way of feeding? Often the vermetids are small, almost opaque species of only a few millimetres size, and difficult to spot. But larger forms may occur (see page 189), and on the reef the large *Dendropoma maxima* is commonly seen. As these snails spend their whole life except for the larval stage in their calcareous tube, they are often mistaken for tube-dwelling bristle worms. This is also the reason for the family name "Vermetidae", as "Vermes" means "worms". Their sessile lifestyle prevents them from moving around and searching for food. Instead they secrete a slime net in which plankton and detritus are caught. As soon as there is enough food in the net, the snail pulls it into the tube and feeds on the captured prey.

Freeliving gastropods are common on live rocks. Most of these are harmless, but be aware that a lot of snails feed on corals and it is not uncommon that such are introduced to the reef aquarium either with coral colonies or with rocks. Commonly introduced are the mitres of the family Mitridae. Mitres, which have received their names for the episcopal headgear, the mitre, are a group of snails

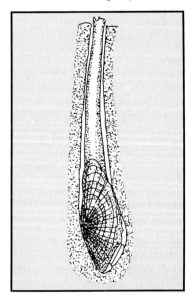

Boring clam of the genus *Pholas*.
(Drawing after BARNES, 1980)

which feed on detritus and small invertebrates. They plow through the sediment trying to find food. Even fully grown mitres are hardly ever larger than one or two centimetres. But what they lack in size they make up by their beautiful colours and patterns.

The algae-eating, nocturnal turban snails of the genus *Turbo* are also often found on live rock. The genus contain a number of species where the largest can reach a size of some 20 cm. We have seen aquaria where the *Turbo* populations reproduce sexually at regular intervals and where the gametes develop, hatch and grow into adult snails.

The primitive (primordial) abalones of the genus *Haliotes*, and the small stomatellas from the genus *Stomatella* (page 188) are almost always present on the rocks. Small cowries of the genus *Cypraea* also occur. The cowry snails have a variable diet. Some species eat algae while others are carnivores and feed on corals. All in all the gastropod fauna on live rock can be extremely diverse.

Only very rarely do we find nudibranchs (class Gastropoda, order Nudibranchia) on live rock. They are much more commonly found as parasites on sponges and cnidarians, and can often be introduced to the aquarium with soft corals upon which they often feed. There are only a few nudibranchs that feed on algae and are therefore suitable for the coral reef

Clams of the genus *Arca* bore themselves into live rocks and stay sedentary for years. The zoanthid is *Zoanthus sociatus.*

These *Mitra* sp. were collected from newly imported live rocks (about actual size).

aquarium. One snail that resembles a Nudibranch, but that actually is a limpet is, however, rather commonly introduced with live rocks. This is *Scutus unguis* commonly found in the shallow waters of the Central Indo-Pacific. These attractive snails, shown on page 188, eat algae and do not seem to feed on corals or sponges. They thrive so well that they even reproduce after only a short time, but unfortunately the species is most active at night and only rarely seen during daytime.

Another very specialized group of molluscs which is easy to identify and which is also imported on live rock are the chitons from the class Polyplacophora. In the reef the chitons can be found in large numbers in the intertidal zone, a typical habitat for the most common species such as *Acanthopleura granulata* which is abundant in the Caribbean. Other species live below the tidal zone. They move around at night and feed on algae. We have found different species in our aquaria of which the largest were several centimetres long. Unfortunately some chitons

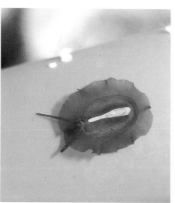

Above: This snail is sometimes introduced with live rock imported from Indonesia. It resembles a Nudibranch, but is actually the limpet *Scutus unguis* commonly seen in the shallow reefs of the Central Pacific where it usually hides below boulders during the day. The large dark brown or black mantle covers the shell and makes the animals look like a Nudibranch. It feeds from algae and possibly also from dead animals. In the aquarium it can also reproduce and a juvenile only some 10 mm across is seen to the left. Below: The quick moving, small and rather delicate snails from the genus *Stomatella* sometimes reproduce rapidly in the reef aquarium and are introduced with live rocks.

Below: The nocturnal snail *Turbo* sp. is often found on live rock. It is about 3 to 4 cm long.

do not seem to live very long. Probably they lack the tidal water
movement which might be essential at least for some species to
thrive.

⑪ Bryozoans (Bryozoa)

Bryozoans are often found on algae and seaweeds in colder seas,
where they form encrusting colonies. There are also many tropical
species, and among these a more
bushy growth-form is common.
Not suprisingly bryozoans are fo-
und regularly on live rock too, but
unfortunately most of these are
small inconspicuous grayish colonies although other bryozoans
might be red, orange or other colours. The bryozoans are very difficult to keep alive in the closed reef
aquarium, and so far we know of
no case where this group has started to grow and multiply in captivity.

⑫ Entoprocts (Entoprocta)

Entoprocts are a small group of
animals that resemble hydrozoans and are closely related to the
bryozoans. About 60 species ha-

Snails of the family Vermetidae spend all their life in a tube and do not move
around, like other snails. They often seem to be the most common gastropods
in coral reef aquaria decorated with live rock, and can build large populations
(above: enlargement: 20 x). The vermetid snails secrete a slime, that is dragged
through the water like a trail net, in order to catch food (below: actual size).

Colonies of bryozoans are nearly always found on live rocks. Unfortunately there is only little chance for
them to survive in the coral reef
aquarium.

ve been found, all of which are living in the sea.

Entoprocts usually grow in colonies and most of them propagate asexually by budding. This is
why they can easily be mistaken
for hydroids. In coral reef aquaria
we have occasionally observed
them on rocks or on the glass
walls of the aquarium itself, always on spots where there was
strong water movement and little
light. With their maximum length

of 5 mm all the species are rather
small and therefore very hard to
track. They feed on organic particles which they filter from the water.

⑬ Echinoderms (Echinoderma-
ta)

Starfish, brittle stars, feather stars,
sea cucumbers and sea urchins
all belong to the echinoderms.
Even though many of these ani-

The tiny Entoprocta resemble hydrozoans, but are much more advanced animals that occasionally grow from live rocks.   Photo: R. Brons

mals may appear on live rock, only small specimens of brittle stars (Ophiuroidea) are really common. In an aquarium decorated with live rock you will nearly always introduce brittle stars to your system. Often you will only see the tiny arms sticking out from small cavities in the rocks. Most of the brittle stars are detritus- and/or plankton-eaters and they persist very well in a coral reef aquarium. We found convincing proof of this when we had to remove sand rich in organics from behind the decoration. Hundreds of brittle stars with a diameter of less than 10 mm were living in this substrate. The

Hundreds of these small brittle stars were found between sand and coral rubble in the substrate where they had reproduced. The white colouration indicates that the animals usually live in the dark (enlargement: 2 x).

This starfish is often introduced with live rocks and can multiply to large populations in the reef aquarium.

brittle stars were buried completely in the gravel and were only discovered when we passed the material through a fine-meshed sieve. When we later examined the aquarium carefully we easily observed a lot of tiny arms here and there projecting from the gravel. It is quite obvious that these animals in an important way contribute to the decomposition processes taking place in the aquarium. Larger brittle stars should for the same reason be added to every reef aquarium. In our personal aquarium we use as much as 50-60 serpent and brittle stars in an 800 litre aquarium. We will return to this topic in volume 3 in the book series. Starfish

can also occasionally be brought into the aquarium on live rock.

⑭ Ascidians or sea squirts (Ascidiacea)

Even though they do not look like us at all, the sea squirts (class Ascidiacea) are among the closest relatives of the vertebrates. They belong together with human beings, birds, reptiles, amphibians and fishes to the phylum Chordata. In the class Ascidiacea the backbone chord string, which is so typical for the vertebrates, can only be seen in a primitive form in the larva-stage. When the animals settle and start their sessile life, the chord-string has vanished.

Sea squirts are usually found on fresh live rocks, often those species that form colonies, spreading over the rock in an encrusting growth. Most often these are members of the family Styelidae and of the genera *Botryllus* or *Botrylloides*. They can easily be mistaken for sponges.

Also species may appear in the aquarium, like the beautiful small yellow species we sometimes find or one completely transparent species (see below). On the coral

These small yellow ascidians of about 1.5 cm size propagate asexually by budding. They are occasionally found on live rocks and prefer places with less light.

reef there is a variety of small, colonial species with the most beautiful colours, found in cavities, on vertical slopes or beneath coral heads. These are rarely seen on live rocks though. Larger solitary species, like *Polycarpa* spp., are, however, often found on fresh live rocks. Our experience shows that most ascidians do best in a more or less shady place. They are very difficult to keep alive for a prolonged period of time, however. From our point of view this has to do with nutrients. Sea Squirts are true filter feeders which rely on minute organic particles for food. The food-particles enter in the buccal siphon at the animal's top and pass a filtering organ before leaving through the atrial siphon usually placed on the side of the animal. Our experience is that in a nutrient poor aquarium filtered through protein skimming, sea squirts hardly survive. Occasionally we have, however, seen that encrusting species can multiply enormously, but again it is our experience that the growth stops and the species vanish after some time.

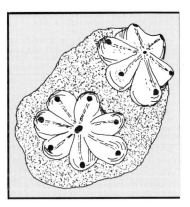

This colony of transparent ascidians (picture top right) developed on live rock, their inner organs can be seen quite well. Ascidians of the genera *Botryllus* or *Botrylloides* are commonly found on newly imported live rocks (picture to the right at the bottom and drawing above). Unfortunately they are normally very difficult to keep and survive only for a short time in the aquarium.

Résumé

This chapter can only give a rough survey of the organisms that are imported on live rock. It is supposed to support the aquarist when he tries to find his way through this miniature world so very rich in different species. Yet there are numerous other life forms that potentially could be found on the rocks that we unfortunately have to bypass here. As a rule we might say that there is a high probability that nearly all sessile and smaller freeliving animals that are found in coral reefs can also be found on a piece of live rock and therefore introduced to the modern coral reef aquarium. This is certainly a field in which reef aquarists will always be in for a surprise.

Further reading

ALLEN & STEENE, 1994; BARNES, 1980; CHOI & GINSBERG, 1983; COLIN, 1978; DAVIS & HUTCHINGS, 1983; GEORGE & GEORGE, 1979; HUMANN, 1994; HUTCHINGS & WEATE, 1977; JACKSON & WINSTON, 1982; LATKA, 1992; NILSEN, 1988; SCHUHMACHER, 1982; VINE, 1986; WALLS, 1982; WELLS & BRYCE, 1988; WILSON, 1993; ZANN, 1980.

The goal with using live rocks is to introduce the natural micro- and macro-fauna found on the reef. To achieve this it is necessary to store and treat the rocks properly. Not everyone has understood the importance of storing the rock correctly and one can often see that a lot of the delicate and important life on and inside the rocks are killed because of improper treatment. The pile of live rock seen on the left was photographed at the facility of a Singapore exporter. These rocks were stored outside in the burning sun and obviously the macro-life on them suffers. If the rocks were taken indoors and stored in running sea-water the situation would be very different. However, it is very important to use live rocks in our aquaria and we feel it is just a matter of proper information to solve problems like this. The use of live rock in aquaria is essential not only for the biological stability of the system, but also to show the aquarist the diversity of the macro-fauna of a reef.

Live rock is a crucial factor in modern coral reef aquaristics. Unfortunately we have been highly criticized for taking it from nature. In many areas of the world the collection of live rock has been totally banned. Nevertheless, all over the tropical world calcareous rock from reefs — what we call "live rock" — is collected for all kinds of purposes; for lime burning, road construction, house building etc. The amount of calcareous rock which goes into building one or a few houses, could pretty much have covered the need for live rock in Europe for a year! And not just a few houses are built from calcareous rock — whole villages are!

The collection of calcareous rock from coral reefs each year amounts to <u>millions</u> of tons. The yearly demand in the aquarium industry may be as much as a few <u>thousand</u> tons — yet environmental groups focus attention on us! Perhaps we are to blame for creating such a fancy term as "live rock". Live rock seems to be more in need of conservation than mere calcareous rock, doesn't it?

In the tropics, live rock and fresh stony corals are used for various purposes such as building houses or jetties (as shown above and below, in the Maldives; photo below: Dr. D. Brockmann).

Chapter 8:

Light in the Modern Coral Reef Aquarium

Light is of crucial importance in various respects. On the one hand it is a vital factor in biological processes, on the other hand it has psychological and aesthetic effects, as for example in a tropical sunset or the bright midsummer nights in the far north. Above all, the biochemical effects light causes are of primary importance. Without light there is no life! The sunlight provides the energy for photosynthesis and at the same time it is the source of essential thermal radiation. The position of our planet with respect to the sun is, in fact, a prerequisite of all life on earth.

Thanks to human ingenuity we have a great choice of artificial sources of light available today. They all have in common that – just like natural light – they emit a kind of radiation that consists of electromagnetic oscillations. Light is composed of radiations of different wavelengths. Each wavelength corresponds to a particular colour. All these together make up the colour spectrum, of which the human eye can perceive only a small sector. The unit of measurement for wavelength is the nano-

The light of the tropics is intensely strong and burning. The coral island "Kuredu" in the Maldives offers little protection (left). Corals develop colourful pigments to protect themselves against the strong ultraviolet radiation.

(Photo above: S. Tyree)

meter (nm). The part of the spectrum that is visible for us ranges from violet at about 380 nm through blue, green, yellow, orange to red at about 780 nm. Wavelengths below the violet radiation, which can influence biological processes very effectively, are referred to as ultraviolet light. Wavelengths beyond red are infrared light or heat radiation. For the marine aquarist it is imperative to have a good knowledge of ultraviolet light. This type of radiation, 100 nm to 380 nm, is subdivided into three sections.

UV-A is the radiation in the ultraviolet range close to visible light, i.e. from 315 nm to 380 nm. This kind of light is of great importance for autotrophic organisms (see below). UV-A passes through normal silicate glass.

UV-B comprises the wavelengths from 280 to 315 nm, a rather small section of the spectrum. It is UV-B radiation that burns our skin if we expose it to the sun without protection for a long period of time. A large dose of this radiation is damaging to live tissue. Aquarists should take this into account in their choice of aquarium lighting. UV-B radiation, also called medium wave UV light, does not pass through normal silicate glass and is absorbed in water rather fast. In a coral reef, however, with its extremely clear water, UV-A as well as UV-B radiation can penetrate as far as 40 metres deep.

UV-C with its wavelengths of 100 to 280 nm is the UV-radiation the furthest away from visible

light. It is extremely harmful to live tissue. UV-C light is absorbed by most gases as well as by the earth's atmosphere. UV sterilizers for aquarium use emit UV-C radiation with a wavelength of 253.7 nm. **Never use this kind of lighting over the aquarium itself.** Small amounts of UV-C radiation are also given off by the lighting systems used for coral reef aquariums. Here the UV-C radiation is eliminated by filters.

UV radiation and the effect on living corals

In general UV light must be regarded as harmful to living tissue. Light of 400 nm is widely accepted as the lower limit for photosynthetic activity. Inhibition of photosynthesis normally occurs at even shorter wavelengths, as the result of chloroplast damage (JOKIEL & YORK, 1982). Radiation at wavelengths between 280 and 320 nm harms nucleic acids and inhibits the function of chloroplasts. Therefore, as the UV-radiation is strong in the areas where coral reefs exist, we can normally see that shallow reefs exposed to full sunlight are poor in epifauna. This biotope does, however, contain a number of colourful corals, in particular stony corals. Consequently the coral fauna of the shallow

reefs must have ways to adapt to intense UV-radiation.

The most important means of protection is the presence of pigments known as S-320, or mycosporine-like amino acids (DUNLAP & CHALKER, 1986), found in the ectodermal tissue of corals. These pigments are largely transparent to UV-A. They seem to be made by the animal tissue and block the biocidal portion of UV-B radiation without attenuating potentially beneficial wavelength. These pigments thereby produce an ideal environment for culture of symbiotic algae (JOKIEL & YORK, 1982). There is an absorption peak around 320 nm for S-320 pigments.

While UV-B radiation and short-wave UV-A ($<$ 350 nm) radiation are clearly damaging to the zooxanthellae, the effect of the long-wave UV-A and short-wave blue-radiation (350-400 nm) is more uncertain. Response to UV-A is often seen as fluorescent colours in the corals. It is, however, quite clear that the symbiotic algae develop strains adapted to different levels of UV-radiation. A coral from deeper areas of the reefs will thus have difficulties if exposed to the light-intensity of the very shallow reef. An adaptation to the increase in UV must be done gra-

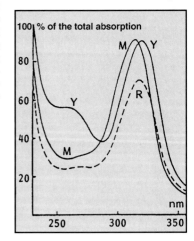

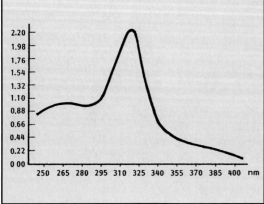

Left: Corals that live in the shallow waters of a reef contain UV-absorbing substances. The diagram to the left shows which wavelengths are absorbed by a colony of *Palythoa* sp. (after LESSER et al., 1990).

In many corals we can find chemical compounds that protect them against UV-radiation. The diagram above shows the light absorption by such compounds in three *Acropora* spp. (Y, M and R). After SHIBATA, 1969

Table 5
Pigment concentration, symbiotic cell population, growth rate and planula release measurements for *Pocillopora damicornis* with and without influence of UV-radiation (After JOKIEL & YORK, 1982).

	UV present			UV absent		
	n	median	range	n	median	range
UV-absorbing pigment S-320 (absorption at 320 nm)	11	0.26	0.19-0.35	11	0.12	0.07-0.17
Photosynthetic pigment chlorophyll a (μg/cm^2)	10	6.0	4.5-7.3	10	4.7	3.0-9.0
Photosynthetic pigment chlorophyll c (μg/cm^2)	10	2.1	1.2-3.4	10	3.3	1.6-7.0
Zooxanthellae population (10^3/cm^2)	10	377	267-522	10	368	311-505
Growth (mm) during 40 days experiment	11	5.7	5.0-8.5	11	8.3	5.3-9.5
Planula release (planula released per night)	10	26.5	9-251	10	4.5	2-77

n= numbers of colonies analysed

Absorption spectra of different colour pigments.
(After RAY, 1972)

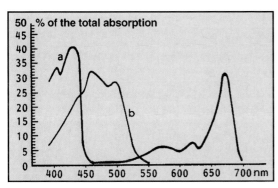

Chlorophyll a (graph a); beta-carotene (graph b)

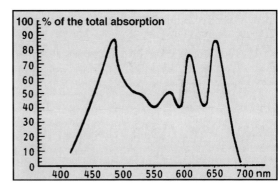

Chlorophyll b

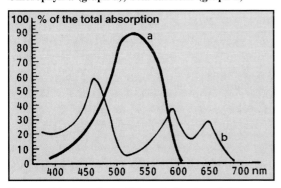

Fucoxanthin (graph a); Chlorophyll c (graph b)

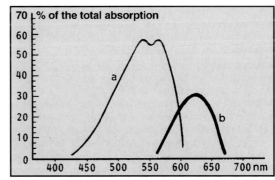

Phycoerythrin (graph a); Phycocyanin (graph b)

dually by the selection of UV-resistant strains of zooxanthellae, and the build up of resistant S-320 pigments in the ectodermal tissue. UV-A radiation is probably channeled into photosynthetic pathways re-emitting the energy at longer wavelengths where it can be absorbed by the algae, (KAWAGUTI, 1969; JOKIEL & YORK, 1982). As a result we often find coral colonies with fluorescent colours in shallow areas.

UV-radiation has effects on growth, production of larvae, on the zooxanthellae and on chlorophyll. JOKIEL & YORK (1982) give an excellent review of these and a summary is given in table 5, page 197.

Light and photosynthesis

The fact that we mostly keep algae and invertebrates with symbiotic algae in our coral reef aquaria, makes additional information on the process of photosynthesis most profitable (for more information see chapter 13).

Photosynthesis takes place in roughly two steps. During the light-reaction, radiation energy produces chemical energy, with oxygen as a by-product. This is a most intricate process, in which iron proteins called ferrodoxines play an important part in the electron transport.

During the dark-reaction, which does not require any light, glucose is produced from carbon dioxide.

The light-reaction involves pigments characteristic of the process of photosynthesis. The most important of these are the *chlorophyll* pigments, of which eight different types are known. Moreover, there are *carotenoids* and *phycobillines*, that can be found for example in red and blue-green algae. The different pigments of the plants effect absorption in different sections of the spectrum. One particular pigment can make use of only one part of the spectrum, not the whole. Thus every pigment has its particular absorption spectrum. This absorption spectrum shows which parts of the light are utilized by the respective pigment (see diagrams page 197).

The most common pigment, *chlorophyll a*, shows maximum

absorption in the range of 430 to 670 nm, i. e. in the blue and red section of the visible spectrum. *Carotenoids*, such as β-*carotene* show maximum absorption between 450 and 500 nm, i. e. in the blue-green section of the spectrum. *Phycobillines* mainly absorb green to orange light. These pigments overlap each other, so that only the most colourful or dominating ones give the algae their external colour. Green pigments are always present, even in algae that appear red to us. Altogether these plant pigments can use most of the visible spectrum.

Light intensity and the underwater light field

The intensity of the daylight can vary considerably. We only have to think of the regions of the far north, which remain nearly totally dark during the winter months. Under these conditions there is only a very small amount of light available for the marine fauna and

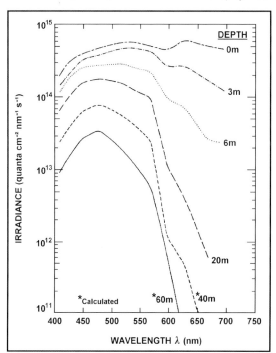

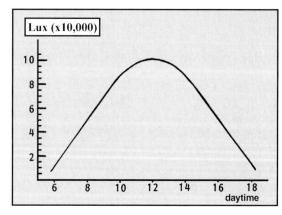

Above: Intensity of the sunlight at the water surface of a coral reef during the course of a day (based on SAUER, 1989a).

Left: Underwater spectral irradiance for an average sunny day on Dancing Lady Reef, Jamaica, between February and April 1978 (after DUSTAN, 1979).

flora. If this nearly complete lack of light is compared to the abundance of light in equatorial regions of the sea, the contrast is striking. There are a number of corals which tolerate the extreme abundance of light in the shallow regions of a coral reef. These corals obviously develop violet pigments, which protect them from the intense UV radiation which we will discuss later. TITLYANOV & LATYPOV (1991) give interesting information on the characteristics of the fauna in correspondence to the respective light intensity.

While light is essential to reef corals and other organisms that contain symbiotic algae, it is also one of the most difficult parameters to measure. The light can be measured in two ways – quantity or spectral quality.

The intensity of light, or flux, varies with the angle of the light-source. Pointing a narrow light-meter towards the light-source, varying the angle, one can measure the flux at various angles. This is called the radiant flux, but is – in practice – seldom used.

More commonly one measures the amount of light at a given surface area. This is referred to as irradiance, and is theoretically defined as the flux of light energy incident on a small element of surface divided by that element (JERLOV, 1968; FALKOWSKI et al., 1990). The units used for light measurements are many and somewhat difficult to understand. The radiant flux comes in quantum units such as quanta/m^2/s (often given as E/m^2/s where E stands for "Einstein" - the product of one proton at a certain frequency and Avogadro's number) or in energy units such as Joules/m^2/s. The irradiance comes in quanta/m^2/s or in watts/m^2, and contains information about the integrated areal distribution of radiant energy. While quantum units are most often used in connection with photosynthetic measurements, energy units are mostly used when calculating energy budgets. Conversion from energy units to quantum units (or vice versa) requires knowledge of the spectral

distribution of the light field. Still we require sophisticated equipment to measure irradiance. A common term for irradiance is lux. On light-sources, such as light-tubes, the irradiance is normally given in lumens. The irradiance of 1 lux is equal to 1 lumen per square meter.

The irradiance on the reefs is normally strong (see diagrams page 198). It is not unusual to measure more than 100.000 lux on midday at the surface over reefs near the equator. Table 6, after van OMMEN (1992), shows an example of variations in light near the equator. The irradiance varies

Table 6
Irradiance at midday on the equator. All values in lux. After van OMMEN, 1992.

Depth (m)	Irradiance		
	minimum	maximum	average (incl. clouds)
Surface	114543	126520	77420
5	28636	31630	19355
10	16039	17713	10839
20	9136	10122	6194
100	46	51	31

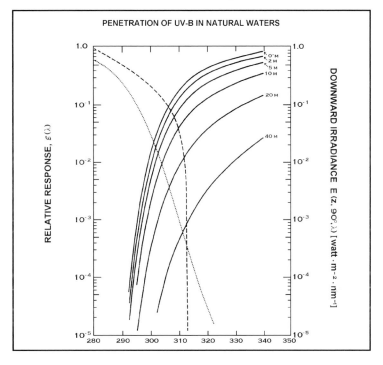

PENETRATION OF UV-B IN NATURAL WATERS

Relative biological efficiencies for an average action spectrum for biological effects involving DNA (dotted curve; see SETLOV, 1974) and for generalized plant response action spectrum vs wavelength (dashed curve; see CLADWELL, 1971). The relative response (left hand scale) is normalized to 1.0 at the wavelength of maximum response. The solid curves (right hand scale) give the downward (noon) spectral irradiance at various depths as a function of wavelengths.
After SMITH & BAKER, 1978.

with depth and with time of the day (see diagram page 198).

Also the spectral energy varies greatly with depth and locations. In general the red light is absorbed rapidly whereas the blue light penetrates deep into the ocean. Ultraviolet radiation plays an important role in reef ecology, but if it is too strong, it may severely damage living tissues (see page 196). The diagram on page 199 (after SMITH & BAKER, 1978) tells us that even the short wavelengths of UV-radiation can penetrate to depths of 40 meters. The amount of UV-B radiation that hits the corals is highly dependent on the transparency of the water and is greatly affected for instance by carbon filtration (see chapter 12).

In oceanic reefs, where the water is nutrient poor and clear, the maximum penetration is between 440 and 490 nm, causing the open ocean to look bright blue. In coastal areas, where the water contains more nutrients, particles, and often more intense blooming of phytoplankton, the maximum penetration is around 550 nm, i.e. more green than blue. However, in general coral reef water must be regarded as clear, oligotrophic, bluish in colour, and relatively rich in ultraviolet radiation.

The light-field on the coral reefs does not only shine from above. Reflection from the sandy bottom causes upwelling irradiance, illuminating the corals from below. This reflected upwelling light is important for coral species colonizing the understory of reefs (ROOS, 1967; FALKOWSKI et al., 1990). This type of indirect light is often missing, or at least found only to a minor extent, in our aquaria. It can frequently be observed that the lower areas of otherwise healthy corals die off. In many cases this could be a result of insufficient light, in particular in lack of reflecting, indirect light from the bottom of the tank.

Factors such as particulate material in the water, plankton blooming and the chemistry of the water itself, also influence the amount and quality of light reaching the corals. Obviously a horizontal substrate receives much more light than a vertical substrate. According to FALKOWSKI et al. (1990) a vertical substrate may get only 25% the amount of light of a horizontal substrate at the same depth.

Waves can act as lenses, causing flashes of light in shallow waters. When photosynthetically available radiation, **PAR**, incident on the surface was 2100 to 2500 $\mu E/m^2/s$, flashes in excess of 4000 $\mu E/m^2/s$ occurred at the rate of 1 to 3.5 flashes per second (FALKOWSKI et al., 1990). Suggestions are that these flashes might play an important role in shallow water reef-ecology. Waves are never present (unless artificially produced by special equipment) in our aquaria and hence this effect is lacking.

The symbiotic algae and other algae are specifically adapted to the light conditions of their particular habitat, and utilize the spectral energy available in their photosynthesis. Only part of the total available radiation is usable in photosynthesis – photosynthetically usable radiation, **PUR**. PUR is a function of the light field and the wavelength-specific absorption spectrum of the algae cell, and is different from PAR. Typically the major pigments (see page 197), including chlorophyll a, absorb most light in the "blue spectrum" between 400 and 550 nm and in the "red spectrum" between 650 and 700 nm. It is interesting to notice that the absorption of energy by the symbiotic algae varies with depth. Zooxanthellae from 52 metres depth absorbed about 50% more energy at 450 nm than zooxanthellae recorded from 8 metres depth, (see diagram below). We will deal thoroughly with the biology of the zooxanthellae in chapter 13.

The light intensity in a coral reef varies according to irradiation and the depth of the water. Even clouds in the sky reduce the intensity of the irradiation. The diagrams on pages 198 and 199 give examples of the light intensity during the course of the day and at different depths at different times of day in full sunlight. The enormous amount of light at the surface around midday is most remarkable. Most of the animals that need very intense light live at a depth of 1 metre or less. Compared to the surface of the water this means a reduction of the light intensity of at least 55 %. Yet the 45000 lux, which is the normal reading there around midday, is equivalent to 38 fluorescent tubes of 36 watt each per square metre. A cloudy sky of course reduces the amount of light on the reef considerably, yet it still remains very high.

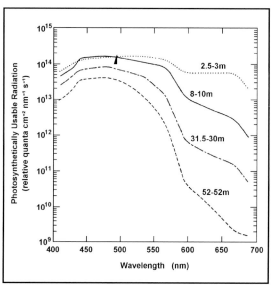

Photosynthetically usable radiation (PUR) of zooxanthellae isolated from *Montastrea annularis*, Discovery Bay, Jamaica (after DUSTAN, 1982).

Readings of the light intensity at three different spots in our experimental aquarium setup. A – directly under the lamps; B – between the two lamps; C – at the narrow sides of the aquarium, 50 cm away from the lamps. In addition to these, readings were taken when the lighting

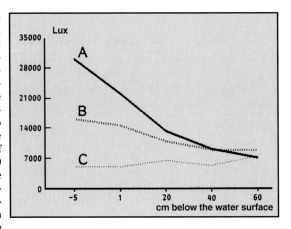

was subdued by a gauze screen. This resulted in a loss of light intensity of 5000 lux at the water surface.

If you want to set up an **aquarium emulating the conditions in the shallow regions of a coral reef** you need an extraordinarily high amount of light as compared to the usual aquarium lighting. As blue light is the dominating section of the spectrum in the ocean at depths of a few metres and deeper, you have to make sure that a certain amount of blue light is available in the aquarium as well. In such an aquarium cnidarians with zooxanthellae may be kept. Corals without zooxanthellae and other animals with meagre amounts of pigment are not protected against the UV-radiation and may only be placed in the more shady parts of the aquarium, e. g. below overhanging pieces of rock.

If however you decide on a **coral reef aquarium for animals from deeper regions of the reef**, less light is necessary. The intensity of the light is greatly reduced with blue light dominating. Only few coral animals with zooxanthellae can exist here. Typical cave dwellers, however, thrive in this biotope.

To find out about the light intensity in an aquarium the reading in lux can be taken with a suitable gauge. We have compared different readings under different conditions in an experimental aquarium setup. The size of the aquarium was 166 x 80 x 65 cm (length x width x height). It was illuminated by two metal halide lamps (HQI-

TS 250 Watt/D). The filter lens of the lamp was exactly 37 cm above the water surface. The distance between the two lamps was 65 cm with each lamp placed 50 cm away from the narrow side of the aquarium. The lamps were tilted over slightly to the front side. The readings are shown in the diagram above. There are considerable differences in the readings of the light intensity directly below the lamps, those between the lamps and those at the sides of the aquarium. Of course these readings cannot be applied directly to other aquaria, yet they point to the fact that certainly not all corals thrive in any place whatever in an aquarium.

Moonlight

It may sound strange, but the light of the moon does play an important part in the reef ecology. It is a key factor in the reproduction of many organisms, and triggers the mass spawning of corals that happens every year on the Great Barrier Reef, Australia, and elsewhere in the central Pacific. Temperature is another important factor connected to reproduction, and the monthly moon cycle should be correlated with a yearly tempera-

ture cycle. We will return with further specifics on reproduction of corals in volume 2, but would like to present the techniques for creating an artificial moon over the aquarium here.

The moon has from nature a 29.5 days cycle. In aquaristic practice this can be said to equal

	Table 7 Nightly luminance value for moon. After TYREE, 1994.	
Lunar phase	Day	Luminance
New	1	0.00
	2	0.01
	3	0.02
	4	0.04
	5	0.07
	6	0.11
	7	0.16
	8	0.22
	9	0.28
	10	0.36
	11	0.44
	12	0.54
	13	0.64
	14	0.74
	15	0.86
Full	16	1.00
	17	0.86
	18	0.74
	19	0.64
	20	0.54
	21	0.44
	22	0.36
	23	0.28
	24	0.22
	25	0.16
	26	0.11
	27	0.07
	28	0.04
	29	0.02
	30	0.01

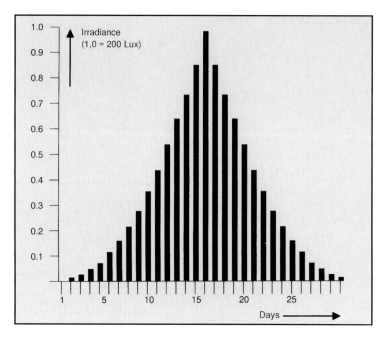

Artificial moonlight in the aquarium: After Tyree (1993, 1994) the increase and decrease in the irradiance should be logarithmic with the maximum (200 Lux; measured at the corals) on day 16.

The lunar cycle should be imitated in the aquarium system. This is possible e. g. with a "blue" electric bulb or "blue" fluorescent tube. However, the irradiance should be adapted to the diagram shown above.

30 days, which means that on day 16 there should be a full moon and on day 1 a new moon. The moonlight should be varied in strength as shown in table 7, page 201 and the diagram to the left. The equipment needed for doing this automatically is Programmable Logic System Units (PLS) such as *Siemens Simatic S5* or equivalent. If coupled to a *Siemens HEFU Dynamic* device or equivalent, the irradiance can be regulated from day to day by the increasing voltage automatically added to a blue light-tube by the computer. It should be stressed that the moonlight can also be regulated manually, but this requires a daily procedure.

According to Tyree (1994), based on Jokiel et al. (1985), the irradiance from the full moon is about 0.01 $\mu E/m^2/s$ which is 2×10^6 times weaker than the normal midday reading of 2000 $\mu E/m^2/s$ and thus very weak. The moonlight is blue, or bluish, to whitish in colour. Tyree (1994) has experimented with actinic blue tubes mounted 60 cm above and 40 cm in front of the aquarium reef, giving some 100-200 lux on the corals. We have ourselves experimented with a single blue 25W bulb mounted only 10 cm above the surface. This gave less than 50 lux on the corals. The same method was used by Flemming Jörgensen, Norway, who got signs of a mass spawning in his aquarium (Fosså & Nilsen, 1995). The technical apparatus for simulating moonlight is not fully explored and we encourage aquarists to try various light-sources and to experiment with the goal of achieving the sexual reproduction of the corals in closed reef aquaria.

The importance of light for the Modern Coral Reef Aquarium

Without doubt aesthetic points of view also play an important role in our considerations about aquari-

Light is life! The coral reef pulsates with life in virtually endless variations (photo above: E. Svensen). To keep delicate stony corals like *Hydnophora exesa* shown below (photo Dr. D. Brockmann) in a coral reef aquarium one has to choose the appropriate lighting system.

um lighting. Thus we usually want to create lighting conditions as similar as possible to those in the original biotopes. This includes a gradual increase of light replacing the rise of the daylight and its slow decrease imitating the fading away of the sunlight at dusk. This effect can be achieved with the help of a timer, which switches the various lamps on and off in a certain sequence. A coral reef aquarium should be lighted for about 12 to 14 hours per day. In tropical coral reefs there is daylight for about 12 hours and there are only very brief twilight periods at dawn and at dusk, because the sun sets at an almost right angle. The fact that the intensity of light in the aquarium can never equal that of natural sunlight can be compensated for by extending the photoperiod. Yet under all circumstances a period of total darkness is absolutely necessary.

The change from complete darkness to full light when the aquarium lighting is suddenly switched on creates stress for all organisms. However, most of them are able to adapt themselves to a longer or shorter period of daylight as long as the lighting period is not changed too abruptly. Usually a bulb or a fluorescent tube switched on before or after the main lighting system will be sufficient as an imitation of the twilight at dawn or dusk.

The different wavelengths of aquarium lighting are of utmost importance for the autotrophic organisms, i.e. for the various kinds of algae. The most important algae in a coral reef aquarium are the different calcareous algae and the zooxanthellae. The zooxanthellae live in the endoderm cells of the tissue of corals and some other invertebrates. As the host animal is dependent on its zooxanthellae to a great extent, it is very important to create optimal living conditions for these algae.

The zooxanthellae absorb light at wavelengths from 350 to 750 nm. Thus they make use of certain parts of UV-A radiation, yet only of those wavelengths that are close to visible blue-violet light. We have

to meet the needs of the symbiotic algae, but at the same time we have to take care that the host animals do not come to harm through light with wavelengths below 350 nm. The spectrum of the light in an aquarium should resemble as much as possible that of natural daylight.

As mentioned above, zooxanthellae live in the endoderm cells of corals and are adapted – as is their host – to a high intensity of light. Tropical sunlight has a high share of UV radiation, including wavelengths shorter than 350 nm. UV-A as well as UV-B radiation can penetrate to considerable depths in the seawater. Some corals develop chemical compounds that work like filters in order to protect against this radiation. These compounds are found in the zooxanthellae as well as in the cells of the coral polyps. A group of compounds referred to as S-320 proves to be especially effective in this respect. These substances have a maximum absorption at 313 nm (see diagram at the bottom of page 196, left). DUNLAP & CHALKER (1986) found three different compounds in the stony coral *Acropora formosa* which absorb between 310 and 340 nm. These compounds can be seen in the corals as white, violet or fluorescent pigments. They are the reason why corals in the shallows of a reef are most colourful (MOHAN, 1990, BINGHAM, 1995b).

Corals living in slightly deeper water only contain a minimum share of UV-absorbing substances. The diagram on page 196, below right shows the absorption of three species of stony corals of the genus *Acropora*. We can see that the protection loses its effect rapidly at wavelengths of more than 350 nm.

If the light over the aquarium is too powerful and contains too much UV radiation a negative reaction of the animals will be noticed before long. A lot of corals do not open under these conditions and their colours fade after a while. The reason for this is that the corals gradually lose their symbiotic algae; the zooxanthellae die.

If this kind of reaction is observed in a coral reef aquarium, either the intensity of the light or its composition, perhaps even both, have to be changed. Another way of dealing with this problem is to transfer the animals concerned to another, less illuminated region of the aquarium. Some aquarists screen their lamps with gauze covers to reduce the intensity of the light when new animals are introduced into the aquarium or when lamps are renewed. We have found this method satisfactory as well.

If you want to screen the aquarium against the main part of the UV radiation without reducing the light intensity, you can use 6 mm sheets of Plexiglass "Röhm PG-233" or filter glass "Uvilex-390". Both types of filter absorb up to a hundred per cent of the wavelengths shorter than 370 nm. To avoid damage to these sheets caused by the heat, you will have to fit them far enough away from the lamps.

Sources of light for the Modern Coral Reef Aquarium

Before you make up your mind which lighting system to buy you should find out all about the technical details of the light sources, especially the spectrum and intensity (lumens). Most of the manufacturing firms publish information leaflets or catalogues telling you about this. We only want to present here a few of the lighting systems available.

There are three main groups of light sources that may be used to illuminate a coral reef aquarium:

❶ fluorescent lamps,

❷ mercury vapour lamps and

❸ metal halide lamps.

The technical data for light sources given by the manufacturers usually states the *colour temperature* and the *Ra-index*. The colour temperature is measured in Kelvin (K). The higher the colour temperature, the whiter or "colder" the light. Thus the violet, blue and green parts of the spectrum prevail. If the colour temperature is lower, the resulting light gives a "warmer" impression, with radiation in the orange and red section of the spectrum dominating. It is interesting to compare this to natural sunlight. The light at dusk, for example has a colour temperature from around 2500 to 3900 K. The colour temperature of sunlight is about 5800 K. Daylight is a mixture of direct sunlight and of light reflected by the sky. Governed by the varying conditions (e. g. weather, time of day) readings of up to 30000 K are possible. Artificial light sources with colour temperatures of about 6000 K are especially recommendable for marine aquaristics.

The Ra-index tells us something about the quality of the colour reproduction of a light source. The scale for this runs from 0 to 100, with 100 standing for the best colour reproduction. The main light source for the lighting system of a coral reef aquarium should have an Ra-index of more than 80.

❶ Fluorescent lamps

There are many good reasons why fluorescent lamps have always been the most common light sources for coral reef aquaria. The lighting effect achieved with these lamps is more than adequate in most cases. Only if an aquarist wants to keep animals from very shallow water, is the light intensity of fluorescent lamps not always sufficient.

Fluorescent lamps are available in different lengths and with different light colours (light temperatures). Fluorescent lamps have a ballast that may be mounted in the hood or separately. Keeping the

Table 8
Useful fluorescent lamps for the marine aquarium.

Fabrication	Name and Type	Watt	Lumen	RA	Kelvin	Length (cm)
Osram-Sylvania	daylight L18/11	18	1300	86	6000	59
	daylight L36/11	36	3250	86	6000	120
	daylight L58/11	58	5200	86	6000	150
	daylight L18/12	18	1000	98	5400	59
	daylight L36/12	36	2350	98	5400	120
	daylight L58/12	58	3750	98	5400	159
	biolux L15/72	15	650	97	6500	43.8
	biolux L18/72	18	1000	97	6500	59
	biolux L30/72	30	1600	97	6500	89.5
	biolux L36/72	36	2300	97	6500	120
	biolux L58/72	58	3700	97	6500	150
Philips	daylight TLD15/96	18	1050	97	6500	59
	daylight TLD30/96	30	1700	97	6500	90
	daylight TLD36/96	36	2200	97	6500	120
	daylight TLD58/96	58	3600	97	6500	150
	daylight TLD15/95	15	900	98	5300	44
	daylight TLD18/95	18	1000	98	5300	59
	daylight TLD30/95	30	1700	98	5300	90
	daylight TLD36/95	36	2350	98	5300	120
	daylight TLD58/95	38	3750	98	5300	150
	Actinic Aqua Coral	380-500nm/w				
	TLD15/03	3.5/15	–	–	–	44
	TLD20/03RS	4.1/20	–	–	–	59
	TLD30/03	7.2	–	–	–	90
	TLD40/03RS	10.5/40	–	–	–	120

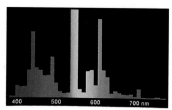

Colour 11 LUMILUX® Daylight

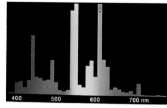

Colour 21 LUMILUX® Cool White

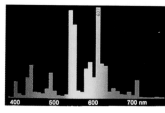

Colour 31 LUMILUX® Warm White

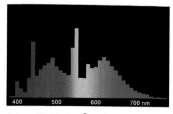

Colour 12 LUMILUX® DE LUXE
Daylight

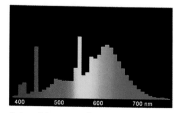

Colour 32 LUMILUX® DE LUXE
Warm White

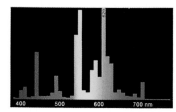

Colour 41 LUMILUX INTERNA®

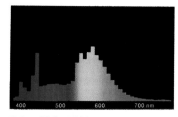

Colour 72 BIOLUX®

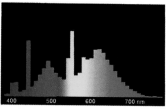

Colour 22 LUMILUX® DE LUXE
Cool White

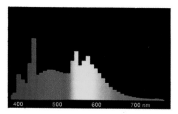

Colour 10 Daylight

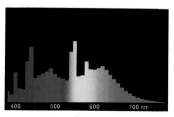

Colour 20 Cool White

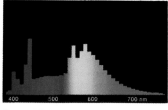

Colour 25 Universal White

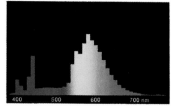

Colour 30 Warm White

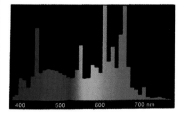

Colour 76 NATURA DE LUXE

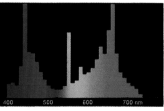

Colour 77 FLUORA®

Spectra of different fluorescent tubes.
(After Osram)

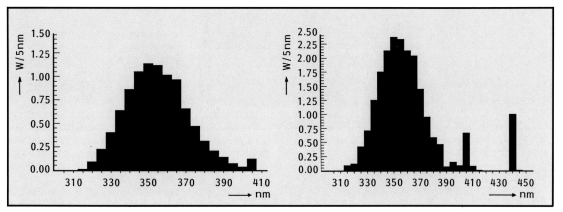

The distribution of the spectral radiation of Osram L73 Black Light, 36 watt (left) and Osram L79/UV-A, 80 watt (right) (based on information provided by Osram).

ballast apart from the lamps removes a source of heat and considerable weight from the canopy.

All electrical installations may only be carried out by an authorised electrician.

Fluorescent lamps are available in different wattages. The length of the fluorescent lamps corresponds to its wattage. This proves to be of practical importance when the lamps for a particular lighting system have to be chosen. To make the best use of the radiation energy fluorescent lamps always have to be fitted with a good reflector. On no account should household aluminium foil be used as a reflecting material. Parts of this foil might tear away fall into the water and cause dangerous metal poisoning.

Waterproof lamps with moisture proof end caps may be fitted at a distance of 20 cm from the water surface. The end caps must also keep salt from entering and depositing there, because this may lead to short circuits. Salt crusts that drop from metal surfaces into the aquarium could also lead to metal poisoning.

It is imperative that all electrical installations and the whole lighting system be grounded.

A lighting system with a single light colour alone does not provi-

de the aquarium with a balanced spectrum of light. If you look, for example, at the spectral analysis of colour 11 (Osram see left), you will find that the maximum radiation is at 430, 545 and 615 nm, i.e. in the blue, yellow and orange section of the spectrum. It contains little red light and also little UV-A radiation, apart from the fact that there is a very little amount of it at 365 nm. A 36 watt lamp by Osram with this colour number has an intensity of 3250 lumens.

The great advantages of fluorescent lamps are that the original cost and the cost of operation are not very high. This enables the aquarist to install a number of lamps with different light colours and to combine them, so that they result in a balanced spectrum. There is a great variety of light colours available in the shops. Most common in Germany are Lumilux 11 and Lumilux 12 (daylight). Other firms produce corresponding types of lamps. In the USA many fluorescent tubes have been developed for aquariums. The ones most commonly available include Triton, Blue Moon, Bio-Lume, Primetinic, Reeflite, Actinic Sun, Coralife 50/50, Aqua Sun, Actinic White, and Super Actinic. The Philips Actinic 03 which is common in Europe is also common in USA. Some of these fluorescent tubes are also available in high output and very high output formats that require a special ballast. In addition there are power com-

pact fluorescents in 9, 15, 28, 55 and 96 watts with 6700 and 7100 Kelvin colour temperature. Some fluorescent lamps also have built-in reflectors.

If you plan to make fluorescent lamps the main light source in your coral reef aquarium we suggest a combination of daylight type lamps with actinic blue lights as a basis. Yet there are many other ways of combining types of lamps successfully. It is essential to experiment and observe carefully how the different organisms react to the different combinations of light. To increase the share of UV-A light, lamps referred to as "black light lamps" (Osram 73) or special UV-A-lamps may be used. There is, however, the danger that animals may thus receive an excessive amount of UV light. We recommend therefore that such lamps should be mounted at a distance of at least 30 cm above the water surface.

In the last few years the "actinic blue lamps" TL 03 and TL 05 have been used with great success for coral reef aquariums. The lamp type TL 05 provides a spectrum between 300 and 500 nm with the maximum at 360 nm. This fluorescent lamp yields a high share of UV radiation and just as with the "black light lamps" special care is necessary when using it. Type TL 03 has a spectrum between 390 and 490 nm with a maximum at 420 nm (see page 208). Thus this lamp yields a small share of

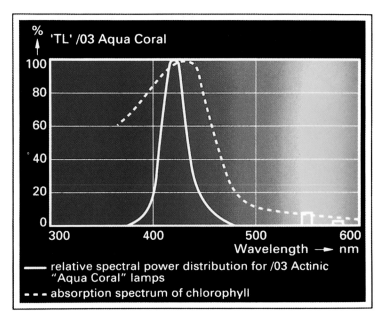

% 'TL' /03 Aqua Coral

― relative spectral power distribution for /03 Actinic "Aqua Coral" lamps

- - - absorption spectrum of chlorophyll

Spectrum of Philips TL03 "Actinic Aqua Coral" fluorescent tube. Note that chlorophyll also has an absorption in the red part of the spectrum (see page 197) and that the dotted curve is in this way somewhat misleading.

UV-A radiation as well as visible parts of the spectrum. Aquarists in North America use this type of lamp in combination with daylight fluorescent tubes very successfully.

We have had very positive results with a combination of type TL 03 and metal halide lamps (HQI). Also lamps like Osram L 67, Philips TL 18 or Thorn T 10 combine very well with HQI-lamps. They all make very decorative complements to the white HQI light. In addition to that, blue lamps are very suitable to create twilight effects. For a coral reef aquarium emulating deeper regions of the reef these lamps are highly recommendable.

There have been some anecdotal observations that indicate that blue and actinic blue fluorescent lamps inhibit the growth of red slime algae.

Plant lamps, like the Osram "Fluora", for example, or Sylvania "Grolux" yield a spectrum that comes very close to the spectrum at which photosynthesis is most active. Apart from a high share of blue they also have a very high share of red. They are therefore

not suitable at all for a coral reef aquarium.

Fluorescent lamps lose a great deal of their light intensity as they get older. Under normal operating conditions (12 to 14 hours of light per day) they should be replaced every year.

❷ Mercury vapour lamps (HQL)

Many invertebrates for our coral reef aquariums come from regions of the reef with a high radiation intensity. For that reason other light sources in addition to fluorescent tubes were tried, among others mercury vapour lamps. Like the fluorescent lamps these are also discharge lamps yet here the gas discharge between two electrodes takes place under very high pressure. HQL lamps have a colour temperature of between 2900 and 4100 K, which is quite similar to that of many fluorescent lamps. The spectral combination of the light of HQL lamps is also comparable to that of many fluorescent lamps. Their RA-index, however, is lower. It should be taken into account that the share of UV radiation in

the light of HQL lamps varies according to the type of lamp.

Among the HQL lamps there are also black light types, e.g. Osram HQV 125 watt, and there is considerable danger of excessive UV radiation. These lamps should only be used as supplemental light sources for very tall aquaria.

HQL lamps have to be fitted with the respective ballast and reflectors (some types, e.g. the Osram HQL-R de lux, have a built-in reflector). The original costs of such lamps are quite high. The fittings needed to mount these lamps above the aquarium are also rather space-consuming. The lamp and the ballast produce a lot of heat and should not be installed too close to the surface of the water. Moreover the lamp should not be mounted closer than at the specified safety distance. The ballast may be mounted separately, yet again the most important precaution is:

All electrical installations may only be carried out by an authorised electrician.

❸ Metal halide lamps (HQI)

Marine aquarists have always been looking for the ideal light source for their aquaria and they have not found it yet. The lighting that comes closest to this ideal today are metal halide lamps, which are also high pressure discharge lamps. HQI lamps have colour temperatures of between 3000 and 20000 K and a good Ra-index, which may be as high as 93.

HQI light includes UV radiation of all three sections. The UV-C radiation, which is harmful, has to be eliminated with a special filter envelope or lens built into the lamp or fixture. These lamps should never be used without these protective filters:

Direct HQI radiation which is not filtered, is harmful to the animals in the aquarium and may also do harm to the aquarist.

Three different metal halide lamps mounted side by side over the authors aquarium. From left to right: "ARCADIA" 250 W, 6500 Kelvin; Radium 400 W, 20000 Kelvin "Marine Blue"; "OSRAM" 250 W, 5200 Kelvin "daylight".

The spectrum of the HQI light resembles the natural light of the shallow waters of the coral reef. There are various types of these lamps. HQI-TS/NDL and HQI-TS/D are the types which may be taken into consideration as lighting systems for a coral reef aquarium. HQI-TS/NDL emits a slightly warmer light and contains a higher share of UV radiation than does HQI-TS/D. HQI lamps are available with 70, 150, 250, 400, 1000, 2000 and 3500 watt.

In the early eighties the "daylight metal halide lamps", like the Osram HQI-TS-250/D with a colour temperature around 5200 K were the lamps most often used. Occasionally the NDL-types, with a colour temperature around 4500 K could be seen. The daylight lamps are still very popular and have proven to give excellent growth of corals. The light is, however, somewhat yellowish compared to the natural light on the reef. This has lead several firms to develop metal halide lamps with a much higher colour temperature than the ordinary daylight tubes.

The English company *Jerrard Bros PLC* introduced *Arcadia* 150W and 250W lamps with 6500 Kelvin which gave a slightly more

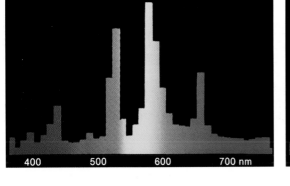

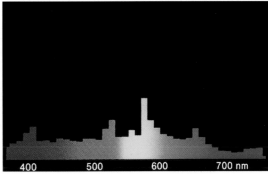

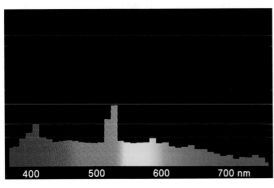

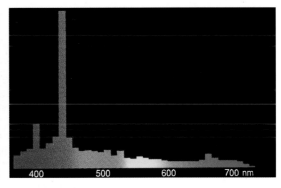

Different types of metal halide lamps with different colour temperatures and spectra. Above left: colour temperature "warmwhite" (.../WDL) not normally used in reef aquariums; above right: colour temperature .../NDL which has a yellow appearance and which is also not much used today; below left: colour temperature "daylight" (.../D), typically shining with 5000 – 5500 Kelvin, which has been used for years with much success, but which at the moment is being replaced with types giving even more natural reef-light; below right: Radium "blue" with a peak of light in the blue spectrum at approximately 450 nm.

Table 9. Useful metal halide lamps for the marine aquarium.

Fabrication	Type	Volts	Watt	Base	Lumen	Kelvin	Comments
Osram	HQI-TS 250/D	220/110	250	Fc2	19000	5200	much used in Europe from the early eighties until today
	HQI-TS 400/D	220/110	400	Fc2	35000	5200	much used in Europe from the early eighties until today
	HQI-TS 1000/D	220/110	1000	Fc2	90000	6000	
	HQI-TS 2000/D	220/110	2000	E40	170000	6000 (?)	
	HQI-TS/T 3500/D	220/110	3500	E40	300000	6000	
	HQI-T 250/D	220/110	250	E40	19000	5400	
	HQI-T 400/D	220/110	400	E40	33000	5900	
	HQI-T 1000/D	220/110	1000	E40	80000	6000	used with good results by some aquarists
	HQI-T 2000/N/E/ Super	220/110	2000	E40	240000	6000 (?)	
aqualine buschke	aqualine 10.000	220/110	150	Fc2	?	10000	very true light, good results obtained by many aquarists
	aqualine 10.000	220/110	250	Fc2	?	10000	very true light, good results obtained by many aquarists
Radium	HRI-T 400 "Marine Blue"	220	400	E40	-	20000	excellent for increasing the amount of blue light. Has a peak at 450nm. Best in combination with other lamps.
Arcadia	HQI 6500 Marine	220	150	E27	11000	6500	much used in Europe since around 1993
	HQI 6500 Marine	220	250	E27	?	6500	much used in Europe since around 1994

whitish light than the daylight lamps. They both have been successfully used in reef aquaria. In Germany *ab* (aqualine buschke) has introduced the 10000 Kelvin *Aquasunlight* in 150W and 250W. Presently, these lamps probably are the closest we have to the natural reef light, and they do indeed give good growth of stony corals in the aquarium.

If one wants to add more blue light (in the area 400-500 nm), one could try the Radium 400 W "Marine Blue" sold by the company *K.J. Feige* of Germany. This lamp has a really bluish light and should be used in combination with other lamps or alone if one wants to simulate the deeper areas of a reef. We have good results with the use

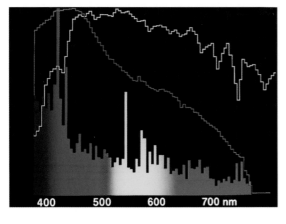

Above: Spectrum of *ab aquasunlight 10000* 150W/250W compared to the lightfield in five metres depth (blue line) and to daylight on the surface (yellow line). To the right: The ILS-2000-System of Hasling Audio Systems.

of this lamp in combination with both Osram daylight, Arcadia and ab lamps. In the USA the firms ESU and Hamilton offer metal halide lamps in 100, 175, 250 and 400 watts, in 5500, 6500, 10000 and 20000 Kelvin. The Iwasaki or "Ultralux" 70, 150, and 250 watt bulbs are most similar to the lamps from Arcadia, and are also rated at 6500 Kelvin. There is also a 400 watt 6500 Kelvin bulb in the same format, and recently a new bulb from Germany was introduced that is 175 watts and 6500 Kelvin.

All in all the development of the metal halide lamps continues and there are at present a number of types to chose from, (table page 210). The number will surely increase during the years to come.

Unfortunately all these lamps are very expensive. Moreover their share of UV radiation is so high that they have to be mounted at least 30 cm away from the water surface. As mentioned before, the animals in the aquarium may be damaged by an excessive amount of UV radiation, which could kill them. A slight overdose of UV radiation will result in an increased loss of zooxanthellae, as the life cycle of these algae is shortened by it. This may lead to a gradual decline in health of the corals. When HQI lamps are installed for the very first time or when old lamps are replaced, the light in-

tensity has to be increased gradually, so that the animals can get used to the higher intensity of radiation. For this purpose the lamps may be screened temporarily with layers of gauze. In addition to that filters which limit the UV radiation may be bought along with the lamps.

The greatest advantages of the HQI lamps are their extraordinary luminous efficacy, their luminance and the favourable composition of their spectrum. Though an excessive amount of UV radiation is detrimental, a certain share of it is essential, as pointed out before on pages 196-198. UV radiation also helps to precipitate protein substances in the water, thus increasing the effectiveness of a protein skimmer.

Hasling Audio Systems (Denmark) has developed a digital controller for all kinds of lighting systems, including HQI lamps, which is available in the trade under the name of ILS-2000. With the help of this system the output of HQI lamps can be reduced to around 60 % of their original power. Thus a variable regulation of HQI lamps of up to 2400 watts during the course of the day may be achieved in such a way that it increases from 40% to 100% and then decreases to 40% again. Another advantage in this situation is that the reduction of the blue por-

tion of the spectrum is lower than that of the rest of the spectrum. Thus not only an emulation of the natural cycle of daylight is achieved, but also the desired dominance of blue light.

There is no doubt that up to now HQI lamps are the best light sources available for coral reef aquaria, particularly for the animals from the shallow regions of a coral reef.

Further reading

Lighting systems for coral reef aquaria in general
JANSEN (1991), LATKA (1991), NILSEN (1985), MOHAN (1990), SAUER (1989 a and b), SCHOMISCH (1991).

Corals, zooxanthellae and light
BROWN (1990), FOSSÅ & NILSEN (1995), GLADFELTER (1975), JOKIEL (1980), THORSON (1964).

Lighting conditions in the reef
SMITH & BAKER (1979), TYREE (1994), JOKIEL & YORK (1982), WEINBERG (1976).

Chapter 9:

Temperature Control
in the
Modern Coral Reef Aquarium

The geographic distribution of coral reefs is limited by the 20° C-isotherm. As a consequence the temperature in a coral reef aquarium should not be allowed to go down below 20° C. Practical knowledge has shown 23 to 27° C to be the most favourable temperature for communities of coral reef animals. Slight variations in temperature of a few degrees during the day are quite common in the sea as well, and do not harm the animals at all. At the borders of the areas where coral reefs can be found, variations of temperature of up to 20° C over the course of the year are not unusual (see table on page 215). Temperature readings on reefs in the Hawaiian region over a period of ten years showed, however, only very slight variations during the warm season. The minimum reading taken was 26.7° C, the maximum 27.4° C.

COLES & FADLALLAH (1991) examined the reactions of stony corals in the Persian Gulf after temperatures had dropped to an average of 13° C for some months (December 1988 to March 1989). This induced a high mortality rate of the coral fauna. *Acropora* and *Platygyra*-species were affected most of all. Brain corals of the family Faviidae, and species of the genus *Porites* proved to be surprisingly resistant to these low temperatures.

Above: section of a reef in the Maldives. **Underwater photo: Dr. D. Brockmann**

Left: this photo from about 15 metres depth on a reef of Thailand shows how extreme temperature and light conditions combined can result in coral bleaching. The temperature at the site was close to 30° C and the massive brain coral shows obvious signs of severe bleaching. However, in the small shaded area beneath the *Pocillopora* sp. (which also has bleached), the brain coral has retained its normal colouration. **Photo: E. Svensen**

A rise in temperature to 30° C leads to serious consequences, as it damages the transport system that is needed for photosynthesis. If corals are exposed to intense UV radiation at the same time, aggressive oxygen develops in the cell tissue. This can kill the stony corals. This phenomenon, described by the term "bleaching" (see next paragraph), has repeatedly been observed (BROWN, 1990). Though it was first noticed as early as 1931, it did not arouse the interest of scientists before the 1980's, when vast populations of corals were bleached in the Indo-Pacific region in 1983 and in the Caribbean in 1987.

Coral bleaching

This colony of *Acropora microphthalma* has bleached severely in an aquarium as the temperature reached 30° C. As the temperature dropped again, the coral recovered nicely.

"Coral bleaching" is directly linked to high temperatures. The term describes a situation where corals lose their normal colouration, either due to a decrease in the number of zooxanthellae or due to a reduction of the pigmentation of each single alga cell, or a combination of both. Healthy zooxanthellae are brownish in colour. Thus, if they are present in sufficient numbers, the coral tissue will also appear brownish. With coral bleaching, the colour of the corals changes and the animal looks pale or even practically white.

Bleaching is well known and has been thoroughly described from the natural habitat. During 1982-1983 at "Thousand Islands" in Indonesia, more than 80% of the corals on the investigated locations died due to bleaching (BROWN & SUHARSONO, 1990). The cause of bleaching in nature is thought to be stress, from the corals being exposed to abnormally high temperature (30° C and above) over extended periods of time.

Bleaching is also connected to the amount of UV-radiation. LESSER et al. (1990) found that the level

of certain hormones, which neutralize active forms of oxygen, increased as the temperature and the UV-radiation levels in the surroundings increased. This is taken as an indirect evidence that changes in temperature and radiation lead to changes in the concentration of active oxygen in the coral tissue. Abnormal concentrations of active oxygen, leads to zooxanthellae die-offs. Apparently corals are more capable of sustaining increased temperatures when exposed to lesser amounts of UV-radiation.

Bleaching is also known from the coral reef aquarium. During heat waves the temperature in the aquarium can easily increase and reach the critical 30° C or more. Some corals are extremely sensitive to this and may, within few hours, lose a lot of zooxanthellae. We have found the branching *Acropora microphthalma* to be among the most vulnerable ones, and also many other species of stony corals show negative re-

actions. In the aquarium, though, bleaching seems also to be linked to the concentration of certain elements in the water. In tanks where the water is particularly heavily filtered over activated carbon, bleaching seems to occur more rapidly. This is likely to be linked to a lower concentration of, for instance certain organic compounds (see also chapter 12).

The best way to prevent bleaching is to avoid extreme temperatures. Preferentially it should never be allowed to reach beyond 28° C.

Heating the Modern Coral Reef Aquarium

The ways to heat a marine aquarium are similar to those used in freshwater tanks. The usual submersible heaters with thermostats

Table 10
Variations in temperature in coral reefs at the borders of the area where coral reefs may be found.

(After COLES & FADLALLAH, 1991)

Region	Degree of latitude	Temperature °C		
		Minimum	Maximum	Fluctuation
Saudi Arabia	27° N	11.4	36.2	24.8
Quatar	24° N	14.1	36.0	21.9
Abu Dhabi	25° N	16.0	36.0	20.0
Florida	25° N	13.3	32.8	19.5
Heron Island GBR	23° S	16.0	35.0	19.0
Japan	35° N	18.0	29.5	16.5
Bermuda	32° N	16.3	29.0	12.7
Abrolhos Island	29° S	17.0	28.0	11.0
Midway Island	28° N	18.2	28.3	10.1
Bay of Aquaba	29° N	20.0	28.0	8.0

have proved to be reliable for this purpose. Continuous flow heating systems with metal heating coils on the other hand are unsuitable. Be sure to take into account the heat produced by the aquarium lighting system and that supplied by direct sunlight when you are calculating the wattage of the heater that is needed. A high rate of evaporation also causes a certain amount of heat loss. A trickle filter with its large water surface also contributes to this heat loss. The best idea is to place the submersible heater at the end of the filtration system, e. g. in the last compartment of the filter, from where the clear water flows back into the aquarium. One of the advantages of this position is that the animals in the aquarium cannot come into close contact with it. Non-sessile invertebrates like sea anemones or snails may be damaged seriously if they do so. Fishes with strong jaws and teeth, like triggerfishes or puffers, are able to bite through electric cables or to damage the glass body of the heater.

As mentioned before, care must be taken not to immerse any soft plastic parts. Most aquarium heaters have a plastic cap and a suction cup made from plastic. Unless the manufacturer clearly has specified that they are made from seawater proof materials, the suction cup should be removed and the cap should remain above the surface of the water.

Cooling the Modern Coral Reef Aquarium

In tropical and subtropical climates, as well as during heat waves all over the world, high temperatures in the surroundings can lead to extreme temperatures in the aquarium. This is particularly common in aquaria with a lot of metal halide lighting, and in closed, built-in set-ups with limited air circulation above the surface. If the temperature in your aquarium frequently approaches the critical 28 – 30° C limit, cooling of the water may become necessary.

The most effective way of cooling the aquarium water is by using a thermostat controlled aquarium chiller. Normally these are attached to the water circuit going to the filter or skimmer. There are also chillers in which the heat exchanging unit is encased in a probe that can be placed in the sump. Through the aquarium trade several brands of water chillers are available; check with your dealer.

An alternative method for cooling the water is the installation of an air fan above the surface. The increased air motion speeds up the evaporation from the aquarium, thereby lowering the temperature.

Further reading

BROWN (1990), BROWN & SUHARSONO (1990), COLES & FADLALLAH (1991), COLES & JOKIEL (1977 a and b), LATKA (1992), LESSER et al. (1990)

Chapter 10

Water for the Modern Coral Reef Aquarium

If you taste sea water you realize at once that it is different from the freshwater of rivers, brooks, lakes and ponds and from the tap water we use every day. The reason for this is quite simple: unlike fresh-water, sea water contains a great amount of dissolved salts. Natural sea water may also be defined as a type of water in which a certain number of elements is dissolved in the form of ions, i.e. with a posi-tive or negative electric charge.

We are well aware today that natural sea water contains all known elements. Some of them are present in high concentration, making a significant contribution

Above: The ocean offers the organisms that live on the reef everything they need for their healthy growth. The water in a coral reef aquarium has to be managed and conditioned artificially at considerable expense.   Photo: E. Svensen

Left: Upper reef slope in the Great Barrier Reef.   Photo: E. Svensen

to the measured salinity. These are called major elements or major ions (Culkin, 1965). Among these are: sodium (as Na^+), magnesium (as Mg^{2+}), calcium (as Ca^{2+}), strontium (as Sr^{2+}), potassium (as K^+), chlorine (as chloride Cl^-), sulfur (as sulfate SO_4^{2-}), bromine (as bromide Br^-), fluorine (as fluoride F^-), boron (as boric acid $B(OH)_3$ and $B(OH)_4^-$). At a salinity of 35 ‰ there are about 35 g of major elements in one kg of sea water.

The elements which we call trace elements or trace salts account for only a very small portion (about 0.1 %) of the dissolved compounds. Nevertheless these elements are of crucial importance for the life in the ocean.

The various elements are not always dissolved in the sea water separately. Many of them form compounds with the oxygen (O) or the hydroxide-anion (OH^-) in the water. The element carbon (C), for example, is not found in sea water in its elementary form, but only as hydrogen carbonate (HCO_3^-), carbonate (CO_3^{2-}) or carbon dioxide (CO_2). At a salinity of 35 ‰ sea water contains about 28 mg/l of these carbon compounds (see also the passage on "buffer capacity", pp. 223).

Some elements are hardly detectable because of their extremely low concentration. This holds true for heavy metals, like cobalt (Co^{2+}) or copper (Cu^{2+}) with their concentration of only 0.00005 mg/l. If these metals occur in a higher concentration they can have toxic effects on all kinds of organisms. High concentration of heavy metals may be detrimental or fatal for different types of marinelife. This is one of the reasons why we are very skeptical about the use of aquarium medicines containing copper in the coral reef aquarium.

Organism living in the sea, especially algae, have the capacity to store a lot of trace elements. When the algae die off, these may be released again in the water. This potential problem must be taken into account, also in the marine aquarium.

Salinity of the sea water

Salinity is a measure (in parts per thousand, ppt, or ‰) for the amount of salt dissolved per kilogram of sea water. The average salinity of sea water is 34.7 ppt. It varies, however, in different geographical regions of the oceans. In tropical seas, from where the animals for our coral reef aquaria originate, the salinity is higher than e.g. in the North Sea, where it varies between 20 and 34 ppt or in the Baltic Sea, with its mere 10 ppt. The salinity of the Red Sea is rather high, just under 40 ppt, while most other tropical seas have a salinity of between 30 and 35 ppt.

Salinity cannot be measured directly. There are, however, indirect methods to determine the salinity of the aquarium water. The most common one simply makes

use of the determination of the density of the water, using a hydrometer. For most aquaristic purposes a density of 1.022 to 1.024 at a temperature of 25 °C has been proven to be just right. This corresponds to a salinity of about 33 to 36 ppt. It should be taken into account, however, that the density of sea water is highly dependent on its temperature. It is therefore important to use a hydrometer calibrated to the temperature of the water, if the salinity of aquarium water is to be adjusted correctly. A differently calibrated hydrometer may be used, but then the reading of the salinity must be recalculated with the help of a conversion table. Disregarding this dependence of density on temperature may result in considerable accidental variations of salinity. For example a density of 1.022, as mentioned above, corresponds to a salinity of only 31.5 ppt at a temperature of 20 °C, but to 35.7 ppt at 30 °C.

During the last few years it has become increasingly common to

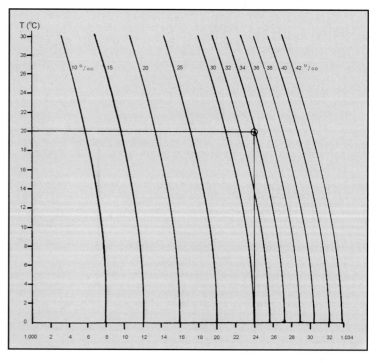

Conversion table showing the salt concentration at particular temperatures and densities. The example in the graph shows that at a temperature of 20 °C and a density of 1.024 the salt concentration is 34 ‰.

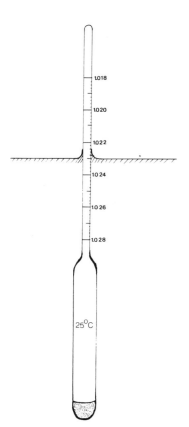

Hydrometer. The reading of the density must be taken at the level of the water surface. In this example the reading is 1.023.

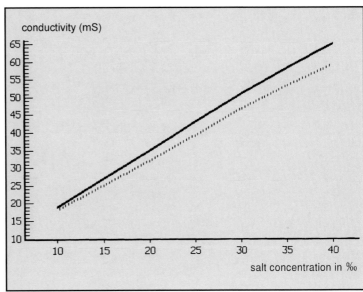

conductivity (mS)

salt concentration in ‰

The relation between salt concentration and conductivity at 30 °C (unbroken line) and at 25 °C (dotted line).

measure the electric conductivity of the water instead of its density. The instruments required for measuring the electric conductivity are not cheap, but they provide us with exact readings of the amount of ions dissolved in the water. It is extremely important to keep the electrodes of these instruments clean and to calibrate them meticulously. The electric conductivity is measured in millisiemens (mS).

We have seen over and over again that well established aquaria gradually suffer from decreasing salinity. This is commonly due to the fact that aquarists tend to disregard the importance of regularly checking the salinity. Do not overlook the fact that elements are removed when the skimmer and filters are cleaned and when water sprays out from the action of pumps etc.! Additio-

nally, it is unfortunately also true that some cheap hydrometers are highly inaccurate. A decreasing salinity is often reflected by changes in the growth of algae, such as a blooming of blue-green or other slimy algae, and in a general lack of prosperity in the corals. Great care should be taken to keep the salinity within the range of normal values.

Osmoregulation

All organisms have a certain exchange or transport of water and salts between their cells and the medium that surrounds them. This may be an active transport, requiring an expenditure of energy, or a passive transport, which does not require any use of energy. The direction in which the water flows is determined by the concentration of salt in the cells and in the surrounding medium respectively. The flow of water goes from a place with high osmotic pressure, i.e. a low salinity, to one with low osmotic pressure, i.e. a higher sa-

linity. This results in a state of balance in the concentration of salts in both places. Most marine organisms try to stabilize this condition by the active transport of ions, so that the osmotic pressure in their cells corresponds most closely to that of their environment.

If a marine animal is moved from a pet shop, where it has become accustomed to aquarium water with a salinity of 37 ppt, and placed directly into an aquarium with 34 ppt, the surrounding water will at once start flowing into the cells of this animal. At the same time the animal will try to compensate this by the active transport of ions from its cells into the surrounding medium. Most animals cannot take a sudden large change of salinity. So if they are moved from one aquarium to another, care should be taken to acclimatize them slowly to their new surroundings. A very simple way of doing this is to put them in a bucket or another container for a while and to add water from their new aquarium drop by drop. For particularly delicate animals this acclimatization may take hours.

A density of 1.022 to 1.024 at 25 °C, corresponding to a salinity between 33 and 36 ppt has been

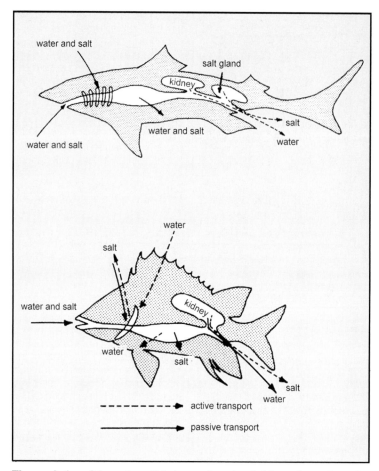

The regulation of the water-salt balance of marine fish by active and passive transport.   (After Spotte, 1979)

shown to be most favourable for coral reef aquaria. It is important to keep the density as stable as possible, to provide osmotic stability. As we usually do not use any glass to cover our aquaria, because we need a high intensity and a certain quality of light, evaporation is high. It is quite common for three to five litres of water to evaporate every day from an aquarium of about 500 litres. Only the water molecules escape into the air, whereas the dissolved salts stay in the aquarium water. If the water lost by evaporation is not replaced by freshwater, the salinity in the aquarium will rise considerably in a few days. We will deal with this problem in more detail in connection with our discussion of the daily addition of "Kalkwasser" to the aquarium (see pp. 224).

Artificial or natural sea water?

Only a limited number of marine aquarists ever get the chance to obtain natural unpolluted sea water. We are among the lucky ones and have in part been using natural sea water for many years, with no ill effects. We do not hesitate to recommend this to other aquarists as well. Natural sea water has to be used cautiously, though, in the seasons when phytoplankton is abundant (in spring and fall along the northern coasts). Natural sea water may be used directly, but we always advise aquarists to check its pH, its carbonate hardness and density, and if possible its calcium-ion concentration, so that they are in a position to evaluate its quality and to make corrections where necessary.

In most cases aquarists have to prepare their own sea water. This is a perfectly safe way to obtain

Left: A 300 litre tank belonging to A. J. Nilsen.

Pterapogon kaudneri is a rare fish living in shoals and among the spines of sea urchins from the genus *Diadema*. The fish is restricted to the Island of Banigai on the east coast of North Sulawesi and was first described by KOUMANS in 1933.

Lysmata amboinensis in a coral reef aquarium of D. Stüber, Germany.

water for the aquarium, and it makes it easier for you to have control over the stable quality of the water. There is a considerable number of commercial sea salt mixes available to serve this purpose. No unbiased and systematic research comparing their quality has been carried out so far, so that reliable evaluations are not possible. It is a fact that the composition of these salt mixes frequently differs from one product to the next. We always recommend the use of tried and tested sea salt mixes of well-established brands, which are most reliable.

Sea salt mixes should never be dissolved directly in the aquarium. Instead, plastic containers should be used to prepare the artificial sea water. Follow the instructions carefully in dissolving a suitable amount of salt in the correct volume of water and let the water mature, aerating it heavily, for a week before you use it. The concentration of free metal ions in a newly prepared water mix may be quite high, but it decreases as the water ages. The quality of the sea salt mix is not the only crucial factor in the preparation of artificial sea water; the quality of the freshwater used is just as important. If tap water contains contaminations like nitrate or phosphate, these substances may also cause problems in the artificial sea water. A nitrate concentration of 10 to 20 mg/l should never be exceeded in a coral reef aquarium in which stony corals are kept. Even if fishes and many invertebrates – with the exception of stony corals – tolerate higher concentrations of nitrate without showing obvious signs of detrimental influences, we hold the opinion that a healthy coral reef aquarium should always have a nitrate concentration as low as possible.

In many places tap water contains a considerable amount of silicates. These may cause immense problems in a coral reef aquarium, as they can be the reason for a sudden increase in the number of diatoms. At times the carbonate hardness is extremely low at 1 to 2 dKH, which makes the addition of certain substances necessary (see pp. 224). It is very helpful for the aquarist to know the exact chemical qualities of the tap water he uses. Information about the water can usually be obtained from the offices of the respective waterworks.

Chemical reactions and parameters of the sea water

It is impossible to list and describe all the substances that are essential for the organisms in the sea. It is just the same with the various chemical reactions that take place in the sea. Some elements and chemical processes, however, are of such extraordinary importance, that we want to deal with them in some detail.

❶ pH

The importance of pH is always stressed by expert aquarists. It is a crucial parameter for the coral reef aquarium. pH is a measure of the acidic or basic reaction of the water. Chemically speaking pH can be defined as the negative common logarithm of the hydrogen ion concentration:

$$pH = -\log_{10}[H^+]$$

This sounds more complicated than it really is. Pure water consists of hydrogen and hydroxide ions and has the chemical formula H_2O. When water dissociates, this results in positively charged hydrogen ions and hydroxide ions which are negatively charged:

If "the chemistry is right" in the coral reef aquarium, it will be a real pleasure to watch the activities of the fish, like this yellowhead jawfish, *Opistognathus aurifrons*.

Photo: F. Nijhuis

$$H_2O \leftrightarrow H^+ + OH^-$$

Hydrogen ions (H^+) cause an acidic reaction of the water, hydroxide ions (OH^-) a basic (alkaline) reaction. In pure water, without any other substances added, both types of ions are present in equal amounts, thus neutralizing each other. This results in a neutral pH, pH = 7. This balance of concentration is represented in the following formula:

$$[H^+] \times [OH^-] = (1\times10^{-7}) \times (1\times10^{-7}) = (1\times10^{-14})$$

(in the formula H^+ represents the concentration of hydrogen ions and OH^- that of hydroxide ions). If other basic or acidic substances have an effect on the water, the balance of H^+ and OH^- ions is disturbed. The water then has either a basic (alkaline) or acidic reaction. Water with a pH of 5, i.e. acidic water contains a considerably higher concentration of H^+ ions than of OH^- ions. The comparison of the concentrations is now described by the following formula:

$$[H^+] \times [OH^-] = (1\times10^{-5}) \times (1\times10^{-9}) = (1\times10^{-14})$$

❷ Buffer capacity

Sea water usually does not show great variations in pH, but remains rather stable at an average pH of 8.2. It is therefore a basic solution which contains more OH^- than H^+ ions. Large amounts of acids and bases are introduced into the ocean every day without causing obvious variations of the pH value. There may be local changes of this value, but after a certain time pH will readjust to the original value of 8.2. The ions that help to stabilize the pH of sea water most of all are carbonate ions (CO_3^{2-}) and hydrogen carbonate ions (HCO_3^-). This stabilizing effect is referred to as the buffer capacity of the seawater. This buffer capacity is described by the following formula:

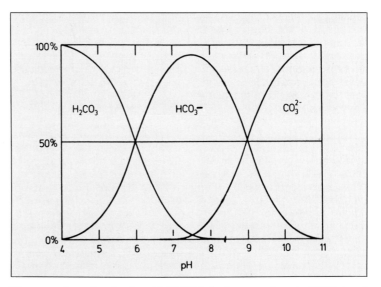

The percentage of carbonic acid (H_2CO_3), hydrogen carbonate (HCO_3^-) and carbonate (CO_3^{2-}) and their dependence on the pH (after SPOTTE, 1979).

$$2\,HCO_3^- \leftrightarrow CO_2 + H_2O + CO_3^{2-}$$

The buffer capacity is also influenced by CO_2. CO_2 reacts with water, producing carbonic acid (H_2CO_3), which then dissociates into carbonate and hydrogen carbonate ions. The chemical reaction can be described like this:

$$CO_2 + H_2O \leftrightarrow H_2CO_3 \leftrightarrow H^+ + HCO_3^- \leftrightarrow 2H^+ + CO_3^{2-}$$

An addition of carbon dioxide (resulting in an increased amount of H^+ ions) causes a loss of balance and an acidic reaction. A consumption of carbon dioxide, e.g. by the photosynthesis of the algae, causes a reverse effect. The balance moves to the basic side, the water shows an alkaline reaction. It has to be added, however, that in a sea water aquarium many of the algae satisfy their need for CO_2 from the hydrogen carbonate

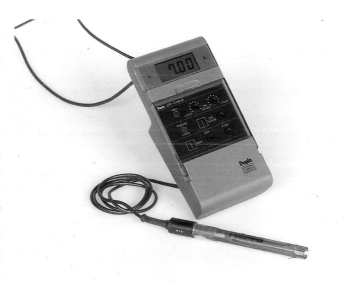

pH-meter "Dupla-pH-Control".

available. Experiments have proved this to be true for red algae of the genus *Iridaea* and brown algae of the genera *Sargassum*, *Alaria*, *Nereocystis* and *Costaria*, whereas the opposite was confirmed for red algae of the genus *Porphyra* and for green algae of the genus *Enteromorpha*. This is also the case for the symbiotic algae (the zooxanthellae) living in the endoderm of most corals. The zooxanthellae can draw their carbon dioxide as **free** carbon dioxide directly from the hosts respiration or from the amount of carbon dioxide naturally found in the water. However, when photosynthesis exceeds respiration and the colony becomes autotrophic – which in fact is the case in many well-illuminated reef sites – the amount of **free** carbon dioxide will be insufficient to sustain the photosynthesis of the zooxanthellae. Then the symbionts will utilize bicarbonate as a source of carbon dioxide (MUSCATINE, 1990).

At a pH of 8.2, 90 % of the dissolved CO_2 is hydrogen carbonate anyway. About 9.4 % is carbonate, whereas 0.6 % is free carbonic acid (DRING, 1986).

As long as everything goes well in a newly set up marine aquarium, the pH will remain stable at around 8.2. If algae start growing the pH may be higher in the evening than in the morning, as carbon dioxide is consumed by photosynthesis during daylight hours. A pH of 8.0 in the morning and 8.4 to 8.5 in the evening is quite normal. Most aquarium animals seem to tolerate these fluctuations.

As a great number of organisms live together in a coral reef aquarium, acids are released through the bacterial decomposition of their metabolic wastes (see chapter 11).These acids are neutralized at first, but this reduces the buffer capacity of the water. If the aquarist does not take measures against this, the buffer capacity will gradually exhaust itself, and the pH will go down significantly. The consequences can be catastrophic. It is therefore necessary to check the pH and the buffer capacity

regularly. It is most advisable to check the pH with an electronic pH meter. The readings from test kits using colour indicators and colourimeters, though useful, are not exact to the same degree.

❸ Carbonate hardness

The buffer reserve is determined through carbonate hardness (KH), which is the alkaline reserve or acid-neutralizing capacity. Thus carbonate hardness reflects the concentration of negative ions (carbonate and hydrogen-carbonate ions), that buffer the water. Carbonate hardness can be measured with test kits available at most pet stores. The fact that KH tests are also influenced by OH^- ions has to be taken into account, however. In solutions with a high pH (pH 10 or higher, like, e.g. in saturated "Kalkwasser", see below) the readings for KH will be extremely high because of the high concentration of OH^- ions. The KH-test kits measure the amount of acids needed to neutralize the base and therefore a solution rich in OH^- will indicate a high KH. This can be tested easily. If one mixes a highly concentrated solution of sodium hydroxide (NaOH) and distilled water, the KH value will be measured to be extremely high, even though no hydrogen carbonate or carbonate is present.

The KH-test is carried out by adding drops of the test solution to a water sample. The number of drops that have to be added until the colour of the solution changes, indicates the KH reading. The carbonate hardness (or rather alkalinity) of sea water is usually around 8 dKH (to convert dKH to meq/l, divide by 2.8). Its total hardness, however, is of little consequence, as it represents the total amount of calcium and magnesium ions. In sea water it is always very high (about 350 dGH at a density of 1.020).

To avoid a reduction of the buffer capacity, and thus a decrease of the pH, carbonates and hydrogen carbonates have to be introduced into the water. Thus the

buffer reserves are refilled. It may be quite helpful to use materials that contain calcium for the decorations, for the bottom layer or as a filter medium, but the effect of this is very limited. Calcium carbonate ($CaCO_3$) dissolves only slowly in sea water, so that by this method the buffer reserves are not renewed fast enough. Thus it is important to replace water that has evaporated from the aquarium by lime water, a.k.a. "Kalkwasser".

"Kalkwasser" is a saturated aqueous solution of Ca^{2+} and OH^- ions. It is produced by dissolving calcium oxide (CaO) or calcium hydroxide ($Ca(OH)_2$) in freshwater. Calcium oxide is a solid, slightly clumpy white substance, which is available in different degrees of purity. It is important to use the purest substance available without any contaminations (e.g. metals ions), which may be harmful to the organisms in the aquarium. In theory 1.7 g CaO can be dissolved in one litre of water. The reaction induced when this takes place produces heat (exothermic reaction!), so that glass containers may burst, if they are used to dissolve the calcium oxide. Plastic containers are therefore much more suited.

The following reaction takes place:

$$CaO + H_2O \rightarrow Ca(OH)_2 \rightarrow Ca^{2+} + 2OH^-$$

If calcium hydroxide ($Ca(OH)_2$) is used, 1.26 g can be dissolved in one litre of water (at 20 °C) and the reaction starts with the second step of the formula given above. This reaction, unlike the first, does not release any thermal energy. The formula above also shows that the amount of negative hydroxide ions produced is twice the amount of positive Calcium ions. Hydroxide has a strong basic reaction and causes the pH to go up. Thus saturated lime water has a pH of 12.4.

To avoid pH shocks for the animals, only small amounts of "Kalkwasser" may be added to the aquarium water at a time. It is good to add it drop by drop. The calcareous reactor we have developed (see page 230) is used with a dosing system to provide fresh saturated "Kalkwasser".

Adding "Kalkwasser" to the aquarium has three main advantages (see also pages 229):

① A strong basic solution containing OH^- is added to the water. A lot of the organic acids, which would otherwise exhaust its buffer capacity are thus neutralized.

② Calcium ions (Ca^{2+}) are added to the aquarium water, which are essential for animals and algae to form their calcareous skeleton.

③ "Kalkwasser" precipitates phospate ions. Phosphate is not wanted as it inhibits the growth of stony corals but increases the potentials for an uncontrolled growth of filamentous algae.

Adding "Kalkwasser" may lead to a pH higher than 8.2 (up to 8.6 is acceptable). This has no harmful effects on invertebrates. There may even be a positive consequence because in our experience a high pH seems to upset the living conditions for the filamentous algae, which are not only annoying, but also detrimental. These algae usually do not grow at a pH of more than 8.5. This may be caused by the fact that at a pH of 8.5 the amount of free CO_2 is noticeably lower than at a pH of 8.2. There is an additional aspect of "Kalkwasser" worth mentioning. If free CO_2 is available, e. g. from the atmosphere, the following chemical reactions take place:

① $Ca^{2+} + 2OH^- + CO_2 \longrightarrow$
   $Ca^{2+} + CO_3^{2-} + H_2O$

② $Ca^{2+} + CO_3^{2-} \longrightarrow CaCO_3(s)$

③ $CaCO_3(s) + H_2O + CO_2$
   $\leftrightarrow Ca^{2+} + 2HCO_3^-$

As formula ② describes, calcium carbonate, which is hard to dissol-

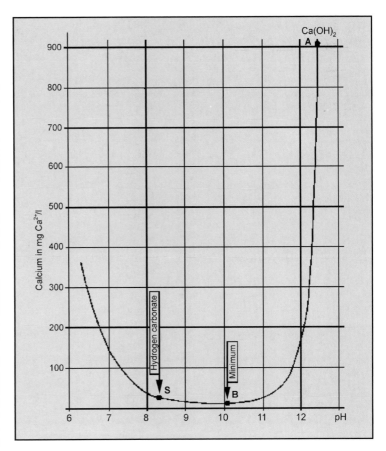

Calcium concentration as a function of the pH value in saturated "Kalkwasser".

ve, is produced. This reaction has not yet taken place in freshly prepared saturated "Kalkwasser". Both types of ions are still present as Ca^{2+} and CO_3^{2-}. The pH of this solution is 12.4 (which reflects the high amount of OH^- ions), the Ca^{2+} concentration is 900 mg/l. In addition to this we find high readings of carbonate hardness (KH). If more CO_2 is added to the "Kalkwasser", it becomes a supersaturated solution and the calcium carbonate is precipitated, which is represented by the symbol (s) in formula ②. This becomes obvious when the "Kalkwasser" turns cloudy. From this moment on pH as well as carbonate hardness and calcium concentration go down. At a pH around 10 the share of Ca^{2+} is no higher than 5 to 6 mg/l and carbonate hardness falls to an absolute minimum (see

diagram above). "Kalkwasser" with these values is useless for aquaristic purposes. If more CO_2 is added to the solution the solid $CaCO_3$ dissolves again, producing Ca^{2+} and HCO_3^- (as calcium hydrogen carbonate) at the same time. Now the carbon dioxide is responsible for the drop in pH, whereas carbonate hardness rises because of the production of HCO_3^-. There is no doubt, that "Kalkwasser" with the highest possible pH should be used in a coral reef aquarium, because it not only adds Ca^{2+} and hydroxide ions to the aquarium water, but also carbonate, which leads to an immediate rise of its carbonate hardness.

Let us look at the chemical reactions that go on in the aquarium water while we are adding lime water. As pointed out before, we thus add Ca^{2+} and OH^- ions, but

As calcium ions must be available for the calcium-consuming organisms in a coral reef aquarium, "Kalkwasser" has to be added regularly. Picture above: A panoramic view of a splendid coral reef aquarium (Photo: K. Dobler). Picture below: Stony corals in A. J. Nilsen's aquarium (photo from 1994).

also, for the reasons explained above, carbonate. As the aquarium water already contains CO_3^{2-} and HCO_3^- ions, calcium hydrogen carbonate is produced:

$$Ca^{2+} + HCO_3^- \leftrightarrow Ca(HCO_3)^+$$

If the highest degree of solubility of the calcium hydrogen carbonate is reached, the reaction first produces calcium hydrogen carbonate ($Ca(HCO_3)_2$) and then calcium carbonate, which precipitates, releasing CO_2 at the same time:

$$Ca(HCO_3)^+ + HCO_3^- \leftrightarrow Ca(HCO_3)_2 \leftrightarrow CaCO_3 + H_2O + CO_2$$

If too much Ca^{2+} or HCO_3^- is added, this reaction can completely shift to the right side. This becomes obvious when the $CaCO_3$ precipitates in the aquarium water causing it to turn cloudy and white. This precipitation however, soon dissolves again. It has to be taken into account in such a situation that as the formula above describes, CO_2 is produced, which may result in a drastic drop of pH. BROCKMANN's (1991a, b) ideas about this should be studied carefully by anyone interested in these problems. (We will discuss the pros and cons and will compare the "Kalkwasser" method with other methods stabilizing the carbonate hardness in a separate paragraph at page 229).

An increase of the buffer capacity may be reached by adding sodium hydrogen carbonate ($NaHCO_3$) and sodium carbonate (Na_2CO_3) in a 5:1 ratio. A solution of these substances has a pH of 8.0. In this way a temporary increase in carbonate hardness is achieved without adding calcium ions to the aquarium water. This method of increasing the buffer capacity has not gained general acceptance, as it may lead to a rise in pH if it is used in an uncontrolled manner. This again might turn out to be extremely harmful to most invertebrates. Thus the addition of this mixture of sodium carbonate and sodium hydrogen carbonate is nothing but an emergency measure. If the maintenance of your coral reef aquarium were neglected for a while this temporary solution will increase the buffer capacity for a short time.

❹ Calcium

In natural sea water the concentration of calcium (Ca^{2+}) is about 420 mg/l. A lot of the organisms which we keep in a coral reef aquarium (e.g. stony corals and calcareous algae), need calcium ions to form their skeletons. The calcium ions available in the aquarium water are therefore consumed rapidly. Thus it is necessary to add calcium ions regularly. The concentration of free calcium ions is also linked to pH (see diagram on page 225). In concentrated "Kalkwasser", with a pH of 12.4, the concentration of free calcium ions is about 900 ppm (= 900 mg/l). If the pH of the "Kalkwasser" is decreased to around 10, the calcium concentration drops correspondingly, to only some 6 ppm (6 mg/l). If the pH is decreased further, the concentration of free calcium again rises.

Calcium is always ready to react with other substances, producing e.g. calcium chloride ($CaCl_2$) calcium carbonate ($CaCO_3$) and calcium hydrogen carbonate ($Ca(HCO_3)^+$), for example. The last two have been dealt with before as components of "Kalkwasser".

The most effective way to increase the calcium ion concentration of the aquarium water is achieved by the addition of calcium chloride ($CaCl_2$), which produces Ca^{2+} and Cl^- ions (see also page 229). Only small amounts of calcium chloride are necessary to increase the calcium concentration considerably (LARSSON, 1984). One should keep in mind, however, that the addition of calcium chloride also raises the concentration of chloride ions, which may disturb the ionic balance of the system. Calcium chloride can either be dissolved in distilled water and then added to the aquarium in solution or it may be introduced into the filter as a solid substance.

> **Chemical substances must never be dissolved directly in the aquarium!**

Calcium chloride must be measured out in very small doses anyway. The calcium ion concentration of sea water can be determined with the help of measuring reagents. As many test reagents do not measure any concentrations higher than 250 mg/l, the test sample of aquarium water must be diluted with an equal volume of distilled water to get into the range of measurement. The calcium ion

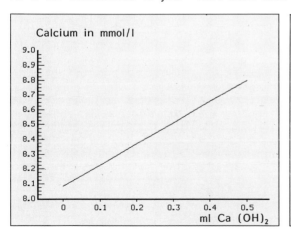

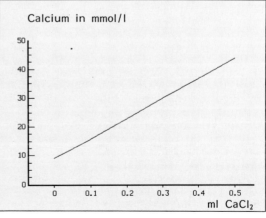

Calcium is an essential element in the coral reef aquarium. There are several ways of adding calcium ions to the aquarium water, two of which are shown: the graphs show the increase of the calcium ion concentration (in mmol/l) when small amounts of calcium hydroxide (Ca(OH)₂; left) or calcium chloride (CaCl₂ right) are added to the water in a test tube. The increase of the concentration is rather small with calcium hydroxide, yet considerable with calcium chloride.
(After LARSSON, 1984)

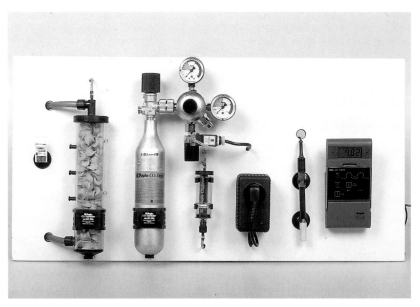

content of the aquarium water is of course twice as high as the reading. A direct measuring of the calcium ion concentration is possible with several commercial test-kits, such as Merckoquant 10083 from Merck, SeaTest from Aquarium Systems, "Test Ca" from Sera, "Sr + Ca Profi-Test" from Salifert and "Calcium Mini Lab Test" from Red Sea fish pHarm Ltd.

When calcium ions are used by corals to form their skeleton and by calcareous algae to strengthen their thalli, the element is fixed as calcium carbonate that occurs in various crystal structures. In the marine environment aragonite and calcite are the most common crystal forms of calcium carbonate. The skeletal material of corals has the aragonite structure, and does – besides of being composed of calcium carbonate – also incorporate strontium (see page 235), magnesium, boron and a lot of other inorganic compounds. Furthermore the skeletal material also contains several organic compounds incorporated in between the inorganic compounds, forming a structure reminiscent of a sandwich. The organic compounds are highly essential to allow the corals to secrete and to maintain the skeletal material as aragonite crystal. Experiments have shown that pure inorganic arago-

nite is readily transformed (by itself) to calcite crystals if it comes into contact with water. The incorporation of organic compounds in the coral's skeleton inhibits the transformation of aragonite to calcite (H. SEKHA, pers. comm.).

❺ Carbon dioxide

Carbon dioxide (CO_2) is the fundamental compound needed for photosynthesis. In a coral reef aquarium some kinds of algae also consume carbon dioxide as hydrogen carbonate. We have already mentioned that at a pH of 8.2 only an insignificant amount of free carbon dioxide is left in the water. If we remove CO_2, the pH of the aquarium rises, if we add CO_2, it falls. Thus the photosynthesis of the algae has direct consequences for the pH of the aquarium water. If the aquarium is exposed to strong sunlight, photosynthesis is intensified and the consumption of CO_2 (hydrogen carbonate assimilation) increases.

The pH rises and carbon dioxide is taken into the water through its surface. The amount of atmospheric CO_2 dissolved in the water is governed by the partial CO_2 pressure of the air and by the temperature and salinity of the water. Of course CO_2 can also escape via the water surface into the air.

In modern freshwater aquaria CO_2 is often added to stimulate the growth of plants (carbon dioxide fertilization). In a marine aquarium the improper addition of CO_2 brings about the risk that the pH may drop below 8.0. Nevertheless adding CO_2 also has a favorable influence on stony corals and other reef building organisms. If you decide in favor of adding CO_2 to your aquarium, you should buy a reliable electronic control unit. A selection of these from various manufacturers is offered for sale in aquarium shops. The systems consist of a pressure bottle with a pressure gauge and reduction valve, needle valve, magnetic valve, a permanent pH controller with electrode and the CO_2 reactor. A pH limit is set, and the magnetic valve stops the supply of CO_2 as soon as the pH falls below this limit. The supply is resumed only when the pH rises above the limit again. The main disadvantage of the addition of CO_2 is the unwelcome stimulation of the growth of filamentous algae.

❻ Comparing different methods for calcium ion and CO_2 addition

In principle there are four different methods for calcium addition, which are discussed in the aquarium literature (reviewed in BROCK-MANN & NILSEN, 1995, 1996), although several modifications of these methods also have been described. The basic methods are:

① the addition of $CaCl_2$ and $NaHCO_3$,

② "Kalkwasser",

③ "Kalkwasser" in combination with a CO_2 injection system and

④ the "limestone-reactor".

In addition to these methods there are other substances like calcium gluconate available to supplement the calcium ion concentration of sea water. However, these methods will not be discussed as they belong – in principle – to one of the four methods described below.

① The addition of $CaCl_2$ and $NaHCO_3$

This method (see also page 227), which has recently been published by, among others, PAWLOWSKY (1994), uses two different salts: calcium chloride ($CaCl_2$) and sodium carbonate or sodium hydrogen carbonate (Na_2CO_3 and $NaHCO_3$, respectively). Two stock solutions, made from the two salts dissolved in water, are added in required amounts at regular intervals to the aquarium water. If both salt solutions are combined, the chemical reaction, which is shown in equation (1) takes places (on the assumption that sodium hydrogen carbonate is used):

$$① \quad CaCl_2 + 2NaHCO_3 \rightarrow Ca^{2+} + 2HCO_3^- + 2NaCl$$

At first sight the addition of $CaCl_2$/$NaHCO_3$ solutions seems to be the method of choice, as it allows the dosage of large amounts of both calcium and hydrogen carbonate ions. The only thing one has to do is to dissolve both salts in water (make two separate stock solutions, otherwise a reaction

starts which ends up with calcium carbonate which precipitates) and add the required amount to the aquarium water. As both salts are easily soluble in water, and as both can be highly concentrated in water, most times it is sufficient to add small amounts of the stock solutions to the tank water in order to keep the calcium ion concentration in the right range. This is certainly the main advantage of the $CaCl_2$/$NaHCO_3$-method, and it explains the benefit for tanks in which the evaporation rate is very low. In these aquariums it might be very difficult to keep the calcium ion concentration at 400 mg/l, through the use of "Kalkwasser" alone. PAWLOWSKY (1994) demonstrated that 48 ml of his calcium chloride stock solution corresponds to one litre of saturated "Kalkwasser". His example shows, that one is independent from the evaporation rate of the aquarium if one uses $CaCl_2$/$NaHCO_3$ solutions.

Both stock solutions, calcium chloride as well as sodium carbonate/sodium hydrogen carbonate, are – if they are stored separately – chemically stable. Therefore it is possible to make and store large amounts of stock solutions. This is in contrast to "Kalkwasser" which is unstable and has to be prepared – under optimum conditions – freshly every day.

What are the disadvantages of the $CaCl_2$/$NaHCO_3$-method? If one carefully considers reaction equation (1), it is obvious that large amounts of NaCl are produced using this method. Actually approximately 2.9 grams of NaCl per gram of Ca^{2+}! In contrast to the calcium and hydrogen carbonate ions, which are consumed by the processes of calcification and photosynthesis, the NaCl accumulates in the water. At first sight this may seem not to be negative, as sodium as well as chloride ions are main components of sea water (with 10.76 and 19.35 g/kg at 35 ‰ salinity, respectively; TARDENT, 1979). An increase of the specific gravity which is due to this NaCl, can be compensated by water changes. But the ratio bet-

ween the single ions, which is disturbed by the NaCl, cannot be compensated by small water changes.

Using a dosage as described by PAWLOWSKY, the chloride ion accumulates daily approximately 0.004 % (the same is in principle true for the sodium ion). Through the span of a year, this will, in fact, amount to a significant accumulation of both ions. This in turn results in a disturbance of the ion equilibrium of the saltwater. For billions of years, the sodium ion has been in a specific constant ratio to other ions, like magnesium or potassium. The invertebrates, on their part, have adjusted to this constant ratio. The concentration of ions in their body fluids is in a constant ratio to the ions of the surrounding saltwater (TARDENT, 1979). This constant ratio is changed if we add sodium and chloride ions. It is unclear, up to which values the invertebrates will tolerate this! To our knowledge there are no exact scientific data available dealing with this subject. Thus, one can only speculate how much is tolerable when the invertebrates get slowly accustomed to the changes. But we assume that when a specific tolerance limit may be exceeded, the invertebrates will start to degenerate and – in the worst case – to die. This might be due to the fact that ion pumps, which are responsible for keeping the ratio of ions in the animal constant with respect to the ions of the surrounding water, are overcharged.

As long as such problems cannot completely be excluded, we would recommend that the method of $CaCl_2$/$NaHCO_3$ is used only in specific cases of emergency.

② "Kalkwasser"

The use of "Kalkwasser" (see also page 224), which today is the most common means for adding calcium ions, was described already by WILKENS (1973). "Kalkwasser" is a saturated solution of calcium hydroxide (WILKENS, 1973; BROCKMANN, 1991). It is generated by dissolving solid calcium hydroxide ($Ca(OH)_2$) in water. The chemical reaction equation is given below:

$$② \ Ca(OH)_2 \ (s) + H_2O \rightarrow Ca^{2+} + 2OH^- + H_2O$$

Normally all the evaporated tank water is replaced by saturated "Kalkwasser". The "Kalkwasser" is either trickled into the aquarium, over a prolonged time period, at night and early in the morning when the light still is off, or through the whole day using a dosage system.

In comparison to the $CaCl_2$/$NaHCO_3$-method, the use of "Kalkwasser", does not lead to any major disturbance of the ion equilibrium. With "Kalkwasser" one adds practically nothing but Ca^{2+} ions to the aquarium water! The OH^- ions, which are also generated by dissolving solid Ca-$(OH)_2$ in water, are in principle "a constituent of the water". These ions are neutralized by the buffering system of the saltwater.

"Kalkwasser" possesses several other advantages. For example, the production of "Kalkwasser" is very cheap and – in comparison to

Calcium hydroxide (left) or calcium oxide (middle), commercially available from your pet dealer, are used to prepare "Kalkwassser".

the $CaCl_2$/$NaHCO_3$ – it is rather easier to handle. In addition, the hydroxide ions are also beneficial. They neutralize acids which are produced by biological processes and help in this way to maintain the alkalinity and pH. Moreover phosphate ions, which are poisonous to the calcification process of the corals, are precipitated from the tank water by the addition of "Kalkwasser".

Besides these advantages, "Kalkwasser" also has some di-

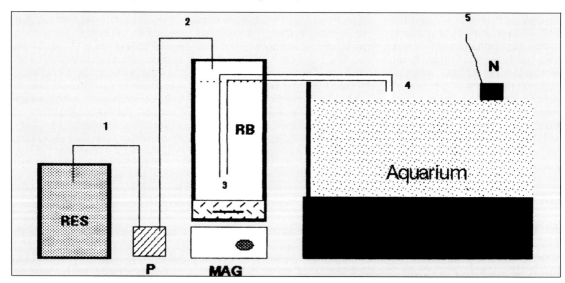

Diagram of a "calcareous reactor": the reactor container (RB) is placed next to the aquarium, so that its upper brim is at a higher level than that of the aquarium. At the bottom of the container there is calcium hydroxide an a teflon-coated magnetic stirring rod. The reactor is placed on a magnetic stirring device (MAG), which is controlled by a timer. A sensor in the aquarium (N), reacting to the level of the aquarium water, is connected to a pump (P) by an electric contact (5). A hose connects the pump to a reservoir container (RES). The pump is controlled by the sensor device and pumps water with a low nutrient content from the reservoir through a hose (2) to the reactor container. The water level in the reactor container rises, and "Kalkwasser" flows through the tube (3) in the middle of the container into the aquarium until the sensor shuts it off again.

sadvantages. First of all the amount of "Kalkwasser" that can be added to the tank is limited. In theory and practice you can refill only the amount of evaporated water with "Kalkwasser". From a tank of some 500 to 700 litres, the daily evaporation may be approximately five litres. Due to the low solubility of solid calcium hydroxide (1.26 gram per 1 litre of water at 20 °C; HOLLEMAN & WIBERG, 1976), the total addition to the aquarium water will amount to maximum 0.68 g Ca^{2+} ions per litre "Kalkwasser"; to stay with our example, 3.4 gram per 5 litres. This is much less than what is possible with the $CaCl_2$/$NaHCO_3$ method. However, it is possible, especially with a calcium reactor described below, to add milky fresh "Kalkwasser" that has extra, undissolved $Ca(OH)_2$ in it, which will dissolve when added to the aquarium. This is dangerous because even small doses of this milky solution have large impact on pH, but it is a way to provide more calcium ions with the dose of "Kalkwasser". A pH control system utilizing CO_2 provides a means of preventing the high pH that can result from an overdose of "Kalkwasser".

The large amount of OH^- ions limits the amount of "Kalkwasser" which can be refilled. Saturated "Kalkwasser" has a pH of 12.4 (BROCKMANN, 1991). Therefore you have to protect yourself when handling it. One must be careful with chemical solutions and keep them away from children! Used incorrectly, the high pH of the solution can also injure the inhabitants of your tank. A very rapid refilling with large amounts of "Kalkwasser" may have harmful consequences in the aquarium, as the buffering system of the tank water can neutralize only a limited amount of OH^- ions (consumption of hydrogen carbonate and production of carbonate; no buffering of OH^- ions). If you add "Kalkwasser" to the aquarium, although its buffering system is depleted, the pH of the aquarium water will increase very fast until it reaches dangerous levels.

The high pH of saturated "Kalk-

wasser" is the reason why it, preferentially, should be added only in small amounts ("drops"), and when the lights still are off. With the lights off, the pH of the aquarium water is low (approximately around 8.0 or less) due to the CO_2 production of its inhabitants.

A big disadvantage of the "Kalkwasser" is its chemical instability. "Kalkwasser" can be stored only for a limited time period. Due to its alkaline pH it attracts CO_2 from the air, and reacts with it to form calcium carbonate ($CaCO_3$), which precipitates. Old "Kalkwasser" will be of no use because of this chemical reaction. Therefore the most effective "Kalkwasser" is obtained when it is prepared fresh on a daily basis, particularly if one uses no dosing system. With an automatic dosing system described below the solution can be maintained in the saturated state.

We have developed a "calcareous" reactor which helps to optimize the quality of the "Kalkwasser" while adding it automatically to the aquarium. The basic idea for this development is derived from the fact that "Kalkwasser" is a very unstable solution. If calcium oxide or calcium hydroxide is dissolved in water, this results in a strongly basic Ca^{2+} solution (see page 224). If this "Kalkwasser" is left standing for a while, the amount of dissolved calcium ions decreases because of the high affinity of the basic solution to the CO_2 in the air, and a reaction towards calcium carbonate ($CaCO_3$) takes place. How can this reaction be slowed down or delayed?

We set up an experiment with two ten litre containers with "Kalkwasser". One container was stirred thoroughly every day, the other was not. The "Kalkwasser" in the stirred container turned out to be much more stable than that in the other, but it also deteriorated after a time. These were the main facts on which we based the development of the calcium reactor.

The calcareous reactor (see the picture on page 230) consists of the following main parts: reactor container, magnetic stirring device, timer, water level measurer,

pump or magnetic valve and (if necessary) a water store tank.

The reactor container must have a volume larger than the amount needed every day to top up the aquarium. It is placed outside the aquarium and contains the calcium water with the sediment of calcium hydroxide. At the bottom of the container there is an outlet with a tap. A pipe is inserted from above so that it reaches down 3/4 of the depth of the container. The other end of the pipe runs to the top of the aquarium. The reactor container is placed on a magnetic stirring device (up to 1100 rpm) which is switched on and off by a timer. The Teflon-coated magnetic stirring rod is placed in the reactor container. The water, which should be oligotrophic, i.e. poor in nutrients, is introduced into the container through a narrow pipe in the upper part. This pipe is either connected to a pump, which draws water from the water store tank, or as an alternative the pipe may be connected to the mains with a magnetic valve. The pump or the magnetic valve are controlled by a level-indicator switch that is installed at the surface of the aquarium or in its sump. **But take care! If you use a system with a magnetic valve on the household mains water line, when the valve or the level switch fails you end up with a freshwater tank and a flooded house.**

The timer is set so that the magnetic stirring device is activated once or twice a day and stirs the sediment thoroughly. The device should not be turned on for too long, we found two or three minutes to be quite sufficient.

When water evaporates from the aquarium, the level-indicator starts the pump which fills freshwater into the reactor container. The water level in this container rises and high-quality "Kalkwasser" is poured through the pipe into the aquarium. The outlet of this pipe has to be placed higher than the surface of the aquarium water to keep the water from siphoning back. Another risk that should be noticed is that the tap water may contain substances that feed the algae. This risk is even higher in areas with intensive farming. In such areas it may be necessary to process the water by reverse osmosis before using it.

Once a week the sediment of the reactor container is let out through the tap at the bottom (this tap is not shown in the diagram on page 230). New calcium oxide (or calcium hydroxide) is dissolved in one or two litres of water in a separate container, the solution is left standing for some hours and is then filled into the reactor container. We found the amount of calcium oxide needed for this to be less than 1 g per litre of evaporated water in 24 hours. Experience will show how much is needed for other aquaria. At the end of a week only a small amount of sediment should be left in the reactor container. It is important that the solid CaO is not put directly into the reactor as it does not completely dissolve and blocks the possibility for draining the reactor easily.

So far our experiences with the calcareous reactor have been very good, especially the growth of calcareous red algae has improved greatly. We have used this type of reactor in combination with the adding of CO_2 (see next paragraph) for several years and have never experienced any problems. The growth of stony corals and calcareous algae has been excellent. It is necessary, however, to clean the reactor container three or four times a year with diluted hydrochloric acid. Pipes and tubes as well must be decalcified now and then. If operated and checked carefully the calcareous reactor serves to add high-quality "Kalkwasser" to the aquarium and to guarantee a good supply calcium ions.

Sometimes one come across articles claiming that adding "Kalkwasser" through a dosage system (which means adding very small amounts of saturated "Kalkwasser" through the whole day) results in an increase of the carbonate hardness. This is a very indirect effect. As you can see from reaction equation (2), there is no CO_2 in the "Kalkwasser" that could be responsible for such an in-

crease of the carbonate hardness. We think that the increase of carbonate hardness (or – to say it better – the regeneration of normal values) is due mostly to lower pressure on the buffering system through the very small amounts "Kalkwasser" added in a given time period. It is obvious that the usual method in which up to five litres of "Kalkwasser" are refilled into a large aquarium during one hour or less at night or in the morning influences the buffering system much more than very small amounts during the whole day.

③ **"Kalkwasser" in combination with a CO_2 injection system**

In principle this method combines two independent procedures:

❶ The addition of "Kalkwasser" and

❷ the dosage of CO_2 with the help of an injection system depending on the pH value of the tank water.

Using these methods two chemical reactions are taking place:

$$③ \ Ca(OH)_2(s) + H_2O \rightarrow Ca^{2+} + 2OH^- + H_2O$$

$$④ \ CO_2 + H_2O \leftrightarrow H_2CO_3 \leftrightarrow H^+ + HCO_3^- \leftrightarrow 2H^+ + CO_3^{2-}$$

Reaction equation ③ corresponds to the "Kalkwasser"-method which we have already discussed, page 229.

The reaction equation ④ describes the dosage of the carbon dioxide, that together with Calcium ions are needed for calcification. As shown in this chemical reaction the carbon dioxide forms a certain ratio of hydrogen carbonate (HCO_3^-) and carbonate (CO_3^{2-}) depending on the pH value of the tank water. Through the combination of both methods the tank water is therefore provided with Calcium ions as well as carbonates!

The dosage of CO_2 has some crucial advantages. First, a **con-**

trolled CO_2 dosage prevents high pH values of the tank water (pH = 8.3 and higher) which might be dangerous for the invertebrates and fishes. In addition, some observations indicate that pH values above 8.2 to 8.3 result in a very low carbonate hardness of the tank water (5 dKH and less). This drop is also counteracted by the addition of carbon dioxide. Another advantage of a controlled CO_2 dosage is a permanent growth stimulation of stony corals and soft corals containing symbiotic algae.

But, as expected the dosage of carbon dioxide possesses some disadvantages. First of all a good injection system is very expensive. A high quality pH-meter and pH-probe is essential. It is obvious, that an incorrect CO_2 dosage might result in a dangerous drop of the pH of the tank water. Therefore it is very important to calibrate the pH electrode on a regular basis to guarantee its accuracy. If such an injection system is used, the electrode should be cleaned and calibrated at least once every 8 weeks (a new electrode should even be calibrated more frequently, at least once in 4 weeks; take notice of the temperature dependence of the control system and the calibration solutions and follow strictly the manual of the manufacturer!). The calibration solutions can only be used once or twice then they should be replaced. They can, however, be stored in a closed bottle at room temperature as long as indicated by the labeling.

A pH electrode which is permanently in use lasts a maximum of two years. Therefore it has to be exchanged on a regular basis. Carelessness can have dire consequences very quickly!

Finally, another big disadvantage of the CO_2 injection system is the fact, that the CO_2 regularly supplied to the aquarium water is a potential fertilizer for algae, as it is one compound used for photosynthesis by plants.

④ **The "limestone-reactor"**

The use of "limestone-reactors" is rapidly becoming more widespread in Europe. These reactors are a method for supplying the aquarium water with calcium ions and hydrogen carbonates, and – at the moment – many people seem to think that a "limestone-reactor" can achieve miracles. Unfortunately this is not true. The "limestone-reactor" has, like all the other methods we have discussed, advantages and disadvantages.

How does a "limestone-reactor" work? A schematic drawing of a well-known model called the "Löbbecke Reaktor" is shown on the right. The reactor, which was developed by HEBBINGHAUS (1994) contains a medium of calcareous gravel, through which the aquarium water is fed. Within this confinement, through the addition of CO_2, the pH is lowered to about 6.5, a pH value at which calcium carbonate dissolves (it is important to note that the CO_2 dissolves also a lot of elements like Sr^{2+} and trace elements, which are chemically bound as carbonates in the calcareous gravel). The following chemical reaction takes place:

⑤ **$CaCO_3 + CO_2 + H_2O \leftrightarrow Ca(HCO_3)_2$**

The result is an increasing of KH and free calcium ions in the aquarium water. In order to maximize the concentration of calcium ions and hydrogen carbonate in the water, much of it is recirculated through the reactor several times before it returns to the aquarium. Thereby, the amount of free CO_2 returned to the aquarium, is kept as low as possible.

Through the "Löbbecke Reaktor", calcium hydrogen carbonate is constantly being added to the aquarium. This is **not** to replace evaporated water, however. Evaporation is replaced with pure fresh water only. The amount of carbon dioxide to be used, as well as the water flow through the reactor, depends on factors such as aquarium size, reactor size, number and kinds of animals, other technical equipment etc. Thus, this must be calculated through experience, by the individual aquarist. In his test aquarium,

containing 20,000 litres of water, HEBBINGHAUS started with a return water flow of 15 l/h, and a CO_2 addition of 150 bubbles/min, but after some practical experience, these values were adjusted to a water flow of 45 l/h, and 350 bubbles of CO_2/min. HEBBINGHAUS concludes that a calcareous-gravel-volume of only 2 litres is sufficient for aquaria up to 1000 litrers water volume. In the aquarium where the reactor was first used, the pH stabilized around 8.2-8.3, the KH around 12 and the concentration of calcium ions was measured to about 400 mg/l. Recently, several commercial producers have launched various models of limestone

reactors, all based more or less on the same basic model.

Personally we would recommend that all additions of carbon dioxide, including through "limestone reactors", should be controlled by the automatic shut-off on a minimum-pH-level in the aquarium (see below).

There are two, in principle different, "limestone-reactors" in current use:

❶ **open systems**, which are placed directly into the aquarium
❷ **closed systems**, based on the Löbbecke model.

In the open system, superfluous CO_2, which does not react immediately with the $CaCO_3$ of the reac-

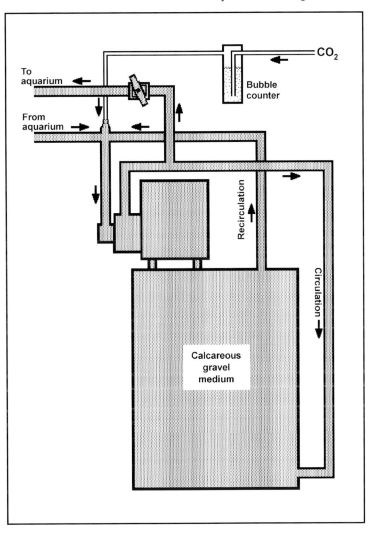

"Löbbecke Kalkreaktor", principle after HEBBINGHAUS (1994).

tor, follows the water stream to the aquarium water. In the closed system, most of the excess CO_2 stays in the reactor, where it passes through an internal circulation. Although both systems have advantages as well as disadvantages, the closed system is much more effective, as the CO_2 can react over a prolonged period of time with the calcium carbonate.

The use of a "limestone-reactor" has several advantages. First of all, as already mentioned, it produces both essential elements (calcium ions and carbon dioxide) needed for the process of calcification. Secondly, "limestone-reactors", which are adjusted correctly, are time and labor saving. The only major maintenance work one has to do on a regular basis is – depending on the consumption – to replenish the $CaCO_3$ gravel medium and the CO_2. In addition, the injection system has to be checked periodically, to avoid a too high or too low dosage of CO_2 due to mechanical problems, like obstruction of hoses or valves. Daily routine works such as the preparation of the "Kalkwasser" and the addition of "Kalkwasser" or $CaCl_2/NaHCO_3$ solutions to the tank water are no longer necessary if a "limestone-reactor" is used.

"Limestone-reactors" have some additional advantages. The dosage of carbon dioxide leads to an increase of the buffer capacity of the tank water, which can be estimated through the measurement of the carbonate hardness. It is quite often observed that the usage of such a reactor leads to an increase of the carbonate hardness to 10 dKH or more, much higher than the normal values of 5-7 dKH measured on most reefs. Unfortunately this increase of the CO_2 concentration can have some negative side effects. This carbon dioxide acidifies the tank water which might result in a drop of its pH. As already mentioned, excess carbon dioxide serves also as an algae nutrient. When there are other nutrients (like nitrate or phosphate) available as well, there will most probably be problems with algae. Phosphate may, in

	M1	M2	M3	M4
Table 11				
Comparison of calcium-ion dosage methods.				
initial cost	low	low	high	high*
running costs	low	low	high	high*
expenditure of work	high	high	high	low
disturbance of the ion balance	yes, strong	low	low	low
disturbing ions	yes, lots	low	low	low
amount of calcium-ions	high	low	low	?
alteration of pH	no*[1]	yes	yes	yes
influence on carbonate hardness	+	-,*[2]	+/-, *[3]	+
stability of chemical solutions	stable	unstable	unstable	-/-
provided compounds for calcification	Ca^{2+} CO_2*[4]	Ca^{2+}	Ca^{2+} CO_2	Ca^{2+} CO_2*[5]

M1) NaCl/NaHCO$_3$-method; **M2)** "Kalkwasser"; **M3)** "Kalkwasser" in combination with a CO$_2$ injection system; **M4)** "limestone"-reactor; *) if a CO$_2$ control system is used; *[1]) if NaHCO$_3$/Na$_2$CO$_3$ is used under controlled conditions; *[2]) 5 dKH and less are described; *[3]) if a CO$_2$ injection system is used; *[4]) CO$_2$ as hydrogen carbonate or carbonate; *[5]) CO$_2$ reacts to hydrogen carbonate in the "limestone"-reactor; +) positive effect; -) negative effect; +/-) positive as well as negative effects; -/-) no chemical solution is used.

fact, be produced by the "limestone-reactor" itself. Quite often (but not always) it is observed that aquaria which are equipped with a "limestone-reactor" have an increased concentration of phosphate. It is assumed that these phosphates are originally chemically bound in the limestones of the reactor, and are dissolved in the same way as the Calcium ions. This generation of phosphates cannot be prevented very easily but protein skimming helps to remove them.

In aquaria which are equipped with "limestone-reactors" the pH of the tank water is often very low in the morning, before the lights are switched on (pH = 7.7 or even less). The low pH is most probably due to the CO_2 dosage into the "limestone-reactor", which results – in combination with the carbon dioxide produced through the respiration of the tank inhabitants (fishes, invertebrates and plants), in an acidification of the tank water. To counteract this low pH, several aquarists use "Kalkwasser" during the morning which raises the pH. In our eyes this seems to be paradoxical as the "limestone-reactor" should substitute for the "Kalkwasser".

If a "limestone-reactor" is used, the CO_2 dosage should be dependent on the pH of the tank water. The usage of a pH control system will diminish the negative side effects of the CO_2 dosage. The pH should be measured continuously in the aquarium and only when an upper pH-value of 8.3 is reached should CO_2 be added. This again requires the careful calibration and maintenance of the pH-probe, as described above.

In summary one can draw the conclusion that both "Kalkwasser" in combination with a CO_2 injection system as well as the "limestone-reactor" are useful ways of adding calcium to the reef aquarium, but that both methods also have their advantages and disadvantages. The use of a "limestone-reactor" often causes a shifting of pH and thus an increased amount of CO_2 added to the aquarium. This can very well result in an increased growth of filamentous algae. But the result can also be an excellent growth of stony corals which is probably linked to the increased amount of CO_2 available for the zooxanthellae.

However, if phosphate is being dissolved causing an increasing concentration of dissolved phosphat, which can be the case using the "limestone-reactor", one might observe that the growth of stony corals decreases and that filamentous algae start to flourish. On the other hand we have never observed an increasing concentration of phosphate from adding "Kalkwasser".

❼ **Strontium**

Strontium has long been regarded by aquarists as a highly essential element that plays an important role in the formation of coral skeletons. As result we have the common practice of adding this element to reef tanks, a practice that has been well established, particularly in Germany, since the

Table 12			
Strontium concentration in some stony corals and in Heliopora coerulea (modified from SHIMEK, 1995).			
Species	Concentration Sr^{2+} (ppm)	Locality	Comments
Porites porites v. furcata	10280	Puerto Rico	mid branch
Acropora cervicornis	10600	Puerto Rico	mid branch
Acropora palmata	20890	Puerto Rico	mid branch
Acropora palifera	9750	Palau	2 samples
Acropora spp.	7776	16 locations	413 samples
Acropora sp.	7872	Heron Island	51 samples
Dendrophyllia micranthus	10300	Palau	2 samples
Dendrophyllia spp.	7844	3 locations	10 samples
Dendrophyllia spp.	8057	Heron Island	6 samples
Favia pallida	11050	Palau	2 samples
Fungia fungites	8900	Palau	2 samples
Fungia spp.	7381	10 locations	85 samples
Fungia spp.	7433	Heron Island	6 samples
Porites spp.	7516	Heron Island	24 samples
Porites spp.	9010	Hawaii	389 samples
Porites spp.	9230	Midway Atoll	55 samples
Tubastraea spp.	7672	Heron Island	6 samples
Heliopora coerulea	8300	Palau	2 samples

early eighties (WILKENS, 1983a, 1983b, 1983c). We are not sure who actually introduced the idea of strontium ions being important to the corals. Today, several authors are questioning the importance of strontium ions, and a most interesting debate on the value of adding it is going on. See for instance SHIMEK (1995), BUDDEMEIER (1995) and SEKHA (1995).

The coral skeletons are mainly built of calcium carbonate in the crystal form "aragonite", but also contain strontium carbonate (see table page 235). There might be a link between strontium ion concentrations and the formation of aragonite in coral skeletons, but further work has to be done to test this hypothesis (SEKHA, 1995). In general there is little agreement among authors whether the concentration of strontium ions in coral skeleton is of any significance to the coral.

Natural sea water contains strontium ions in a concentration of about 8 mg/l. Measurements in coral reef aquaria have shown that this concentration is reduced to only 1.5 mg/l in the course of about six months. In our 800 litre stony coral test aquarium, we have been adding 25 ml strontium chloride solution (prepared as described below) per week, for several years. Nevertheless, the concentration of dissolved strontium amounted to only 4 mg/l when the water was properly tested in May 1995. There is no conclusive evidence of whether the added strontium ions are actually incorporated in the coral skeletons, or if it, perhaps, precipitates, or is bound to organic elements and skimmed off from the aquarium.

Strontium ions may be added to the aquarium water as strontium chloride ($SrCl_2$). A solution is prepared by dissolving 50 g strontium chloride in 500 ml distilled water. Of this 1 ml per 100 l aquarium water is added weekly.

⑧ Oxygen

Oxygen (O_2) is involved in nearly all functions of life. It is produced by the autotrophic organisms and is consumed by them and by the heterotrophic organisms during respiration. Oxygen is taken into the aquarium water and given off

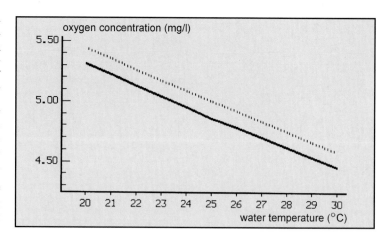

The relation of oxygen concentration and water temperature at a salt concentration of 36 ‰ (dotted line) and 32,5 ‰ (unbroken line).

through its surface. More oxygen is introduced into the water if there is strong water movement, e.g. when waves break. The oxygen content of the water depends on the air pressure and on the temperature and on the salinity of the water. In our aquaria we often keep so many organisms that they may cause an oxygen deficiency if no suitable measures are taken to increase it. Normally it will be sufficient to ensure that the surface water circulates vigorously. This is achieved by placing a circulation pump just below the surface (not so high that the water splashes, which would cause salt creep or water loss). The supply of oxygen can also be increased by effective aeration with the help of an air pump. If a protein skimmer is used, which is a must anyway for a coral reef aquarium, the oxygen exchange in the skimmer is so effective that an additional aeration is not necessary. Occasionally the water will be supersaturated with oxygen. This situation is most likely to occur if there are great amounts of algae growing in the aquarium and the intensity of the light on the aquarium is high. Such an overproduction of oxygen is often caused by blue-green algae and diatoms.

⑨ Products of chemical reduction

Products of chemical reduction, like nitrate and phosphate, may ha-

ve extremely harmful effects in the aquarium. We try to reduce or remove these polluting substances or the substances from which they are derived with the help of all kinds of filter devices. The most detrimental of these substances and their recycling in nature will be dealt with in chapter 11.

For aquarists who use tap water or take their freshwater from a well in an area with a lot of farming, nitrate and phosphate can be present in excess. Freshwater with a nitrate concentration of 20 mg/l or more is not suitable for a coral reef aquarium. This holds true for the new preparation of artificial sea water as well as for the topping up of the aquarium that becomes necessary because of evaporation. Even the slightest suspicion that the freshwater may be polluted is reason enough to check it for nitrate and other harmful substances. If the water is polluted, purified water should be used (i.e. distilled, demineralised, or reverse osmosis; see also chapter 12).

⑩ Silicates

Silicates (SiO_2) can normally be found in sea water with a concentration of 2 to 3 mg/l (as silicic acid ($H_2SiO_3)_n$). An increase of the silicate concentration above this value often leads to a bloom of a type of algae called diatoms. These algae make use of the silicate (silicic acid) to build up their cell walls.

When a new marine aquarium is set up it is very common to have a great number of diatoms develop initially. When the silicate concentration has decreased after a few weeks, other algae predominate. If, however, new silicates are added again and again when the evaporated water is replaced by tap water, there is the risk that this problem may be perpetuated. This circumstance will discourage the growth of the calcareous algae.

Tap water with a considerable silicate content is not at all unusual. This is due to the geological conditions of our soils. The silicate content of the water of the well near the home of one of the authors (A. J. Nilsen) is higher than 30 mg/l. This water is absolutely unsuitable for a coral reef aquarium as it caused a sudden immense growth of diatoms which could hardly be stopped. We must concede, however, that we have also seen splendid coral reef aquaria, for which water rich in silicates had been used. So we have to suppose that other factors as well (e.g. competition by other algae) influence the growth of diatoms.

So far there is no simple method to remove silicates from the water. Only processing the water by reverse osmosis may be taken into consideration. If permanent problems arise through the blooming of diatoms on a huge scale, we recommend to measuring the silicate concentration in the water (calculated as silicates SiO_2), e.g. with Aquamerck test kit 11119 Silicate/Phosphate. Moreover it is helpful to replace evaporated water by "Kalkwasser" which has been prepared with distilled or reverse osmosis water.

⓫ Trace elements

Most elements can be found in sea water only in very small amounts, which is why they are called trace elements. These "trace elements" have been the subject of many a discussion among marine aquarists. As it requires a lot of technical effort to measure these small quantities, there are not many statements about this subject that can be both made and proved.

It is undisputed that protein skimming and also filtering the water through activated carbon remove a certain amount of the trace elements from the aquarium water. It is also definite that algae and animals consume trace elements from the aquarium water and accumulate them. Food substances added, the water used for refilling evaporated water, as well as reactions of the aquarium water with objects in the aquarium, introduce new trace elements into the aquarium. There is no way of telling, however, which amounts of trace elements are consumed and which amounts are introduced from outside (see table on page 238 for further information on trace elements in the aquarium).

Even if we do not know much about all this we can take it for granted that the amounts of trace elements in the aquarium water decrease, so that they have to be replaced. There are numerous mixtures of trace elements available on the market today. Some of them contain a meticulously balanced mixture of chosen substances and were based on careful research. Yet others are nothing but nitrogenous compounds concocted with some iron. To find out about the quality of the different brands it is best to learn by experience and to exchange these experiences with other aquarists.

Over the years we learned that it is more advisable to add less than to add more trace elements. An overdose is always the worst solution. As a rule of thumb we recommend to add only half of what the instructions say. Again it seems important to mention that there is no need for experiments as long as the animals are thriving.

There is good reason to say that the supply of one particular trace element, iodine (I), will run short quickly in a coral reef aquarium. Among others red and brown algae need iodine to grow. If a coral reef aquarium is set up with live rocks it can be observed that red and brown algae develop marvelously during the first few months, only to disappear quite suddenly later. The reason for this in most cases is lack of iodine. We have also observed that iodine (perhaps in combination with other trace elements) seems to play an active role in the formation of UV-protective pigments. When an aquarium was heavily filtered over activated carbon, so much trace elements were removed that the corals suffered and showed clear signs of bleaching (see page 214). When iodine was added, after the filtration over activated carbon had been halted, the corals got their normal colours back (for more information about activated carbon and its ability to remove yellowing substances from the water which might enhance the bleaching response see chapter 12).

In the oceans the iodine concentration is about 0,06 mg/l. Iodine may be added to the aquarium water quite easily as potassium iodide (KI), yet it has to be measured out with extreme care! **Potassium iodide is a highly toxic substance, which must be kept in a safe place.**

If potassium iodide is dissolved in water, it will dissociate into potassium and iodide ions. The normal concentration of potassium ions in the sea water is 390 mg/l, so the slight addition of potassium iodide will hardly affect the potassium ion concentration. First a stock solution of 25 g potassium iodide in 500 ml of distilled water is prepared. Of this solution 0.5 ml for every 200 litres of aquarium water should be added weekly. Our experience shows that this is also the amount which is consumed in the aquarium system.

Iodine is unstable and it is essential that the solution is stored in a dark and cold place.

Further reading

BROCKMANN, 1991a and b; DRING, 1986; EMMENS, 1989; KIPPER, 1989; SPOTTE, 1979; WIKKENS & HELM, 1981; WILKENS, 1982a and b, 1983a, b and c.

Table 13
Concentration of some specific ions in natural seawater (B, E, F; average concentration = A; after TAIT, 1971) and in different coral reef aquaria (C, G, H, I, J, K, L1, L2, M1, M2, N).

Element	Symbol	A (μg/l)	B (μg/l)	C (μg/l)	D (μg/l)	E (μg/l)	F (μg/l)	G (μg/l)	H (μg/l)	I (μg/l)	J (μg/l)	K (μg/l)	L1 (μg/l)	L2 (μg/l)	M1 (μg/l)	M2 (μg/l)	N (μg/l)
Lithium	Li	170	200	200	200	250	300	400	410	300	450	240	1250	440	1000	1000	1500
Boron	B	4600	4255	2960	3145	3515	3885	2960	6660	3330	8140	3422	1390	1480	2220	1850	2590
Silicon	Si	3000	1560	1500	1510	500	500	500	1000	600	560	600	600	440	600	600	50
Vanadium	V	2	60	50	60	60	70	70	70	60	80	60	70	40	70	60	10
Cobalt	Co	0.5	2	0.6	0.7	0.8	0.1	1	0.6	1	1	1	2	0.6	6	15	40
Rubidium	Rb	120	90	90	90	100	110	150	120	120	120	130	1200	510	1300	1200	1500
Strontium	Sr	8000	11800	11500	11900	7700	8300	11900	7800	8700	22100	21000	2600	4100	4700	4000	21700
Iodine	I	60	30	20	20	80	40	200	30	90	100	70	1300	500	60	70	1200
Barium	Ba	30	33	32	33	5.6	5	8	70	13	25	9	12	6	13	6	12
Calcium	Ca	4×10^5	4.6×10^5	4.6×10^5	4.5×10^5	4.5×10^5	4.1×10^5	4.25×10^5	3.6×10^5	5.25×10^5	4.25×10^5	6.5×10^5	4.25×10^5	4.75×10^5	3.75×10^5	2.25×10^5	4.8×10^5
Density (25°C)			1.0226	1.0226	1.0227	1.0224	1.0229	1.0241	1.0226	1.0238	1.0238	1.0217	1.0256	1.0247	1.0236	1.0226	1.0238
In operation									>3 y	>5 y	1 y	>10 y	4 y	4 y	8 y	8 y	4 y

Table 13 shows the concentration of some specific ions in natural sea water (in μg/l). A) average concentration after TA-IT, 1971; B) Waikiki Aquarium, Hawaii, water from well entering the open aquarium system; E) reef water off Puerto Rico, 2 metres depth (July 1995); F) reef water from the surface, the Maldives (April 1992).

The table also shows the concentration of the same ions in some coral reef aquaria. C) Waikiki Aquarium, Hawaii, water inside the open aquarium system; D) Waikiki Aquarium, water leaving the open aquarium system; G) closed aquarium system Mr. G. Santiago, Puerto Rico; H) closed aquarium system Mr. D. Ramirez, Miami, USA; I) closed aquarium system Mr. J. Sprung, Miami, USA; J) closed aquarium system Salifert, Mr. H. Sekha, BL Duiven, The Netherlands; K) closed aquarium system, Mr. D. Stüber, Berlin, Germany; L1 & L2) closed aquarium system Mr. F. Jørgensen, Stavern, Norway (for more information on L2 see below); M1 & M2) closed aquarium system Mr. A. J. Nilsen, Hidrasund, Norway (these probes were from the same tank, but taken months apart); N) closed aquarium system Mr. K. Nagy, Flekkefjord, Norway. Y = years.

The sample L2 was taken just after a 75 % water change has been completed. In addition the aquarium was added 150 gram $CaCl_2$ (aquarium volume: 700 litres) during a few days around the water change. Most of the trace elements have decreased in concentration, especially Li and Co. All the corals in the aquarium "exploded" in growth after the water change. From this observation and the comparison of the concentrations of trace elements in columns L1 and L2 it might be concluded that a too high concentration of certain trace elements might limit the growth of stony corals. However, the values in the table show that the trace elements vary a lot from aquarium to aquarium. Nevertheless, in all aquaria there seemed to be a healthy and prolific growth, both stony as well as soft ones. From this observation one can draw the conclusion that a minimum concentration of specific ions is necessary to obtain healthy growth of corals and other invertebrates.

All values (except for Iodine SD = +/- 20 μg/l, Calcium +/- 5 mg/l or Strontium SD = +/- 5 %) represent the ion concentrations of one distinct sample. Therefore it is not possible to estimate their variations during the operation time of the respective aquarium. In addition, these values can only be considered as approximate values and not as absolute values as only one sample was analyzed and no statistics were performed from independent probes!

Tests were carried out by H. Sekha, Salifert Aquarium Products, The Netherlands.

The outdoor aquarium system for stony corals at Waikiki Aquarium, Honolulu (columns B, C and D). Photo from 1991.   Photo: E. Svensen

The aquarium of Mr. D. Stüber, Germany (column K).

The aquarium of Mr. D. Ramirez, Miami (column H).   Photo: J. Sprung

The aquarium of Mr. F. Jørgensen, Norway (column L1). In this aquarium a mass-spawing of stony corals took place in 1994.   Photo: K. Nagy

The aquarium of Mr. J. Sprung, Miami (column I).

A section of the aquarium belonging to Mr. K. Nagy (column N).

Chapter 11:

Biochemical Processes in the Modern Coral Reef Aquarium

The balance of a biological system is highly dependent on the decomposition and the utilization of waste materials that accumulate. A biological balance in the original meaning of the term cannot be reached in an aquarium, at least not as long as this aquarium is also supposed to be a pleasant sight. An aquarium as a biological system cannot keep going if we do not control and interfere. This implies that specific measures must be taken for the removal and decomposition of waste materials. Thus we have to remove a considerable part of these materials from the aquarium, while at the same time we must support the work of the organisms which decompose these substances in the aquarium system. Due to their metabolism all organisms excrete wastes. As a rule vertebrates pro-

The reef and the reef aquarium: To the left (photo Dr. D. Brockmann) delicate octocorals and minute sessile organisms in a reef of Madang, Papua New Guinea. Above: on the bottom of a small cave in the author's aquarium two nudibranches, *Jorunna funebris*, are searching for sponges to eat while the large calcareous tube worm, *Protula bispiralis*, filters plankton from the water.

duce metabolic wastes which are chemically more complex than those of invertebrates. Most marine organisms excrete ammonia (NH_3), but also ammonium (NH_4^+), urea ($(H_2N)_2CO$) and uric acid ($C_5H_4O_3N_4$) are common products of excretion. All these compounds have one thing in common, they all contain nitrogen (N). These wastes are not just excreted by animals, they may also result from dying and decaying algae, food substances, etc. Here nitrogenous compounds occur in the form of proteins. Proteins and other complex compounds also accumulate when organisms decay.

In natural surroundings the organic substances are decomposed and become inorganic compounds again, which in turn are available for the producers and thus the wheel turns full circle. In this process bacteria have the most decisive part, yet all other organisms present and their metabolisms are involved in it and they thus have an important role in this biological cycle. The diagram at the top of page 243 shows the nitrogen cycle. Nitrogen is one of the elements that causes most of the problems and troubles in a coral reef aquarium.

An aquarium is a small and closed biological system in which the population density of organisms is considerbly higher than in natural surroundings. Therefore the pollution in this system is excessively high. During the decomposition of the waste materials a number of intermediate and by-products result, some of which are highly toxic. If these accumulate this can have very negative consequences for many of the organisms in the aquarium. That is why it is absolutely necessary to clean the water with some kind of filtering device.

Which filtering system to choose is of course guided by the number and kinds of organisms that are kept in the aquarium. Some animals require much better water quality than others. An aquarium densely populated with fish demands a more elaborate filtering

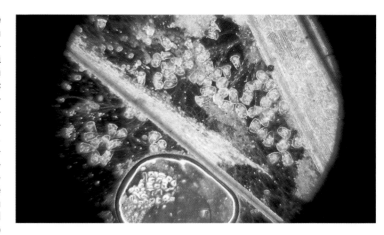

Bacteria and unicellular animals are visible with the help of a microscope.

system than an aquarium with only a few fish and some invertebrates.

Bacteria and their environment

Oxygen is indispensable for most living beings, yet it is not available everywhere. A milieu in which oxygen is available is called aerobic, if

there is no oxygen it is called anaerobic. In natural surroundings as well as in the aquarium there are aerobic and anaerobic zones. Usually most of the water in the water column which moves freely about is nearly saturated with oxygen. In the coral sand of the seabed, or especially in live rocks, the conditions are quite different. If a live rock is broken to pieces, one can often see that the stone which is pale outside is black in the middle. The black colour results from precipitations of sulphur, an unmistakable sign of an anaerobic milieu. The oxygen contents

Populations of different species of bacteria in the filter substrate of an aquarium, numbers of bacteria per gram of filter substrate.

(After SPOTTE, 1979)

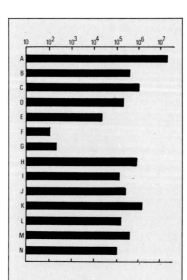

A: total number of aerobic bacteria
B: total number of anaerobic bacteria
C: aerobic bacteria that hydrolyse starch
D: anaerobic bacteria that hydrolyse starch
E: bacteria that decompose gelatin
F: sulphate-reducing bacteria
G: bacteria that decompose cellulose
H: bacteria that decompose urea
I: denitrifying bacteria
J: ammonium-reducing bacteria
K: aerobic, nitrate-reducing bacteria ($NO_3^- \rightarrow NO_2^-$)
L: anaerobic, nitrate-reducing bacteria ($NO_3^- \rightarrow NO_2^-$)
M: nitrifying bacteria ($NH_4^+ \rightarrow NO_2^-$)
N: nitrifying bacteria ($NO_2^- \rightarrow NO_3^-$)

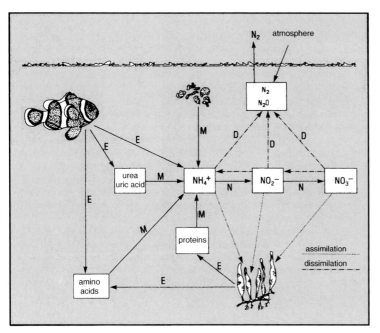

Left: Nitrogen cycle in the aquarium (after SPOTTE, 1979):
D = denitrification
E = excretion
M = mineralisation
N = nitrification

❶ **Mineralisation**

During this stage of decomposition amino acids (constituents of proteins) are reduced to inorganic compounds. Organic compounds differ from inorganic ones by containing carbon. This carbon from the amino acids is consumed by the heterotrophic bacteria, usually of the genus *Bacterium*, which thus reduce organic compounds to inorganic ones. The products of the mineralisation process are ammonia and organic acids. These acids have a dangerous influence on the buffer capacity of the aquarium water and can make the pH go down. Ammonia (NH_3) is not only introduced into the water by bacteria. It is the most common metabolic waste from other marine organisms and, depending on the pH, it always stands in a certain relation to the amount of ammonium (NH_4^+). At a pH of 8.3 the relation ammonia:ammonium is about 1:9. The balance can be shown in the following formula:

$$NH_4^+ + H_2O \leftrightarrow NH_3 + H_3O^+$$

Ammonium in its free form is toxic,

in live rocks decreases continuously from the outside to its inside.

Among the bacteria there are aerobic species that need oxygen to stay alive and anaerobic species that need an environment low in oxygen. The two types of bacteria have completely different functions in the decomposition processes, which will be dealt with later. Moreover there are facultative (=optionally) anaerobic bacteria which are able to adapt to a changing oxygen content in their surroundings.

A further distinction is made between heterotrophic and autrophic species of bacteria. Heterotrophic bacteria cover their needs of energy by consuming various organic compounds, while autotrophic organisms either obtain energy from the oxidation of inorganic substances (chemoautotrophy, e. g. nitrifying bacteria) or make use of light energy via photosynthesis, without setting free oxygen, (photoautotrophic bacteria). In aquaria many different species of bacteria can be found.

To the right: This *Acropora cervicornis* in the aquarium of J. Sprung, Miami, grows beautifully.

The decomposition of nitrogenous compounds

In the decomposition process of nitrogenous compounds three main stages can be distuinguished (see diagram above):

❶ **Mineralisation**
❷ **Nitrification**
❸ **Dissimilation**

In a closed system, which is exactly what an aquarium is, waste substances pollute the water. *Pterois miles* is a species with high food requirements and thus it pollutes the water with a high amount of excreted matter.

yet it is also an import source of nitrogen for algae. Usually ammonia and ammonium are oxidised to nitrite and nitrate before long.

❷ Nitrification

The next stage of decomposition is the oxidation of ammonia and ammonium to nitrite (NO_2^-) and nitrate (NO_3^-). These reactions are mainly carried out by two groups of bacteria. Up to this point aquarium literature suggests that species of the genus *Nitrosomonas* oxidize ammonia or ammonium to nitrite, while *Nitrobacter* oxidise nitrite into nitrate (see the formulas below).

$$2NH_4^+ + 2OH^- + 3O_2$$
$$\textit{-Nitrosomonas} \rightarrow$$
$$2H^+ + 2NO_2^- + 4H_2O$$

$$2NO_2^{2-} + O_2 \textit{ -Nitrobacter} \rightarrow$$
$$2NO_3^-$$

There are certainly other bacteria involved, particularly in the species rich live rock and live sand substrates.

Heterotrophic bacteria also take part in these processes (JOHNSON & SIEBURTH, 1976; TATE, 1977). It has been shown that heterotro-phic bacteria are able to convert amino acids directly into nitrite and nitrate, without going indirectly via the ammonia/ammonium pathway (QASTEL et al., 1950; JENSEN & GUNDERSEN, 1955; DOXTADER & ALEXANDER, 1966).

In an aquarium there is always a certain amount of nitrifying bacteria, no matter what filtration method is used. It depends on a number of factors, how effectively these bacteria "work":

- the pollution of the water with toxic substances

- temperature, pH and oxygen content of the water

- the surface available for the bacteria to settle on.

Toxic compounds

Toxic compounds that pollute the water may be subdivided into two categories:

1. substances that are introduced into the aquarium from outside and

2. substances which are produced by the metabolism of the organisms in the aquarium itself.

Toxic metabolic end products, i. e. compounds produced by the metabolism of the inhabitants of the aquarium, include ammonia, ammonium, nitrite and nitrate. If the concentration of nitrite in the aquarium rises significantly, this may inhibit the nitrification processes.

More or less toxic substances which have been introduced into the aquarium (e. g. substances that are added to treat fish diseases) may also disturb the nitrification processes considerably. Methylene blue, which is a component of many fish medicines, killed most of the nitrifying bacteria in an experiment we carried out. Yet copper sulfate, which is extremely toxic for invertebrates, does not seem to inhibit nitrification very much. As we know only very little about the side effects of most fish medicines, we recommend not to use them in coral reef aquaria as a matter of priciple.

Temperature, pH and oxygen content

The process of nitrification is dependent on the temperature, pH and oxygen concentration of the water. We can find that it works more effectively the higher the temperature gets (up to a maxi-

Zebrasoma flavescens, the Yellow Tang, also pollutes the water with its excretions, yet at the same time it is also welcome in the coral reef aquarium because it grazes on the filamentous algae that annoy the aquarist.

Photo: K. Upstad

mum of 30 °C). It is similar with pH. Nitrification works best at pH 9. Yet in a coral reef aquarium only readings between 8.0 and 8.5 are acceptable. Regarding the oxygen concentration, it has to be taken into account that nitrifying bacteria are aerobic, yet possibly not as strictly aerobic as often supposed (GUNDERSEN, 1966).

Substrates

Substrates on which they can settle are of utmost importance for the development of the bacteria. In the open body of water normally no nitrification takes place. In order to be decomposed the substances dissolved in the water first must be adsorbed by a surface covered with detritus. Thus it is necessary that a certain amount of detritus be present in the aquarium and in the filter for bacterial decomposition to take place effectively. Bacteria form a thin, slimy film on the substrates they settle. This film is the place where decompostion takes place. Such a bacterial coating undergoes a continual change, as it grows permanently and is decomposed at the same time. There are changes in the thickness of the layer according to the density of the bacteria population (see diagram at the bottom of this page on the left).

Toxic effects of nitrite and nitrate

Nitrification produces nitrite as an intermediate and nitrate as the end product. Both compounds are toxic. Nitrite has a toxic effect because it oxidises hemoglobin to methhemoglobin. While hemoglobin is responsible for the transport of oxygen, methhemoglobin lacks this ability. Nitrite poisoning in fish causes respiratory problems with an unusually high rate of gill movements. Many invertebrates react to nitrite by contracting their bodies heavily; anemones turn their intestinal cavity inside out through their mouth. So far there is no satisfactory explanation why invertebrates react that way. Nitrite concentrations higher than 0.05 mg/l are not acceptable in a coral reef aquarium.

Authors who write on aquaristic subjects often regard nitrate as rather harmless. This certainly does not hold true for a coral reef aquarium. High concentrations of nitrate (1000-2000 mg/l) are an

Diagram of the development of a bacterial film:
At the beginning, when aerobic bacteria start to settle on the surface, the populations of bacteria are still rather small (a), when oxygen and nutrients are generously supplied they will grow substantially (b and c). When there is a deficiency in the supply of oxygen to the lower levels of the bacterial film, the aerobic bacteria start to die (d), which leads to an increase of the anaerobic bacteria (e). Finally stable populations of these will develop. This state will remain unchanged until a nutrient deficiency occurs in the lower levels of the film, which will cause it to come off from the substrate. (After SPOTTE, 1979)

impediment to the development of the tissues of many organisms. Yet delicate corals – especially stony corals – usually stop thriving already at concentrations which are much lower. In a closed coral reef aquarium with stony corals our experience shows that nitrate levels that exceed 10 to 20 mg/l may lead to problems, especially when it comes to the control of filamentous algae. In a well established coral reef aquarium there will usually be little risk of a dangerous concentration of nitrate accumulating. The concentrations of nitrite and nitrate can be tested with specific test kits available from several producers and sold in the pet shops. These kits are easy to use, and they are accurate enough for aquaristic purposes.

❸ Dissimilation

In the last stage of decomposition nitrate is reduced. Many different types of bacteria are involved in the process of dissimilation from which the following end products may result:

- Dinitrogenoxide (N_2O) (a.k.a. nitrous oxide or laughing gas)
- Nitrogen (N_2)
- Ammonia/ammonium (NH_3/NH_4^+)
- Nitrite (NO_2^-)

Dinitrogenoxide and nitrogen are gases. If the decomposition process results in these substances, it is called *denitrification*. During this process nitrogen escapes from the aquarium. If ammonia/ammonium are the end products of the process, *nitrate reduction* takes place. In this case the ammonia/ammonium concentration may increase so enormously that it can have harmful effects. Fortunately such nitrate reduction only rarely prevails in the aquarium.

The environmental conditions are of great importance for dissimilation as well. Temperature and pH influence dissimilation in the same way as they influence nitrification. This is completely different, however, with oxygen. The

bacteria involved in dissimilation are anaerobic, or optionally anaerobic. This is why we can say very generally that oxygen inhibits dissimilation. Thus this reaction occurs in the aquarium only in places with an oxygen deficiency, e. g. inside live rocks, in parts of the aquarium bottom substrate or in special denitrification filters. Some experts hold the opinion, however, that dissimilation can also take place under aerobic conditions.

Bacteria living in an anaerobic milieu produce enzymes which reduce nitrate ions, making use of the oxygen from the nitrate for respiration. Enzyme production stops as soon as aerobic conditions are established. As a consequence the nitrate concentration in the aquarium rises. Most of the bacteria involved in dissimilation are heterotrophic. So they need organic nutrients which must be available in dissolved carbon compounds. As the different kinds of bacteria take in different nutrients the bacteria populations vary according to the food substances

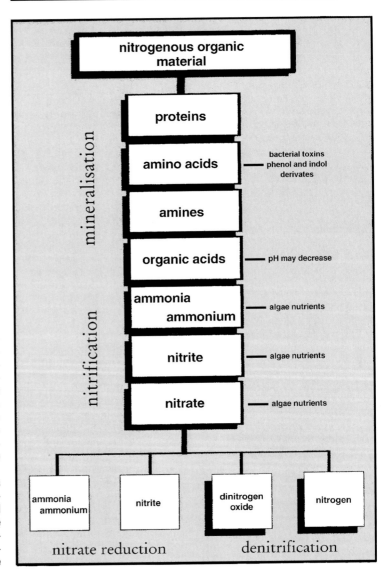

Decomposition of nitrogenous organic material

available. In a denitrifying filter lactose is often dosed as a food supplement to enhance the function of the bacteria.

The denitrification process in the aquarium has so far not been the subject of intense research. We obviously still have a lot to learn about this subject. Yet we have learned from experience that in aquaria decorated with live rocks in combination with protein skimming and sufficient water motion an accumulation of nitrate does not normally occur. In aquaria without skimming, nitrate can, however, accumulate heavily, see ATKINSON et al. (1995) and chapter 12.

The complete decomposition of nitrogenous compounds is shown in the diagram on page 246. In the process of decomposition a number by-products arise. Thus mineralisation may produce colour substances as derivates of Phenole or Indole, which may give the water a yellow hue. This tinge can only be removed effectively by filtering the water through activated carbon or by using ozone.

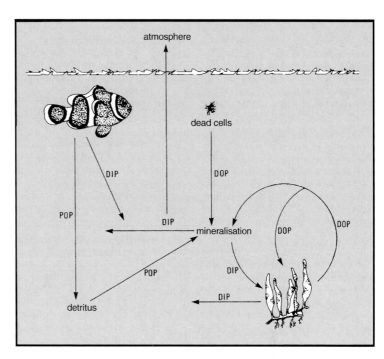

Phosphate cycle (after SPOTTE, 1979). Abbreviations used: DIP = dissolved inorganic phosphate; DOP = dissolved organically phosphate; POP = phosphate fixed to particles = particulate organic phosphate.

Phosphorus cycle

Nitrogenous products of decomposition are under discussion most often among aquarists, yet there are also other decomposition products containing nutrients that have to be taken into account in the maintenance of a coral reef aquarium.

When talking about "phosphate" we usually have in mind an inorganic compound of phosphorus (P) and oxygen (O). Inorganic phosphate can be found in seawater of a normal pH as PO_4^{3-}, HPO_4^{2-} and $H_2PO_4^-$, of which the second one is most commonly found. The negative phosphate ions are combined with positive ions, often calcium (Ca^{2+}) or magnesium (Mg^{2+}), resulting in the respective calcium and magnesium salts (KESTER & PYTKOWICZ, 1967). Phosphate can also be found in organic compounds. It is set free in the decomposition process of plants, planktonic organisms, detritus or micro organisms (see diagram above).

SPOTTE (1979) gives 0.06 mg/l as the average phosphate concentration in seawater. In coral reefs, however, the concentration of dissolved phosphate is lower by far, often less than 0.015 mg/l (FURNAS et al., 1990). The same author found extremely low readings also for other dissolved inorganic substances, e.g nitrite and nitrate, which he found to be under 0.002 mg/l. Even though the concentration of nitrite, nitrate and phosphate is low in the water surrounding most coral reefs, these substances are essential nutrients to the symbiotic algae associated with hermatypic corals and with other reef organisms. In the aquaristic phosphate has been much discussed in connection with the "limestone-reactor" and "Kalkwasser". In the aquarium there is always a pool of phosphate present, normally as salts or bound to organic molecules. If the pH is lowered, this pool is mobilized and the concentration of phosphate increases which again can result in an uncontrolled growth of algae. The use of "Kalkwasser" raises the pH and prevents phosphate from dissolving.

BAYLOR et al. (1962) showed that phosphate can be removed from natural seawater very effectively by aeration – therefore simply by protein skimming. In artificial seawater the results were less convincing. The reason for this is probably that pure fresh mixed artificial seawater (not aquarium water) does not contain any organic pollutants. This shows that phosphate must be bound in an organic compound to be easily removed from the aquarium system by protein skimming.

Reduction and oxidation

Processes of great importance for the coral reef aquarium are **reduction** and **oxidation**, summarised also under the term **redox reaction**. In this process one substance is reduced, another oxidised. That means, that electrons (tiny particles of matter that are negatively charged) move from one substance to the other. The substance that loses the electrons is oxidised and the substance that receives them is reduced. The following formula describes the oxidation of zinc (Zn) and the reduction of copper (Cu):

$$Zn + Cu^{2+} \longrightarrow Zn^{2+} + Cu$$

The zinc atom, which is neutral at first provides two electrons (negative charges) for the copper atom, which had two positive charges originally. We then get a zinc atom with two positive charges, while the copper atom is electrically neutral now. Zinc is a **reducing agent**, as it reduces copper, and copper is an **oxidising agent** as it oxidises zinc. This redox reaction can be demonstrated in the following way: a zinc electrode is immersed into a glass with with an electrolyte solution (e. g. potassium chloride) and a copper electrode into a second glass with the same solution. If these two glass containers are connected by a

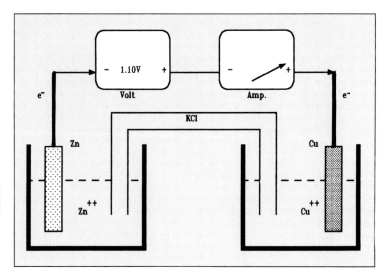

Diagram of an experimental demonstration of the flow of electrons and of the measuring of the redox potential. (After MAHAN, 1980)

glass tube also containing the electrolyte solution, there is a voltage of 1.10 volt between the two electrodes (see the diagram above). This voltage is the measure for the power (potential) of the redox reaction of zinc as reducing agent and copper as oxidising agent, it tells us the redox potential (also referred to as redox tension) of this reaction. What is the importance of this for a coral reef aquarium?

It is also possible to measure the redox potential of seawater, or rather the voltage between the electrode and an electrolyte in the measuring device, thus between the redox measuring device and the aquarium water. Redox measuring devices may take a rather long time to provide exact and reliable results. This is why redox should be measured continuously

It takes a lot of patience and a continuous observation of the animals to keep a coral reef aquarium going successfully. Without well-founded knowledge about the biological, physical and chemical processes going on in the aquarium, it is hardly possible to draw the right conclusions that induce further progress in reef aquaristics. Photo: R. Latka

rH values as a function of the redox potentials at pH 8.0 (unbroken line) and 8.6 (dotted line). The border between strongly and weakly oxidizing conditions is between 300 and 350 mV (the diagram is based on BAUMEISTER, 1990).

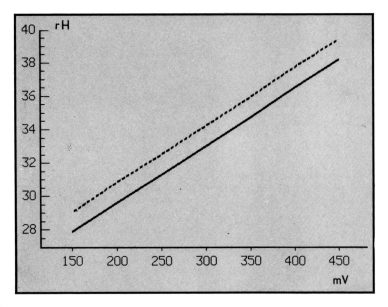

rH values as a function of the redox potentials at pH 8.0 (unbroken line) and 8.6 (dotted line). The border between strongly and weakly oxidizing conditions is between 300 and 350 mV (the diagram is based on BAUMEISTER, 1990).

over a period of several days. The result may (loosely!) be taken as an indication of the "state of health" of the aquarium as it hints at the balance of oxidation and reduction capacity. The redox potential of the aquarium water is strongly influenced by the oxidation and reduction processes of the various bacteria. Yet also reactions between metals that are present in the aquarium may be involved. If ozone is applied the redox potential is increased.

It is simply not possible to give a certain value as **the** correct value for the redox potential in a coral reef aquarium, yet in a "healthy" coral reef aquarium the readings will usually be between 300 and 400 mV. In aquaria with eutrophic water and a heavy growth of algae the redox potential is often between 200 and 300 mV. Ozonisation can increase it to 450 mV and more. Of course the redox potential decreases when there is an oxygen deficiency. Thus in a functioning denitrifying filter very low readings can be taken. Extremely low readings of -50 mV may also be taken in the skimmate liquid of a protein skimmer.

Redox potential is influenced by pH. If the pH increases the redox potential goes down and vice versa. This is why "rH", a value which combines various aspects is most practical. rH indicates the relation between mV and pH and can be calculated according to the following formula:

$$rH = mV/29 + (2xpH) + 6{,}67$$

The resulting value represents the redox balance of the aquarium. BAUMEISTER (1990) distinguishes between five different kinds of redox balance:

1) rH 0 – 9 = heavy reduction
2) rH 10 – 17 = slight reduction
3) rH 18 – 25 = neutral
4) rH 26 – 34 = slight oxidation
5) rH 35 – 42 = heavy oxidation

The relation pH/mV or the rH, if measured continuously, gives us an insight into the functional processes and developments of a coral reef aquarium. Yet we would like to warn aquarists not to become slaves to their measuring equipment. It is as reliable and perhaps easier to develop valid criteria for the biological conditions in one's coral reef aquarium by watching very carefully the state of health and the well-being of the creatures that are kept in it. Of course measuring the redox potential can be quite useful as it may help to confirm or dispel certain suspicions, if problems arise. Redox measuring equipment is available from different manufacturers.

Some aquarists have little concern for theoretical knowledge. It is of course an open question whether the information dealt with in this chapter is indispensable for the maintenance of a coral reef aquarium. Yet we have learned from experience that it is always helpful to have thorough background knowledge. We would like to stress that the best way to learn how to judge the health of an aquarium is to watch closely if the

animals are thriving and especially if the algae are growing. As long as this is the case, there is no need to change anything about the technical appliances the aquarium is fitted with.

Further reading

General:
ATKINSON, 1987a, 1987b, 1988 and 1991; ATKINSON & BILGER, 1992; ATKINSON & GRIGG, 1984; ATKINSON & SMITH 1987; ATKINSON et al., 1995; NILSEN, 1982, 1983
Nitrification, denitrification
ALDERSTON & SIEBURTH, 1976; BISHOP et al., 1976; DAWSON & MURPHY, 1972; DODD & BONE, 1975; JERIS & OWEN, 1975; MULBARGER, 1971; SPOTTE, 1979

Small calcareous sponges from the genus *Sycon* growing on live rocks.

Chapter 12:

Filtration, Water Maintenance and Hydrotechnology for the Modern Coral Reef Aquarium

In the preceding chapters we have described the water quality that is needed in a coral reef aquarium and some of the chemical and biological processes that are of importance there. In this chapter we would now like to deal at length with the methods and the technical equipment used in water maintenance and filtration.

Biological filtration

Biological filtration is the method of cleaning water by biological processes. These are decomposition processes carried out by bacteria, algae and/or other animals. If a separate container is used for this it is called a biological filter or biofilter, for short. The microbiological processes taking place in such a biofilter are quite unpredictable and there is the risk that drastic changes in the biological milieu may occur after some time. To

Above: The currents in a coral reef are powerful and variable. The water is oligotrophic (= poor in nutrients) and very transparent. We must try to imitate these conditions in a coral reef aquarium as closely as possible by filtration, water maintenance and hydrotechnology (underwater photo: E. Svensen). Left: A cross-section of a biological reef aquarium run by the principles of JAUBERT (1989). The aquarium belongs to J. Sprung.

keep the function of the biofilter as stable as possible it is absolutely essential to exchange part of the filter substrate regularly (this does not apply to filters with live rock as filter medium). Moreover large organic particles should not be allowed to clog up the filter. This can be avoided by using a prefilter and by exchanging its filter substrate at least once a week (see also the passage on "mechanical filters" on page 257).

The best material for the construction of a biofilter container is glass. The container can be divided into smaller compartments by vertical partitions. To achieve an optimal flow through of the water through it the bottom of the substrate compartments consists of a latticework of glass strips or of perforated PVC or Perspex, the water can flow easily through the filter. Soft plastics may not be used as it might release harmful substances into the water.

There are a number of systems which may be regarded as biological filters, e.g. biofilters with live rock or other filter substrates, denitrification filters, trickle filters and filters run with monocultures of selected organisms. We will deal with all of these in more detail on the following pages. Already at this point, however, we would like to point out a major problem of using biofilters as the only, or main, filtration in a coral reef aquarium. All experience shows that this, in the long run, has a tendency to result in massive accumulation of nutrients, e.g. nitrates and phosphates, in the aquarium water.

All decoration materials that are porous, e.g. dead calcareous rock (taken from areas above the water), live rocks, crushed oyster shells, coral or foraminiferan sand, are potential areas where beneficial decomposing organisms may settle. The more porous the material, the larger its effective surface. By using the decora-

tion material just mentioned, it is already possible to get biological decomposition processes going which are highly effective. The processes thus stimulated are of extraordinary importance for many aquarium systems. Live rock especially is very useful in keeping the water clean, and it seems to be an essential element also in the processes of filtration.

❶ Biofilters with live rock

Live rocks have the enormous advantage that they already arrive with a load of bacteria and other beneficial organisms. Due to the structure of these stones the oxygen content gradually decreases from the outside to its center. Thus there are aerobic as well as anaerobic zones. To guarantee an oxygen-enriched milieu there must be a strong flow of water running through a biofilter with live rock, ensuring high efficiency by reaching as much of the substrate as

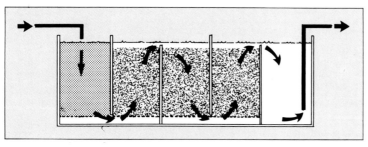

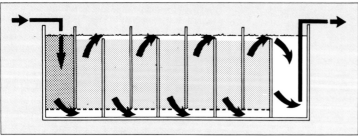

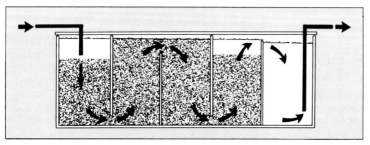

Diagrams of different types of biological filters:

Above – Biofilter with live rocks as a filter substrate. The first compartment is filled with Filter floss, which serves as a mechanical filter medium. It must be cleaned or exchanged very often. Behind it we have three compartments with coarsely crushed live rock. The last compartment is a water compartment without any filter material. Here a submersible heater, nylon bags with activated carbon, or other things may be placed.

Middle – Biofilter with other filter substrates, e.g. crushed oyster shells, coral gravel or artificial porous materials. The first compartment is used as a prefilter and thus must often be cleaned. The following compartments may contain various filter materials. The last compartment is the water compartment again.

Below – Denitrification filter. The filter must be tightly covered with a lid to keep oxygen from entering. The effluent from the last water compartment must never be conducted directly into the aquarium.

possible. The water volume of the aquarium, or rather, the whole system, should pass through the filter at least once per hour. The diagrams on page 252 show the function of this type of filter.

❷ Biofilters with other filter substrates

Other materials are also suitable as filter substrates for a biofilter: crushed oyster shells, coral gravel, coral and foraminiferan sand and artificial porous materials. This type of filter should have even more compartments than a biofilter with live rock. This leads to a smaller volume per compartment, which reduces the risk of dead zones, anaerobic zones where the water cannot flow freely. Such anaerobic zones in a filter sometimes release toxic substances all of a sudden. There has to be strong water movement and in this type of filter the water body should be circulated at least once per hour as well.

The first compartment of such a filter (see the diagram in the middle on page 252) should be filled with filter wool as a "dirt trap". This mechanical filter is easily rinsed or exchanged. This material may also be used for the other compartments, yet the other filter substrates mentioned above are more effective. It is crucial that the water is able to flow freely through the filter substrate.

It depends on the flow rate and the amount of pollutants how often such a filter must be cleaned. It is of utmost importance to replace only a small part of the filter substrate at one time (about 10 to 20 % per month, your experience will show you what is best). Too much cleanliness will reduce the number of microorganisms in the substrate and thus impede the function of the filter.

The purpose of the two types of biofilters described here is to enhance nitrification and the other decomposition processes. The final products of this decomposition are mainly nitrate and phosphate. The redox potential, which should be appropriately

Cryptocentrus cinctus is a beautiful goby that is regularly imported. It is of special interest because of its symbiotic relationship with shrimps of the genus *Alpheus*. Goby and shrimp live together in a burrow in the sand which is dug and restored by the shrimp. As a return service the goby warns the shrimp of approaching predators.

high (300 – 450 mV), will prove that these decomposition processes are in fact taking place. Sometimes the nitrate content of the aquarium water will rise. Then further steps must be taken against a nitrate accumulation, which should be avoided.

❸ Denitrification filters

Denitrification filters (page 252, bottom) were developed to prevent dangerous rises of the nitrate content of the aquarium water. Basically these are filters with anaerobic conditions and, accordingly, a low water flow rate. If the filter provides the conditions necessary for denitrification, nitrate is decomposed into nitrogen (N_2) and dinitrogen oxide (N_2O). Both substances escape as gases. The main problem of this type of filter is the fact that anaerobic conditions will only set in after a considerable time. It is generally difficult to establish anaerobic conditions in a denitrification filter. If this has been achieved, however, a denitrification filter will work quite

efficiently. Another proof of anaerobic conditions are very low oxygen readings in the effluent water. The biological conditions, however, can only be recorded by correct measurement of the redox potential in the filter. Redox potentials between -50 and -200 mV are a sign that denitrification is working well, readings higher than -50 mV tell us that no denitrification is taking place, while readings below -200 mV indicate a danger that the highly toxic gas H_2S may be produced. BAUM (1989) made some very interesting remarks on this subject.

The general layout of denitrification filters is similar to that of the biofilters described before, yet here a prefilter is not needed as the inflow always comes from the aerobic filter. The filter media in a denitrification filter must have a fine structure. Suitable media are: finely ground live rock, crushed calcareous rocks and, of course, artificial materials specially developed for this purpose. The water flow rate should be kept as low as possible, usually less than 50 litres per hour. The filter should be kept tightly closed to keep out oxygen from the surrounding air. Nutrients should occasionally be added to feed the bacteria. Lactose ($C_{12}H_{22}O_{11}$) is a very good choice here. The bacteria decompose the lactose into carbon dioxide and water, taking the oxygen needed from the nitrate molecule. This leads to the production of gaseous nitrogen (see chapter 11). The best and simplest method is to add the lactose to the water in the first filter compartment, one level teaspoon per week at first. In order to establish optimal anaerobic conditions it is very important to determine the right amount of lactose to add. One way to judge this is with redox measurement. If the redox potential of the effluent is too high this results from too low an amount of lactose, if the redox potential is too low, there was too much lactose added.

Attention!

You should never use a denitrification filter without a normal biofilter! The water flowing from this filter is extremely low in oxygen and must not be allowed to enter the aquarium directly. Instead, the effluent should always be conducted into the aerobic first compartment of a biofilter.

❹ Trickle filter

A trickle filter substrate is not submerged in the water. The water trickles over the substrate, instead. This causes a maximum enrichment with oxygen and a better nitrification than in normal biofilters. This is a great advantage in an aquarium system with an unusually high amount of polluting substances, e.g. if it is overstocked with fish. We do not think that this type of filter is needed for a coral reef aquarium, which usually has only a moderate amount of pollutants. A high evaporation rate and enormous heat loss are among the disadvantages of trickle filters.

The diagram at the top right of this page shows the design of a

trickle filter. A stack of boxes, each filled with a thin layer of filter substrate, make it easier to exchange the filter material. Today a variety of different trickle filter designs are available in the aquarium trade. Crushed calcareous rock is a very suitable and inexpensive substrate, yet there are also specially developed materials, e.g. bioballs made from a plastic structure with a large surface. Live rocks are of course also highly useful.

❺ Monoculture filter

The term monoculture filter is used for filters that contain a culture of plants or animals of the highest possible purity which have a favourable influence on the quality of the water. The best known monoculture filters are algae filters.

The simplest type of algae filter consists of a container that is exposed to a high light intensity, which boosts algae growth. This filter is planted with *Caulerpa*-algae (see diagram page 255), which consume nitrate (and a certain amount of other substances, e.g. phosphate) when they grow. If these algae beds are thinned out regularly the pollutants are removed with them. Another favourable effect of a monoculture filter is that the intense growth of the *Caulerpa*-algae keeps other, less desirable algae from growing or at least reduces their growth (by competing with them for the available nutrients and by depriving them of these substances). The growth of these algae also means competition for the symbiotic zooxanthellae of the invertebrates.

Filamentous algae may be cultivated in monoculture filters, but it is then difficult to keep them from spreading throughout the whole aquarium. If an aquarium for invertebrates from the shallow water zone of a coral reef is exposed to a lot of light, filamentous algae may become a nuisance. But if invertebrates from greater depths are kept in an aquarium under dim light, a filter with filamentous algae may be of advantage. Of course, *Caulerpa* can be used as well in this ca-

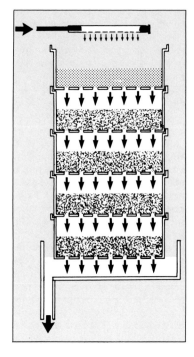

Diagram of a trickle filter: the filter material is placed in removable acrylic boxes that can be stacked. Thus they can be cleaned very easily. The box on the top, filled with Filter floss, is the prefilter. The following boxes may be filled with various filter substrates.

se, but our experience shows that filamentous algae are easier to cultivate and can consume more nitrate. The diagram on page 255 shows the construction of a filter with filamentous algae. The lights above an algae filter must be turned on for 12 to 14 hours per day.

In 1983 Dr. W. Adey of the Smithsonian Institution, Washington, published an article describing what he called a microcosm, an aquarium system which he had been continuously developing since 1974 (ADEY, 1983). The basic idea of the system is to filter the water over a number of algal-turf-scrubbers, which are algae filters where many species of filamentous turf algae are grown. As the growth is harvested, nutrients are removed from the system. In general the system was aimed at simulating the structure and functions of a shallow water Caribbean

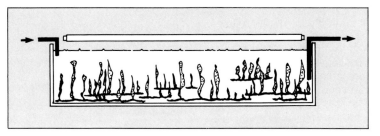

Diagram of a monoculture filter with *Caulerpa*: shallow containers with a maximum bottom area are most suitable. There must be a lighting installation above the filter, e.g. fluorescent lamps.

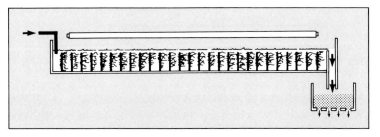

Diagram of a monoculture filter with filamentous algae: a suitable substrate on which filamentous algae may grow, (e.g. an acrylic glass grid) is placed in a shallow container with a high light intensity. As filamentous algae grow best in a strong current, a powerful water flow must be provided. A mechanical filter must be placed near the drain so that algae are not washed into the aquarium.

The *Great Barrier Reef Aquarium*'s 4.5 million litre reef tank, was originally run with the same techniques as the Smithsonian microcosm, using algae filters with an immensely large surface as the only filtration (EAGER & PETERSON, 1988; JONES, 1992). After visiting the *Great Barrier Reef Aquarium* we are not convinced anymore that algae filters are a good solution for a coral reef aquarium. The growth rate of the stony corals in this aquarium seemed to be considerably lower than in many private and public coral reef aquaria in Europe. Perhaps even more important, the general health situation and the variation and multitude in animal and algae life seemed in no way to be better, or closer to nature in this aquarium than what we know from many systems based on protein skimming. The use of algae turf scrubbers has been debated and reviewed by several authors, see for example SPRUNG (1993 and 1994) and ADEY (1994).

The only animal we know of that can be used in a monoculture filter is the anemone, *Aiptasia* (SCHLAIS, 1979). We are, however, very skeptical about such monoculture filters, mainly because it is hardly possible to keep the anemones

coral reef. Adey's ideas received much attention, and since 1983 many public aquaria, including the *Great Barrier Reef Aquarium* in Townsville, Australia, have made use of adaptations of the system.

Below: The "Algae Turf Scrubbers" at the Great Barrier Reef Aquarium, Townsville, Australia, in July 1991. To the right: View of a part of the decoration and inhabitants of the Great Barrier Reef Aquarium, Townsville, Australia, in July 1991.

from entering the aquarium. Here they may easily become a pest.

Subgravel filters

Subgravel filters were very popular once and perhaps even the most common filters for marine aquaria. As the way they function is well known, we only want to sketch it briefly here. The basic principle of a subgravel filter makes use of an airlift pump or a powerhead which draws the water through the bottom substrate, i.e. the water flows from the area above the substrate to a zone beneath it. Thus water rich in oxygen passes through the substrate where it enhances the nitrification processes. Later designs for subgravel filters with a reverse-flow direction were used. Here the water is pumped from the area below the substrate through to the water body above it. Both variants were tested by marine aquarists for years.

The experience with subgravel filters shows that they are not a suitable type of filter for coral reef aquaria. While they continue to be popular for fish-only set ups, so far we have not yet seen any coral reef aquarium with a subgravel filter that really worked well for a long period of time. Not very much is known about the processes that are going on in the subgravel filter. It seems to be very probable that the biological milieu in the substrate is subject to considerable changes. Subgravel filters also seem to stimulate the growth of blue-green algae.

The "Jaubert System"

Dr. J. Jaubert at the University of Nice, France has developed a highly specialized system of biological filtration, which can be looked upon as a sophisticated variation of both normal undergravel filtration and of the Natural System

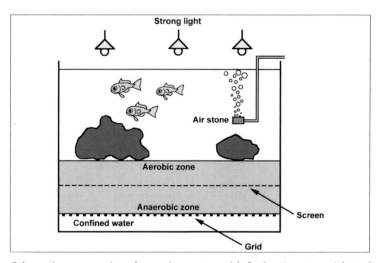

Schematic cross-section of aquarium set up with Jaubert's system. Adapted from JAUBERT (1989).

A nice small reef aquarium at the Oceanographic Museum in Monaco. This aquarium uses Jaubert's system and is also semi-open, receiving 5% water exchange per day with mediterranean natural seawater.   Photo: J. Sprung

of Lee Chin Eng. Since his first publication of the system at the *Deuxième Congrès international d'Aquariologie* in Monaco in 1988 (JAUBERT, 1989), Jaubert has patented the principle (French patent number 03 28474, U.S. patent number 4,995,980).

Jaubert's system is based on the use of a thick bottom substratum, consisting of so-called living sand – coral sand or gravel with a multitude of live organisms who have positive influence on the biological processes in the aquarium. In order to avoid harmful an-

oxic processes, a perforated grid (similar to an undergravel filter plate) is used, under which a body of confined water exist. The thick substratum above is divided by a horizontal screen, which prevents fish and invertebrates from disturbing it. It is important to note that there is no forced water circulation through the substratum. Movement of oxygen, carbon dioxide and nutrients occurs through diffusion. Consequently, clogging is not possible. The only water circulation in the aquarium is above the substratum, and is created through the use of an air stone or water pumps.

It has been demonstrated that this set-up is capable of supporting both mineralisation, nitrification and denitrification in the aquarium. In other words the substratum layer provides for both oxidizing and reducing processes. Several reports show that it, even alone, can create water-quality good enough for keeping excellent coral reef aquaria, provided the aquarist has the necessary knowledge and experience. The reason we discuss it here is, however, that we regard it as more interesting as an addition to other filtration methods (e.g. protein skimming), rather than on its own. For a more detailed discussion of the principles, see JAUBERT (1989) and DELBEEK & SPRUNG (1994).

Mechanical filters

The purpose of a mechanical filter is to remove suspended particles from the aquarium water before these are decomposed. Removing these particles avoids an additional pollution of the biological filter and sets a limit to the amount of pollutants that must be decomposed. It is very important to clean the mechanical filter as often as possible, at least once a week. If this is neglected, biological processes also start in the mechanical filter and the effect intended cannot be achieved. The more pollutants there are in an aquarium, the more the mechanical filter must be cleaned.

We have already described a mechanical filter as a prefilter for a biological filter. In this prefilter and in all other mechanical filters synthetic filter wool is the best filter medium. Foam materials are also used quite often. We cannot rule out, however, that these materials may give off toxic substances.

There are two more types of mechanical filters: internal power

Pyjama Cardinalfish, *Sphaeramia nematoptera* do very well in a coral reef aquarium.

filters and canister power filters. Closed canister power filters are difficult to clean, we think. This, however, is the only disadvantage they have. The plastic tubes that are fitted on these filters should be checked carefully. They may contain softening agents that can be emitted into the aquarium water, thus poisoning the animals in the aquarium. We recommend silicone tubes or PVC pipes for use with canister filters. Internal filters with powerheads and cartridges with filter wool are very useful. They are easily cleaned and there is no need to install tubes or pipes.

Mechanical filters are especially important during the break in period of a coral reef aquarium. During this phase various floating micro algae bloom subsequently and accordingly large amounts of these algae die. If these are not removed thoroughly water quality will deteriorate rapidly. At this stage a mechanical filter may have to be cleaned even daily.

Activated carbon filters

The main purpose of activated carbon filters is to remove from the water any organic pigments (derivatives of phenole and indole), which are not easily decomposed. These compounds are produced as by-products of bacterial decomposition and give the water a yellow tint. Carbon absorbs these substances, which are not electrically charged. Carbon must be processed especially at the time of production to have the enormous absorptive power needed in aquarium filters. Carbon treated in this way is called *activated carbon*. Unfortunately the brands of activated carbon available in aquarium shops are of varying quality. Experiments have shown that the inexpensive brands not only have less absorptive capacity, but may also emit harmful substances into the water, among others large amounts of phosphates. Usually the more expensive well-known brands are the safer choice here, because the processes needed in the production of activated carbon are costly and make higher prices a logical consequence. The salespeople in your aquarium store will give you more advice on this subject.

Carbon filters are brought up for discussion again and again. On the one hand a lot of people hold the opinion that this kind of filtration also removes useful substan-

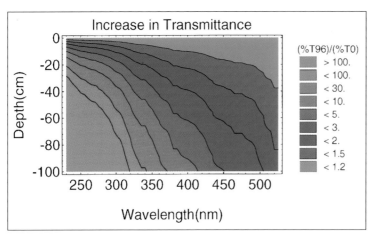

Increase in transmittance of light of different wavelengths through water filtered by activated carbon. The percent transmittance of the clarified water after 96 hours of filtration (%T96) is divided by the percent transmittance at the start of the experiment (%T0) when the water had a yellow tint. The colour key to the right shows the increase in transmittance ranges from slight (1.2 times) to well over 100 times depending on the wavelength and depth (BINGMAN, 1995).

ces from the aquarium water. On the other hand carbon filtration is the only way to remove coloured pigments and thus to keep the water from becoming yellowish. The yellow tint of the aquarium water has a negative influence on the quality of the light.

We have, however, several times observed that heavy filtration with activated carbon may cause bleaching in the stony corals. *Bleaching* is the condition when the corals loose their pigmentation, typically due to a decrease in the number of zooxanthellae. See chapter 9 for a discussion of the phenomenon. A possible reason for the link between extensive use of activated carbon and bleaching in corals is that the carbon removes important nutrients which the corals and/or the zooxanthellae need. An alternative explanation has been discussed by BINGMAN (1995). Increase of the amount of UV-light has been clearly demonstrated to have harmful effects on corals, and may lead to bleaching reactions. Bingman showed that the transmittance of UV-light increases with time when the aquarium water is filtered with activated carbon (see diagram above).

Carbon filtration is essential when the aquarium water conta-

ins toxic substances, as it is able to absorb most of these. Most probably also essential microelements are removed from the aquarium water by the activated carbon. If these elements are missing, the production of certain compounds that have a protective function against UV radiation is stopped and the metabolism of the zooxanthellae may be inhibited and reduced. In the instances where we observed bleaching after the use of activated carbon, we could also notice that the corals again healed and started to grow normally when the activated carbon was removed and trace elements, including iodine as KI, were added.

Carbon may be used in mechanical filter cartridges or placed in a nylon bag in the water compartment of a biofilter. The normal amount of carbon to be used on a continuous basis is between 100 and 200 grams of carbon per 100 litres of aquarium water. Carbon filters may be run continually or only temporarily when the aquarium water changes colour. Activated carbon loses its effect after some time and therefore must be replaced at regular intervals, otherwise it will only have the same effect as a mechanical or biologi-

cal filter. The period over which the activated carbon is effective differs from one product to the next and is, of course, dependent on the degree of pollution in the aquarium concerned.

While in the earlier days of European reef aquaristics it was common to use activated carbon almost continuously, the trend today is to use smaller quantity of this filter medium in shorter intervals. For example, for a 500 litre aquarium this could mean only 200 grams activated carbon for a period of 2-3 days, once a month.

Protein skimming

In the water of our coral reef aquaria large amounts of proteins are accumulated which come from dead algae and animals, from leftover food particles and organic wastes. These proteins either must be removed at once or decomposed by bacteria. Intensive activity of bacteria in the aquarium, however, may lead to an accumulation of harmful intermediate products. As nitrification takes place faster than denitrification, nitrate is accumulated as well. Particularly in aquaria with high amounts of polluting substances it is important to remove the proteins, before they are decomposed by bacteria. This is achieved by protein skimming.

In the process of protein skimming electrically charged protein molecules adhere to air bubbles. In the contact pipe of the skimming device where the air bubbles run through the water, the production of foam is especially intense. There are two different types of foam, and they look different: **normal foam** and **protein foam**. The normal foam, consisting of small bubbles of identical size which break up quickly, settles at the bottom of the contact column. It is always produced when seawater is whirled up and aerated. Above the normal foam brownish protein foam is produced which consists of larger bubbles of different size. This protein foam contains the substances that we want to remove from our coral reef aquaria. This is why it is skimmed and collected in a container. In this container a viscous, dark brown liquid called **adsorbate** is collected, and it must never be allowed to get back into the aquarium!

There is a high probability that in addition to proteins some other substances are skimmed as well in the process. Among these there are also substances that are essential for the chemical balance of a coral reef aquarium. It is difficult to determine, however, which useful substances are skimmed and in what quantity. This could be an argument against the use of protein skimming devices, but we have only rarely observed a lack of nutrients or other negative effects caused by protein skimming. The advantages of protein skimming are considerably larger than any disadvantages.

Foam production is only possible if the water surface is highly charged electrically. This is why protein skimming is not possible in water with a specific gravity of less than 15 ‰. Variations of the surface tension are also possible in seawater. This is mainly due to fatty substances which are suspended (= finely distributed) in the water. After we have fed the animals in the tank with a food that contains a high amount of fat we can observe a considerable decrease or even a total cessation of the foam production for some time, even up to a few hours. But even fatty substances accumulate in the skimming device after some time. Thus it is of special importance that the pipe in which the foam is produced be cleaned regularly, if possible twice a week. Otherwise the fatty substances deposited on the walls will break the foam before it can rise to the collection cup.

Most of the protein substances accumulate in a thin layer on the surface of the aquarium water. Therefore the effect of a protein

Counter current skimming device with airstones; produced by Sander.

skimmer is greatest if surface water is siphoned off directly into the skimming device.

There are different types of excellent protein skimming devices on offer which work with different methods. Consult your dealer in this matter. The most common types of skimming devices are based on the countercurrent principle. The water flows into the skimmer at the top and leaves it at the bottom. The air injected into the skimmer at the bottom rises against the flow direction of the water. Thus the longest possible contact between water and air is guaranteed and the effect of the device optimized, as long as the pipe where the contact takes place is not less than 70 to 80 cm long (except for very small aquaria).

For a highly effective production of foam we need large amounts of fine air bubbles. Depending on the type of skimming device, the length of the contact column and the amount of pollutants in the aquarium it takes between 100 and 1000 litres of air per hour. Thus it is crucial that the air output be high enough. The only ways to regulate the foam production are to adjust the air output or to change the length of the lift pipe just below the collection container. The skimming device must be adjusted in such a way that only protein foam reaches the collecting container, but no normal foam. If the adsorbate in the container is too light-coloured and runs too thin, it contains too much water, which shows that normal foam is collected as well. Then the amount of air must be reduced or the length of the lift pipe increased. The air bubbles that are necessa-

The adsorbate of a well functioning protein skimmer should be thick and have the consistancy of paste.

skimmers. Our 850 litre stony coral test aquarium is set up with one having an inside diameter of 11 cm and a water column 125 cm high. This skimmer has for nearly 10 years operated this aquarium, with no other filtering equipment installed.

Another type of skimming device is the rotation skimmer (as produced by e. g. TUNZE). This type of skimmer has a very short contact pipe. The necessary contact between air and water is achieved by whirling a hard jet of water through a nozzle into the pipe. The water pressure needed for this is produced by a powerhead with an output of at least 1000 or 2000 litres per hour. At the same time air is drawn in by venturi effect, producing a fine mixture of air and water. One of the advantages of rotation skimmers is that they are rather compact. Thus it is easier to find a suitable place for them in the aquarium setup. Rotation skimmers may either be hung in the aquarium, attached to its side, or placed below it in the sump. Like all other skimmers they must be cleaned regularly.

ry can be produced in different ways:

- with an airpump and airstones (as in the protein skimmers produced by Sander),

- or a motor pump that draws in air and injects it via a venturi or through a dispergator into the skimmer.

The air stones in the first type of protein skimmer are either made of limewood or a ceramic material. Foam quality does not always seem to be the best with ceramic airstones. But regardless of the material used, airstones must be replaced quite often. As soon as we notice that the foam production decreases and the airstones are blocked they must be exchanged.

Other factors affecting the efficiency of the skimmer are the diameter and height of the tube where air and water mix, the flow rate, the bombardment rate (the number of times an ascending clean air bubble hits a descending drop of water), as well as the amount of fatty compounds found in the water that enters the skimmer. For a further discussion of this, see Es-COBAL (1995).

Personally we have had great success using counter current

To sum up we can say that the experience with a lot of marine aquaria shows that protein skimming leads to very good results. There is no doubt that it helps to stabilize water conditions and facilitates water maintenance. Protein skimming reduces the nutrient content of the water and

Left: rotation skimmer; produced by TUNZE. To the right: Tunze rotation skimmer mounted inside an aquarium.

This combination of gigantic skimmers (to the right) has been set up to run a 30.000 litre aquarium system (above), constructed and owned by K. Jansen, Germany. For this specific aquarium, with its high stocking density, the skimmers are correctly dimensioned and give excellent results. "The bigger – the better" is, however, not a rule to be generally applied in reef aquaristics.

brings its quality nearer to that of the water of a coral reef in the ocean. With a lower concentration of accumulated organic compounds, the same number of bacteria break down the nitrate into nitrogen gas more rapidly. Experience shows that in reef aquaria where skimming is used in combination with live rocks and sufficient water motion, the concentration of nitrate remains very low. This again makes it possible to control the growth of filamentous algae. To us this is the simple essence of the modern reef aquarium and a major part of the revolutionary thinking by aquarist pioneers in Europe during the late seventies and early eighties – which helped to make it possible to keep corals in captivity.

Today a large number of different types of skimmers are available on the market. The majority of these can be expected to perform excellently, provided the recommendations of the producer are followed. One point of concern which we would like to mention, however, is the frequently seen tendency among aquarists to select over-sized skimmers. Some aquarists, particularly in Europe, tend to think that "bigger is better" also applies to protein skimmers. This is certainly not true. Although we are convinced that an efficient protein skimmer is the very best filtering equipment for a coral reef aquarium, overdoing it has the potential for creating problems. Please do also remember that the well being of the inver-

tebrates and fish are more linked to knowledge and the wise use of selected technical equipment, than to the size of the skimmer or the amount of sophisticated tools.

Reverse osmosis

We have pointed out before in this volume that a coral reef is an eco-system which is not rich in nutrients and that the organisms living there are adapted to these conditions. We think that oligotrophic (i.e. not rich in nutrients) conditions are essential for the success with a coral reef aquarium. The most important means to provide this condition is effective protein skimming. Yet it is also important to replace evaporated water by "Kalkwasser" which contains little or no nutrients. As a consequence the freshwater that is used to produce the "Kalkwasser" should contain as little algae nutrients as possible. Nitrate, phosphate and silicate are the main nutrients that must be taken into consideration here. Which amounts of these and other substances are found in the tapwater available to you depends on the local conditions. Aquarists can take readings themselves or phone up their waterworks for them. If you draw water from your own well you should analyze the water yourself or have it analyzed.

We have again and again talked to aquarists who were at a loss to explain why their aquarium was permanently polluted with nitrate. Quite often the reason was simply that they used tapwater that contained nutrients. Other organic pollutants and inorganic ions and compounds may become a problem, too. Today acid rain is known in most parts of Europe. Acid precipitations make the pH of freshwater go down, often lower than pH 5. At such a low pH some metallic compounds may be dissolved in water, first of all aluminium. If this water is drawn from the tap, copper and zinc may be dissolved in it as well. All these metals are extremely toxic in a coral reef aquarium, even if their concentration is very low.

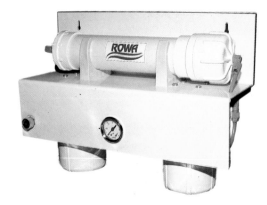

Reverse osmosis installations:
as produced by Rowa (above) and Wiegandt (below).

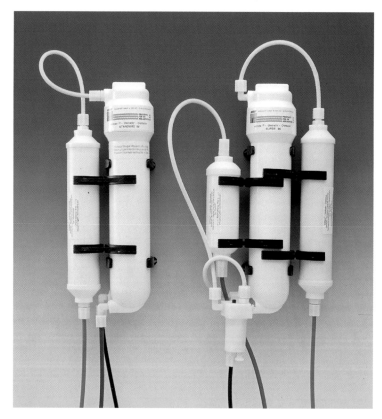

Reverse osmosis is a very good method to remove harmful compounds from the tapwater. In this process water is filtered through an ultrafine membrane at a pressure that is higher than the osmotic pressure. The membrane keeps back most of the organic and inorganic compounds disolved in the water, but allows the water molecules to pass. A reverse osmosis system thus removes (except for a very small amount that remains) all unwanted substances like nitrate, phosphate, silicate, aluminium, copper, etc., however, it also removes useful substances like calcium and carbonate. In areas where the water is highly polluted with nitrate, aquarists often have no other choice but to use a reverse osmosis unit.

There are a large number of different reverse osmosis systems for sale in the aquarium stores. These units work at a water pressure of 3 to 5 bar and may be connected directly to the water mains. The water first passes through a filter with activated carbon, which removes the chlorine, among other substances, and then through a mechanical filter, which eliminates larger particles, before it is then pressed through the membrane. There is a separate outlet for the waste water, which has a high mineral content but may still be used for other purposes (flush toilet, dish washer, etc.). The prefilter as well as the membrane must be exchanged at certain intervals depending on how dirty your tapwater is. We strongly recommend the use of reverse osmosis to clean the freshwater that is used for mixing saltwater and for making water used for refilling evaporated water, whether this is "Kalkwasser" or not. Frequently (at least in Europe) the freshwater quality is rather bad and it can contain, among other pollutants, high concentrations of nitrate and phosphate. We have also seen a few occasions where old water pipes and couplings made from copper, iron or brass have leached metals into the freshwater. Unless the freshwater is filtered over reverse osmosis, these metal compounds may in turn be accumulated in the aquarium.

This aquarium in Miami, Florida utilize highly effective protein skimming.

Ozonisation

Ozone (O_3) consists of three oxygen atoms. It is an unstable gas with a pungent odor which normally disintegrates quickly by reduction. Ozone is produced when oxygen is exposed to a high electric tension, e.g. in the ozone generators that are used for aquarium purposes. After a thunderstorm the smell of ozone may also be perceived in the air. Even in a dilution of 1:500 000 ozone may still be smelled (this is also important for its use in aquaristics).

Aquarists use ozone because it is a powerful oxidant. Ozone can crack organic molecules without producing harmful by-products as happens in bacterial decomposition. The effect that ozone has can be described like this:

We have to give a firm warning:

Ozone is extremely toxic, does harm to all live organisms, and must never be allowed to enter the aquarium.

The most common method of using ozone is to add it to the air that is used in the protein skimmer. The amount of it must be just right to make sure that all ozone molecules have disintegrated before the water flows back into the aquarium. We can check on this by smelling if any of the typical ozone odor can be perceived above the skimmer. This method is, however, not a very safe one.

To guarantee the production of ozone in the ozonizer, the air that passes through it must be absolutely dry. Special air drying devices are available for this. We have seen several coral reef aquaria on which ozonisers were installed. All of them were beautiful and healthy. Yet we have also seen coral reef aquaria without ozonisation which were just as beautiful and healthy. It seems doubtful to us if ozonisation really has such great advantages that they compensate for the great risks its application

$$\text{organic molecules} \xrightarrow{O_3} \text{ammonia} \xrightarrow[\text{bacteria}]{O_2} \text{nitrite} \xrightarrow{O_3} \text{nitrate}$$

(After De Graaf, 1988)

brings along. After all, we must keep in mind that ozone is toxic for humans as well (WENDLER, 1986).

UV sterilizers

UV sterilizers produce a radiation of the wavelength 253.7 nm, which is in the UV-C range (see chapter 8). UV-C radiation has a lethal effect on live tissue. UV sterilizers are mostly used to get rid of planktonic fish parasites. Bacteria and floating micro algae are killed as well. The UV sterilizer is an appliance in which the water passes by an encapsulated UV lamp. The speed of the water current and the intensity of the radiation of the UV lamp determine how great the sterilizing effect is. The temperature is another important influence. The UV sterilizer is most effective at a temperature of 40 °C.

The biological effects of UV ste-

UV sterilizer, produced by Wiegandt.

rilizers have not yet been totally investigated, so we recommend to use and apply them only with great care. They may perhaps really be of use to get rid of some especially troublesome fish parasites.

Water changes

For a long time many aquarists took the view that water changes at regular intervals were a must. Monthly water changes of about 10 % of the aquarium volume were regarded as normal. The attitude towards this question has generally changed and we have realized that it must be answered individually for every aquarium.

An aquarium with biological filtration will normally contain a higher amount of nutrients and will thus require water changes more frequently than an aquarium with a highly effective protein skimmer. How often the water must be changed and how much of it depends on the volume of the aquarium and its filtration system. If the animals in the aquarium do not look healthy this may also be a hint that a partial water change is needed.

During the break in period of a coral reef aquarium partial water changes should be made at regular intervals if there is an intensive algae growth. Only very small amounts of water have to be changed after the conditions have become more stable and the calcareous algae have started to grow, which at the same time keeps the unsightly slime algae and filamentous algae from growing. In our aquaria we exchange only about 10% of the water per year. Our experience shows that changing large amounts of water destabilizes the conditions in an aquarium and often stimulates unwanted algae in their growth. On the other hand, we have also experienced that a water change in the amount of 75%, in an old, well established

reef aquarium led to a drastic increase in the growth of the stony corals. This may be due to changes in the concentrations of trace elements, but it could possibly also have other causes. Obviously there are very few absolute truths in reef aquaristics. (See table 13, page 238 and compare column L1 and L2).

It is a matter-of-course that only good seawater prepared from high quality salt mixes may be used for water changes. It must be aerated thoroughly and given time to "mature".

Hydrodynamics and hydrotechnology

The water currents in a coral reef are powerful and very variable. We should always try to imitate these conditions in a coral reef aquarium, particularly if we keep sessile animals, which are not able to move around at will. Many coral animals are dependent on the water currents on the one hand in order to clean their body surface and on the other hand to get rid of their metabolic wastes. The water current also provides many of these animals with their food. Finally it also distributes heat and oxygen evenly throughout the aquarium.

There are several ways of providing water movement in a coral reef aquarium. Powerheads are especially useful in this regard. They are inconspicuous and, if placed in the right spot, they circulate the water very effectively. As a rule of thumb their total output per hour should be ten times the volume of the aquarium. If only fishes and less demanding invertebrates are kept, a lower output will do.

At least two powerheads should be installed independently of each other, so that the direction of the water current can be changed. Counter currents are produced most easily by a timer that switches the powerheads on and off

Waves, breakers and the tides produce strong water turbulence and variable currents. These circumstances should be re-created in a coral reef aquarium in order to provide optimum living conditions.

Photo above: Dr. D. Brockmann, photo below: E. Svensen

Powerhead, produced by Tunze.

alternately. On the coral reef currents often change in the morning and in the late afternoon. You should keep this in mind when you set the timer intervals.

"Wavemakers" with automatic interval systems are much more advanced devices. They produce counter currents much more effectively and their effect is much more satisfying aesthetically. Devices of this type are available from different companies. An automatic electronic pulsation system adjusts the performance of the powerheads connected to it. So for a short time the pumps may work at only 20% of their maximum performance only to change to full power the next moment (the percentage may be infinitely variable). This produces a pulsating water current which is similar to the movement of the waves on the coral reef. In addition to that the powerheads may be switched on and off at certain times during the day independently of each other.

For a long time nobody paid close attention to the movement of the water in a coral reef aquarium. Our experience shows quite clearly that a strong and variable water current has positive effects on many animals. If you want to reach the highest possible standards with your coral reef aquarium, you should spare no expenses or pains to make sure that there are enough and the right kind of water currents. As a general rule we recommend a water motion at least 10 times the aquarium volume per hour, but the type of aquarium and the shape of the decoration also play a part in this formula.

Combinations of filters

The purpose of all technical appliances for the coral reef aquarium is to provide all the organisms there with living conditions as close as possible to the natural environment. It is not easy at all to say which technology serves this purpose best. Throughout this chapter we have already described some types of filters and other appliances that are helpful in keeping the water of a coral reef aquarium clean and healthy. Some of them are extremely useful (e.g. protein skimmers), others less so (e.g. undergravel filters).

There are a number of examples that show that a coral reef aquarium without much technology, i.e. only with aeration and lighting, may also be a success. The most frequently discussed version of this is the so-called "Natural System", which was basically a creation of Lee Chin Eng of Indonesia. His ideas were widely published in many parts of the world in the sixties and seventies. For the single most thorough discussion of the system, see the book by RI-SELEY (1971).

The Natural System relies completely on the effect of the biological decomposition that takes place in the decoration material (live rock). In spite of all the success Eng achieved, there is no doubt that Natural System Aquaria are extremely delicate systems and that they make great demands on the aquarist's knowledge and time.

The original version of Jaubert's system (see page 256) may be regarded as a variation of Eng's Natural System.

Dutch aquarists were among the first to realize the importance

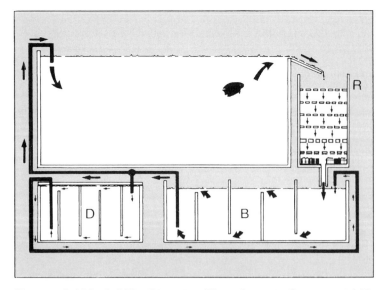

Diagram of a biological filtration system: The surface water flows over a trickle filter (R) into a biofilter below it. The majority of the water is pumped back into the aquarium, while a smaller part is conducted into a denitrification filter (D) from where it flows back into the biofilter.

of biological filtration. From this basic idea a system developed that is often called "mini-reef". We prefer the term "biological system". Biological filters must be cared for and cleaned quite often if the bacterial fauna is to develop somewhat constantly. If biological filtration is the only type of filtration used, it is worthwhile combining a trickle filter with a biological filter below it. Thus the oxygen content can be increased.

Normally biological filtration causes an increase in the nutrient concentration in the aquarium water. This is the reason why we can often see *Caulerpa* and other macro algae that need eutrophic (rich in nutrients) conditions to grow in abundance. Such a system may be very interesting for aquarists specializing in algae. Yet this is clearly not a coral reef environment. We therefore cannot recommend that a biological filter is used as the only nor the main filtering equipment for a coral reef aquarium populated with a moderately high number of corals, other invertebrates and fishes.

Most of the coral reef aquaria we have seen that were doing really well were more or less of the same type that we would like to call semi-biological system. The great majority of the aquaria pictured in this volume were set up according to these principles. The most important appliance for water maintenance here is the protein skimmer. If the aquarium decoration consists of porous material and live rocks, there is no need to combine this with a biofilter. The bacterial flora of live rocks is so diverse and numerous that these or-

Semi-biological filtration system: protein skimming and live rocks

ganisms can easily decompose the remaining substances that the skimmer is unable to remove. Normally there will be no accumulation of nitrate or phosphate, so we hardly ever got a reading of more than 1 – 2 mg/l in coral reef aquaria where these principles are applied. We cannot emphasize enough the importance of live rocks. We deal with them in more detail in chapter 7 of this book. The use of sufficient water motion (at least 10 times the aquarium volume per hour) also seems to be beneficial for the well being of the system.

Of course a protein skimmer can be combined with filters, preferably with mechanical filters. During the break in period of a coral reef aquarium a mechanical filter will virtually always be necessary. Biological filters may also be used, but they do not have any advantage over the others. If other

materials are used for decoration instead of live rock, it may be helpful to set up a denitrification filter. This holds true at least if the aquarium water is highly polluted by a great number of fish or by large fish. The most crucial advantage of protein skimming lies in the fact that proteins are removed before their decomposition starts. Thus the activity of the bacteria is reduced. The nutrient content in the water decreases, a condition similar to the natural conditions in the reef. It is of utmost importance to keep the collecting compartment of the skimmer clean to guarantee perfect function. If this is neglected, algae will soon start to grow abundantly. Many invertebrates do not like this at all. You should make a habit of cleaning the protein skimmer twice a week.

Last, but certainly not least, perhaps the most important thing is

630-litre-aquarium by D. Stüber – two counter current skimming devices; water circulation with seven powerheads (1000 l/h each); regular addition of "Kalkwasser"; no biological filtration; no activated carbon filtration; lighting system 3x250 W HQI/TS-D (photo from 1985).

This experimental aquarium setup contains corals of the families Acroporidae, Pocilloporidae and Favidae, which were collected in the Pacific.

patience. Fully stocking your tank with fish and corals during the span of the first few months will rarely lead to success. Allow a full year for the aquarium to settle down while the skimmer is running, with the stable maintenance of calcium ion concentration and buffer capacity, with the proper light running and with the complete decoration of live rocks surrounded by heavy water motion. Then, as you slowly and carefully add corals, other invertebrates and fishes, you will eventually see a small reef evolving.

The experiences we have conveyed here to the reader are only our own, individual experiences. Every aquarist will develop his own attitudes and that is all right; everyone must go through his own experiences and must find his own solutions. The ideas we have presented here are only supposed to support that.

None should expect spectacular successes right from the start. It may take one or two years until a coral reef aquarium works as perfectly as we want it to. Some are successful at once, others never really succeed. The secret behind the success is patience, patience and once again patience. Looking back 20 years to the time when we started with marine aquaristics we can say that there have been positive developments in our hobby throughout all of this time. Results that can be achieved easily today seemed to be unrealistic 15 years ago. Let us all hope that this positive development of reef aquaristics will continue.

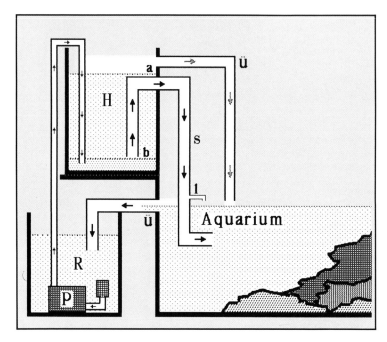

Bruce A. Carlson, director of the Waikiki Aquarium in Honolulu, Hawaii presents an especially interesting way of producing heavy currents in an aquarium. For his outdoor experimental aquarium setup with stony corals he developed a device which pumps about 150 litres of water through the aquarium every five minutes. This installation is a closed water circulation and can easily be adapted to an aquarium setup at home.

It works like this:
Water is pumped from a reservoir container R into a container H, which is set up in an elevated position. When level a is reached, the water will automatically flow into the aquarium by the pipe S according to the principle of communicating pipes. When the water level in the container H has fallen and reaches level b, the pipe S sucks in air and the water flow is stopped until level a is reached again in container H. Of course, the output of the pump must be adjusted so that while the water is flowing into the aquarium less water is pumped into the container H than is necessary to reach level b. Moreover it is very important that there is an opening l in the pipe S, through which air can escape from pipe S when the water reaches level a in the container H. Otherwise the air in pipe S will block the flow of the water and the installation will not work. The surplus water in the aquarium after the water has siphoned over from container H is conducted into the reservoir container R by an overflow pipe. From there the water is pumped into the container H, which also has an overflow pipe s, which is necessary in case pipe s is blocked.

Further reading

ACHTERKAMP, 1986; ADEY, 1983; BIRKHOLZ, 1982; DE-
BELIUS, 1982; DE GRAAF, 1988; DOBLER, 1990; HEINZ,
1990; KAL, 1982; NILSEN 1990a, 1990b, 1991a,
1991b, 1993, 1994 and 1995; REYNEN, 1984; RIET-
BERG, 1982; RISELEY, 1971; SABATKE, 1985; SCHMIDT,
1984; SCHOMISCH, 1989; STÜBER, 1987 and 1989;
SUK, 1989

Life processes in the sea are incredibly dynamic. The wreck of the Japanese supply vessel Rio de Janeiro Maru, which sank in World War II, serves as a substrate on which animals settle at a depth of 29 metres. A stony coral of the genus *Symphyllia* with large polyps (above) and the Bubble Coral *Plerogyra sinuosa* thrive on a vertical wall of the ship.

Underwater photos: Dr. D. Brockmann

Chapter 13:

Algae

Algae are an extremely diverse group of plants. With the exception of the prokaryotic blue-green algae they are the main group of the phycobionta (prokaryotes are organisms whose cells do not have a nucleus separated from the rest of the cell by a membrane). Algae live in a wet milieu, most of them completely submerged in the water. Altogether there are more than 19,000 species of algae, 8,500 of them marine. In the oceans algae account for more than 93% of the plant life. They clearly dominate the marine fauna. On dry land they are a minority, however. The most primitive algae still existing, blue-green algae, (cyanophyta), were already in existence more than 1.5 billion years ago, in the Precambrian. Blue-green algae belong to the prokaryotes and are closely related to bacteria. The most primitive algae of primeval times were those from which the higher terrestrial plants originated.

Algae, like higher plants, have the ability to photosynthesize, i.e.

Above: The reef aquarium can develop a magnificent diversity of algae like here on this small area only some 6 x 8 cm. However, great care must be taken to prevent the aquarium from becoming overgrown by filamentous algae.

Left: Aquarists are not the only ones who have to cope with uncontrolled growth of algae. Here a small sponge crab appears to be carrying a heavy load, a ball of *Caulerpa* sp. used for camentage (Kölle Zoo, Stuttgart, Germany).

The most important primary producers in the coral reef are the small turf algae, which in shallow waters even grow on the underside of rocks because of the high light intensity. Patches of turf algae are made up of many different species of algae. A number of them also occur in the coral reef aquarium.

they can produce organic glucose compounds or carbohydrates from the inorganic compounds water and carbon dioxide. The concentration of free carbon dioxide in sea water at a pH of 8.2 is only 0.6 % of the total amount of carbon (C). About 90 % is present as hydrogen carbonate (HCO_2^-) and about 9.4 % as carbonate (CO_3^{2-}). Many algae, among them calcareous algae and symbiotic zooxanthellae, are therefore able to use hydrogen carbonate as their source of CO_2 in photosynthesis. With the help of a number of enzymes, e.g. Ribulosebiphosphat-Carboxylase and Carbonatdehydratase, hydrogen carbona-

te is cracked into carbon dioxide and water. CO_2 is needed for photosynthesis. It is also worth mentioning that some marine algae are **not** able to use hydrogen carbonate as their source of CO_2; they are only able to make use of free CO_2.

Like all plants algae need nutrients, most of all nitrogen and phosphorus. This is of great importance in the aquarium, because many algae accumulate (store) the nutrients in their cells in concentrations which are considerably higher than the concentrations in the surrounding water. This is especially true for algae with a strong thallus (plant body without

roots), e.g. the leaf-like brown and red algae. Therefore the algae growth in a coral reef aquarium can turn into a "nutrient bomb" in case the algae die or release their nutrients for any other reason. This may have catastrophic consequences. We therefore recommend to **limit** the growth of the leaf-like algae in a coral reef aquarium. Nevertheless a coral reef aquarium will always accommodate a great diversity of most interesting algae, which is one reason why they are always a subject of discussion among reef aquarists. With the exception of calcareous algae, an excessive amount of algae indicates that the concentration of nutrients in the aquarium water is too high.

The importance of algae for the ecology of the reef has been underestimated for a long time. Corals and other animals attracted the attention of scientists more than the algae did. Algae seemed to be less numerous, which made them seem to be less important. Today we know that this idea was wrong. Recent research has shown that the ecology of a coral reef is considerably influenced by a multitude of algae, whose productivity may be compared to that of the plants of the tropical rain forest. Algae are a vital component of a coral reef: it cannot exist without them.

Among the most unpopular algae in the coral reef aquarium are green algae (*Ostreobium* spp.) that grow inside the skeleton of stony corals. They can make the skeleton soft very quickly and destroy it, so that the coral dies. Here a colony of *Euphyllia ancora* is heavily "infected" with such green algae. These algae are, however, a natural component of the coral reef.

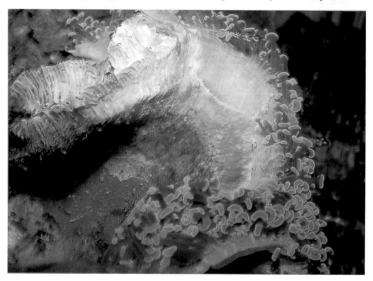

Algae in a coral reef are not as conspicuous as the large algae and seaweed beds of our coastal waters. We do not observe the enormous seasonal increase in the growth of planktonic algae as can appear in colder ocean areas. The algae of a coral reef often grow on the bases of the corals and between them. Most of these algae are short since herbivorous animals graze on them heavily. Because of the similarity of their appearance to a lawn they are called "turf algae". There are many different genera and species that often grow together to form an interwoven bed of turf algae.

There are also higher algae, e.g. large red or green algae, many of which accumulate calcium carbonate. Calcareous algae have an important function in the formation of sediments, as they are the main reason for the enormous production of coral sand in the reef. Thus they reinforce the eroded corals and contribute directly to the building of the reef. In some reefs which are exposed to heavy erosion calcareous algae are of greater importance for reef building than the corals themselves. Moreover algae play an essential part in the ecosystem of a coral reef by chemically fixing nitrogen, thereby importing into the system this important nutrient which is in short supply in the sea water.

Around 1930 scientists found out that corals live in a symbiotic relationship with unicellular algae – a discovery that revolutionized biological theories about the coral reef. These symbiotic algae, called zooxanthellae, hold a key position in the ecology of the coral reef. They are responsible for the fact that corals dominate in the shallower areas of tropical seas. Even though zooxanthellae were discovered more than 60 years ago, a lot still remains to be revealed about their biology and their ecological function. But not only corals may have a symbiotic relationship with algae. This special kind of association has also been proved to exist in many sponges, some bivalves and a few annelids.

In one group of ascidians we even find a special type of algae not related to any other kind of algae anywhere in nature.

Structure and reproduction

As algae, unlike higher plants, do not have clearly defined parts, they cannot be described in terms of morphology, i.e. their outward appearance, and are difficult to describe in general. Algae have

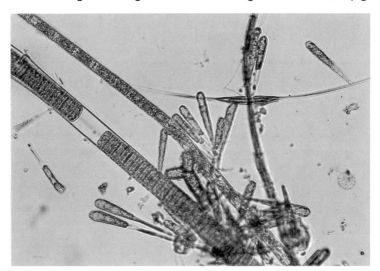

A sample of algae scraped off an aquarium glass viewed under the microscope: blue green algae, *Lyngbya* sp. (the thickest thread), green algae, *Derbesia* sp. (the two thinner threads) and two diatomeans, one of which leads an epiphytic life on other algae, whereas the other is non-sessile (magnification 560x).

neither roots nor stems nor leaves.

Algae reproduce sexually or asexually. Asexual reproduction takes place by cell division. Under favourable conditions unicellular algae may have an extraordinarily high rate of reproduction, with cell division taking place at an enormously fast rate. More complex algae often reproduce by fragmentation, i.e. one fragment of the alga comes off and adheres to a substrate, where it grows into a new plant. Many algae also produce spores asexually.

The reproduction by spores is part of a complex life cycle which also includes sexual reproduction. As any kind of sexual repro-

duction requires a reduction of the number of chromosomes to one half (meiosis), such a life cycle implies that the number of chromosomes in the algae cells is different at different stages of the cycle. In some cases the reduction of the chromosomes to one half takes place in sexual cells. In other cases the algae may have a reduced set of chromosomes for most of their lifetime. We find very complicated life cycles with the red algae, Rhodophyta, and the brown algae, Phaeophyta. Most algae are unicellular at some stage of their life and are then equipped with one or several flagella, which give them the ability to move about. All algae contain various pigments which absorb light of different wavelengths (see table 14, page 274).

The environmental conditions in a coral reef aquarium have a strong influence on the growth of the algae. If a marine aquarist strives for algae growth in his aquarium that comes close to that of a reef, i.e. if he wants calcareous al-

Table 14. Biochemical characteristics of algae.

After WILSON (1978)

group of algae	main pigment	reserve substances	cell wall substances
Cyanophyta (blue-green algae)	chlorophyll a ß-carotene phycobiline	cyanophyte starch	cellulose, pectins, Murein, amino acids, fatty acids, polysaccharides
Dinophyta (dinoflagellates)	chlorophyll a,c ß-carotene	starch, fat, oils	cellulose, pectin compounds
Bacillariophyceae (diatoms)	chlorophyll a,c ß-carotene Fucoxanthin	Chrysolaminarin, oils	cellulose, pectin compounds, silicate
Phaeophyceae (brown algae)	chlorophyll a,c ß-carotene Fucoxanthin	Chrysolaminarin, oils, Mannitol	cellulose, pectin compounds, alginous acids, calcium carbonate
Rhodophyta (red algae)	chlorophyll a,d? ß-carotene phycobiline	starch	cellulose, pectin compounds, mucus, calcium carbonate
Chlorophyta (green algae)	chlorophyll a,b ß-carotene	starch	cellulose, pectin compounds, calcium carbonate in some species

gae, turf algae and zooxanthellae to grow, he must take into account the natural conditions in a coral reef. That is why it matters a lot what kind of technology a coral reef aquarium will be equipped with. The concentration of nutrients, CO_2, O_2, light and the amount of detritus are only a few of the factors that influence the growth of the algae. Moreover we must always be aware of the fact that algae emit growth-inhibiting compounds into the aquarium water. These compounds may have an effect on the growth of other algae, e.g. zooxanthellae, and may impair the quality of the water.

Algae are a subject of extreme interest for the reef aquarist, in spite of the fact that they are mostly regarded as a nuisance. To get rid of unwanted algae may be next to impossible and is one of the greatest difficulties a reef aquarist may face. Fortunately not all algae in a coral reef aquarium are pests. Many of them are vital components of the life there as well and many even add to the decorative effect.

Taxonomy and nomenclature

The nomenclature of the kingdom of plants is somewhat different from that of the animal kingdom. This also applies to the nomenclature of algae. Even though a lot has been changed since then, "Species Plantarum", the book by the Swedish natural scientist Carl von Linné, which was first published in 1753, is still the fundamental work of botanical nomenclature. A scientific name has to be treated according to the rules of the Latin language, even if it is not of Latin origin (words from all languages and even neologisms may be used). Plants – just like the animals – are divided up into taxonomic categories. The following categories are of importance for us:

division – phylum
class – classis
order – ordo
family – familia
genus – genus
species – species

Certain suffixes refer to the respective categories, e.g. the names of divisions have the suffix ...phyta, classes have ...phycae, orders ...ales, families ...aceae (these suffixes are different in the animal kingdom). In this chapter we will deal with the following divisions and classes:

Division Cyanophyta
    Class Cyanophyceae –
                blue-green algae

Division Rhodophyta
    Class Rhodophyceae –
                red algae

Division Heterokontophyta
    Class Bacillariophyceae –
                diatoms

Class Phaeophyceae –
                brown algae

Division Dinophyta
    Class Dinophyceae –
        dinoflagellates

Division Chlorophyta
    Class Chlorophyceae –
        green algae

If we use live rocks as decoration material many algae will grow on them automatically. The most primitive algae, the blue-green algae of the division Cyanophyta are not at all the first to colonize a newly set up coral reef aquarium. We will therefore not deal with the algae in their systematic sequence as shown above. We will present them in the same sequence in which they usually appear in an aquarium.

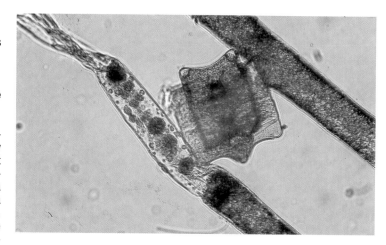

Diatoms are immobile, unicellular algae. In the coral reef aquarium we find the box-shaped species of the genus *Odontella*(?) among other algae (magnification 560x).

Division Heterokontophyta

Class Bacillariophycaea
Diatoms

We know about 6000 species of diatoms, of which about half are marine. AMIR 1982 gives a good survey, which is easily comprehensible. The first algae that appear in a coral reef aquarium are diatoms. They usually show within a few days after the aquarium is put into operation. As these unicellular algae deposit silicic acid in their cell walls, they are also called diatoms. Silicon (Si) can be found in sea water as silicic acid $(H_2SiO_3)_n)$. Silicate is also found in the soil and is dissolved in the ground water, which is why tap water may contain a varying amount of silicate, depending on the quality of the ground water. In a coral reef aquarium the amount of silicates available determines how many diatoms will appear and for how long they will thrive.

Diatoms in the aquarium are not exactly a pretty sight, but they look different if viewed through a microscope (see above). If the silica-

te content of the aquarium water is high, the materials in the aquarium may soon be covered with a thick, chocolate-coloured coating. When their cells divide, diatoms consume silicate, and their colony grows. But if we avoid the addition of new silicate when we add "Kalkwasser" to replace evaporated water, the growth of diatoms will soon stand still and they will finally disappear completely.

The normal period for the appearance of diatoms in a newly set up coral reef aquarium is during the first two to four weeks (also see the diagram on page 164). If at any later time diatoms appear again in larger amounts, this shows that the silicate content of the water has increased for some reason. Also a sudden change in the aquarium conditions, e. g. of the light quality or high organic

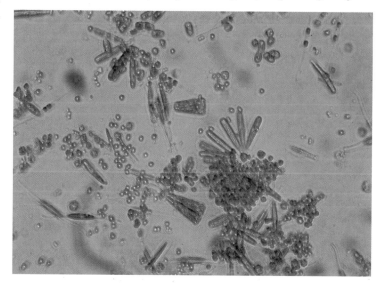

The aquarium glass always turns lightly brown because of algae growth. If you look at this collected algae sample through a microscope, you will discover the "wonderful world" of diatoms and non-sessile dinoflagellates (small, round cells). This picture (magnification 560x) shows a triangular *Licmophora* sp. and two other species of diatoms.

pollution of the aquarium water might cause the diatoms to grow again, as there is always a certain amount of silicate present in an aquarium. If a persistent growth of diatoms keeps reappearing in the aquarium, however, distilled water or water treated in a reverse osmosis unit should be used as source water for the "Kalkwasser".

Diatoms can reproduce asexually at an enormously high speed. If an aquarium is infested with diatoms it is possible to clean it completely in the morning and to find everything in it covered again with diatoms in the evening. Diatoms usually consist of an upper and a bottom shell that fit together like the lid and the bottom of a box (see the drawing to the right). When these algae reproduce asexually the original cell splits lengthwise parallel to the two shells. The resulting two halves become the lids of the new daughter cells, the bottom half has to be re-produced. Thus one half of the individuals is reduced in size from generation to generation. When these cells have been reduced to 30 to 40% of their maximum size, they start reproducing sexually, producing a new generation with maximum size.

In an aquarium that is grown over with diatoms a large amount of waste substances resulting from the metabolism of the algae and the decomposition of dead algae is emitted into the water. The algae are rich in nutrients and vitamins, e.g. vitamins A and B_{12}. Sometimes when nutrients are released a foul smell may be perceived. A protein skimmer removes large amounts of liquid fat and of the polysaccharide Leucosin. In this situation it wll also be helpful to filter the aquarium water over activated carbon. In case of sudden algal blooms in heavily populated aquaria this will even be a necessity. Increasing the redox potential by applying ozone may also contribute to a limitation of the growth of diatoms.

Under normal circumstances diatoms will only be a problem in a coral reef aquarium in the first weeks of the break in period. They will disappear as soon as the sili-

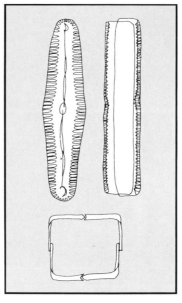

An example of a diatom: the drawing shows the alga as seen from above (left), from the side (right) and in a sectional view (bottom), illustrating the typical structure of a diatom, which consists of two parts fitting to each other like a box and its lid.
(Drawing after Hoek, 1978)

cate has been consumed. Therefore it makes no sense to try to avoid this first growth of these algae. However, one should never introduce animals into an aquarium that is infested with diatoms. Later on after their growth has declined if you look for diatoms you will always find a certain amount of them in a coral reef aquarium, e.g. diatoms that grow epiphytically on filamentous algae. Usually these do not cause any problems, however.

Division Cyanophyta

Blue-green algae

When the diatoms have disappeared, they are usually followed by the first blue-green algae. Despite their name, these are not always blue or green. From an evolutionary point of view, blue-green al-

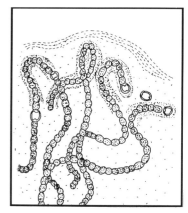

In the blue-green alga *Nostoc* sp. the cells make up long chains which are wrapped in a layer of mucus. The larger cells with thicker walls are called heterocysts.
(Drawing after Hoek, 1978)

gae are a very old group. From a systematic point of view blue-green algae and bacteria together make up the prokaryotes. This is why many scientists regard the blue-green algae as belonging to the bacteria and call them cyanobacteria.

Blue-green algae can be found all over the world, in marine as well as in freshwater. Many species are able to take in free nitrogen dissolved into the water from air. This absorption of nitrogen takes place in specialised cells called heterocysts (see drawing above). Research shows that this special nitrogen fixing is of great importance in the coral reef. The small blue-green alga *Calothrix crustacea*, which is one of the turf-algae, has a key role in this. It can fix nitrogen very quickly as ammonium and uses it as food. As these algae do not live very long and as fish and other animals feed on them heavily, the nitrogen is soon introduced into the life-cycle of the ecosystem (Borowitzka & Larku, 1986).

On the reef plateau of Green Island in the Great Barrier Reef, which is nearly drained at low tide, we found a blue-green alga that probably belongs to the species *Schizothrix calcicola*, which can be found worldwide. It grew together with the marine seagrass

Thalassia sp. (Hydrocharitaceae). This blue-green alga has been proven to be of great importance for the absorption of nitrogen in the reef. In places with considerably varying temperatures and salt content the blue-green alga *Lyngbya aestuarii* can be found.

Another group of blue-green algae lives in symbiosis with sponges and is the reason why many of these are brightly coloured. Due to photosynthesis these algae probably produce nutrients for the sponge cells. At the same time the pigments of the algae protect the sponge by eliminating UV-radiation. These symbiotic blue-green algae – not to be confused with the zooxanthellae – are able to photosynthesize at a relatively low light intensity. This is also the reason why the greatest diversity of sponges is to be found at depths between 10 and 25 m. Yet there are also sponges with symbiotic blue-green algae that can exist at a very high light intensity. These are capable of living in the shallow areas of the reef.

Some species of blue-green algae grow as parasites in the calcium carbonate skeleton of stony corals. A very special example of these is *Phormidium corallyticum*, which makes a black band appear on the coral off which it lives, thus causing what is called the "black-band-disease". This phenomenon occurs quite often in corals in shallow water, especially *Montastrea annularis* and *Diploria strigosa*. On these two species of corals algae can spread at a speed of more than 3 mm per day and it may destroy up to 14 cm² of coral tissue in a single day (RUETZLER & SANTARY, 1983).

Blue-green algae often form long cell chains which result in jelly-like, intensely coloured layers that cover everything in the aquarium. There are, in addition, some smaller, unicellular species. Some species are able to perform a gliding kind of movement. Yet there are no blue-green algae that have flagella. For some genera threads that look like corkscrew curls are typical, while the genera *Oscillatoria*, *Lyngbya* and *Microleus*

Blue-green algae of the genus *Schizothrix* are often found on reef flats that fall dry at low tide, and in shallow reef lagoons where they have an important function because of their ability to accumulate nitrogen.

In the tissue cells of many sponges symbiotic blue-green algae can be found. They give these animals their wonderful colours and enable them to survive with sunlight. Here in the coral reef aquarium of J. Sprung, Miami, this magnificent sponge thrives together with various turf algae in front.

Left: A typical "clean water type" of blue-green algae. It nearly always appears during the break in period, yet it disappears before long. The slimy masses of algae are full of oxygen bubbles. The oxygen is produced by the algae. Right: Red slime algae of this type, called "the red pest" can appear very suddenly. They are very difficult to remove.

grow in thicker threads.

Blue-green algae reproduce asexually by cell division which can take place very quickly. Small fragments that tear off may grow into large mats within a short time. If conditions become unfavourable, blue-green algae can produce permanent spores which are able to endure extreme living conditions, e.g. very high temperatures or a very low salt content.

For aquaristic purposes it has turned out to be practical to subdivide the blue-green algae into two groups: "the clean water" forms and the slime algae. The "clean water" forms usually appear after the diatoms have vanished. These forms are bright green, brown or red. Their photosynthetic activity,

which shows when oxygen bubbles appear on the algae filaments, is very high. They always disappear after a short time.

The slime algae are the more disagreeable type of blue-green algae by far. They show as a bluish-black or bright red layer that can appear all of a sudden and without any apparent reason in aquaria that have been set up quite a long time. Aquarists call this phenomenon the "red pest". Very often it all starts with a seemingly harmless small spot of black or red colour on the bottom of the aquarium. They remain like that and do not start growing until later so that they usually go unnoticed. But very suddenly, within a few days they grow explosively and the

whole aquarium decoration is covered with an ugly, slimy coating. These algae emit substances which very effectively impede the growth of other algae or even kill them. Moreover they are very harmful for many other inhabitants of the aquarium.

It is really very difficult to get rid of these slime algae. We can try to remove them mechanically, i.e. by brushing and then siphoning them off. Yet the aquarium decoration will soon be covered by them again. If removing them mechanically is supposed to make any sense at all we have to start out on it as soon as the slightest trace of these algae appears. Once they have spread in the aquarium, it is mostly too late. Obviously

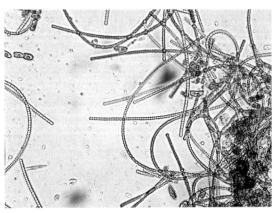
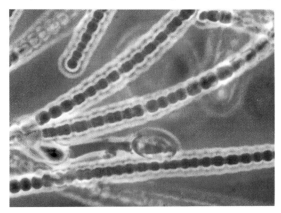

If you look through a microscope at red slime algae as seen in the picture above on the right, thin algae filaments can be seen kept together by a layer of mucus (magnification, left: 450x; right: 2200x). This may may be an *Oscillatoria* sp.

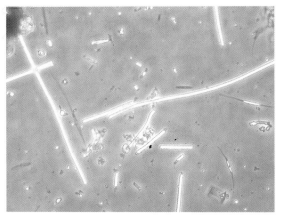
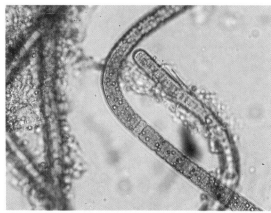

Left: These blue-green algae that look like corkscrew curls are very dark and grow erect in lumps in the coral reef aquarium. They have a very special structure, yet at the moment it is not exactly known to which genus they belong (magnification 450x). Right: This blue-green alga, which is very similar to *Oscillatoria* ssp. was found on the trunk of a *Sarcophyton* soft coral. The form that grew there was dark blue (magnification 880x).

there is no safe therapeutic method to fight slime algae without doing harm to other organisms at the same time. Adding antibiotics to the aquarium, e.g. Tetracycline or Erythromycin, will kill the algae, but also kills many useful bacteria, including the important denitrifying bacteria. As a matter of principle any sort of medication should be avoided in the coral reef aquarium. The effects it might have are completely unpredictable and often completely different from what was expected, even if no obvious damage seems to have been done.

Slime algae seem to appear most easily in unstable aquaria or in tanks that were subjected to sudden changes of the milieu, e.g. when a larger number of animals is introduced within a short period of time, or when the quality or the quantity of light changes considerably. If yellow and red wavelengths are predominant in the aquarium lighting this may support the growth of slime algae, a high share of blue light and UV-A radiation will have a prophylactic effect. A number of observations suggest that stable aerobic conditions with a sufficient supply of oxygen impede the growth of slime algae to a certain degree. This

has, however, not yet been proven. We think that problems with slime algae are usually due to the accumulation of nutrients and biological imbalance.

We have observed repeatedly that the amount of algae generally rises with the increase of the nutrient content, e.g. after a period of ample feeding or if the protein skimmer has not been cleaned sufficiently. This is an absolutely normal reaction which should not surprise anyone. A sudden great increase of red slime algae is mainly due to a change for the worse in the milieu of the aquarium. The accumulation of nutrients

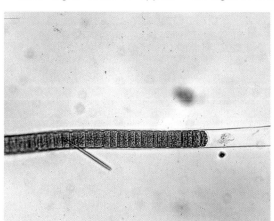
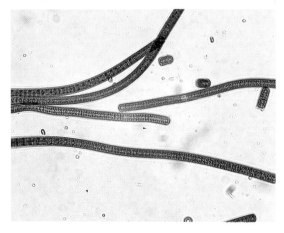

Left: In the coral reef aquarium these blue-green algae, probably from the genus *Lyngbya* may cover live rocks with thick, dark blue or nearly black layers (magnification 450x). Right: This species was found in an aquarium that had been set up a long time. It grew there in blue-black patches (magnification 450x).

in the aquarium water results in the availability of nutrients for all algae. It also influences the bacterial flora in the aquarium system. Red slime algae are closely related to the bacteria (see previous pages). It is possible that a change of the normal bacterial flora may result in an intensive growth of red slime algae.

Our experience shows that in a coral reef aquarium with live rocks there are less problems by far than in an aquarium with "dead" materials as decoration. The rea-son may be that the great diversity of microflora and fauna on and in the live rocks competes with the slime algae and deprives them of what they need for their growth. It has been shown that slime algae can grow even at a redox potential of far more than 400 mV, a potential which indicates highly aerobic conditions which can be reached by ozonisation. On the other hand there have also been some reports that an increase of the redox potential stopped the algae growth (perhaps it is just the sud-den change that triggers this effect). It may be some consolation for us to know that the slime algae can also disappear by themselves as suddenly as they appeared. If a coral reef aquarium is tended carefully, if the aquarist is thoughtful and scrupulous, and if he is lucky enough, he may even be spared confrontation with the "red pest". The literature list at the end of this chapter includes a number of reports that deal at length with he problem of slime algae.

The main genera of algae and their habitats on "One Tree Reef" of the Great Barrier Reef.
(After BOROWITZKA & LARKUM, 1986)

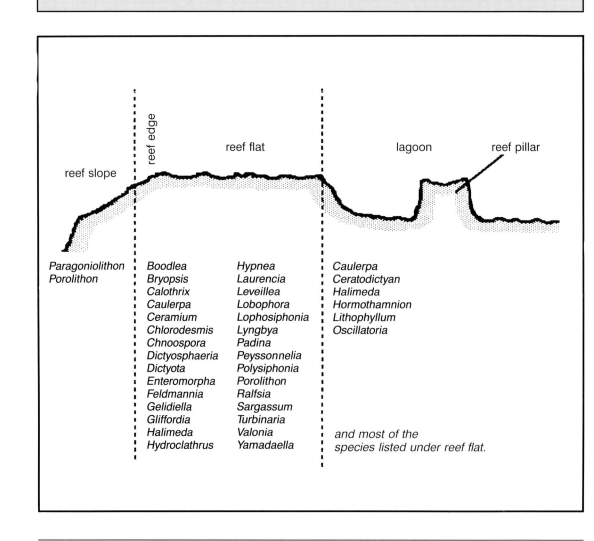

| reef slope | reef edge | reef flat | lagoon | reef pillar |

Paragoniolithon	Boodlea	Hypnea	Caulerpa
Porolithon	Bryopsis	Laurencia	Ceratodictyan
	Calothrix	Leveillea	Halimeda
	Caulerpa	Lobophora	Hormothamnion
	Ceramium	Lophosiphonia	Lithophyllum
	Chlorodesmis	Lyngbya	Oscillatoria
	Chnoospora	Padina	
	Dictyosphaeria	Peyssonnelia	
	Dictyota	Polysiphonia	
	Enteromorpha	Porolithon	
	Feldmannia	Ralfsia	
	Gelidiella	Sargassum	
	Gliffordia	Turbinaria	
	Halimeda	Valonia	and most of the
	Hydroclathrus	Yamadaella	species listed under reef flat.

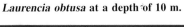

Algae off Bonaire, Caribbean Sea.
Photos: O. Gremblewski-Strate

Padina sanctaecrucis in the spray water zone.

Laurencia obtusa at a depth of 10 m.

Dictyota mertensii at a depth of 10 m.

Stypopodium zonale at a depth of 15 m.

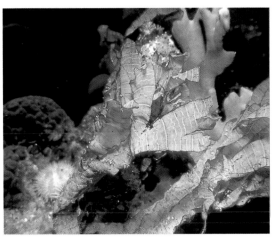

Turbinaria turbinata in shallow water.

Lobophora variagata at a depth of 30 m.

Green algae are the largest and the most varied group of algae, containing about 450 known genera with about 7000 species, of which around 900 are marine. There are unicellular, filamentous and very large upright species. Some species develop forms with flagella, others do not have them. Many green algae have rather complicated life cycles which may include two or more different-looking generations. The drawing and the photos to the right show how zoospores with flagella are produced and discharged by *Derbesia*.

❶ Order Ulotrichales

In this order there are three genera that most commonly appear in a coral reef aquarium if it is decorated with live rock. They do not stay for too long, however, except when the coral reef aquarium keeps on containing more nutrients than would be desirable.

The thallus of algae of the genus *Ulva* is leaf-shaped and not thicker than two layers of cells. *Ulva* spp. thrive at a high light intensity and seem to appear preferably after other green algae have vanished. They are decorative and can grow into magnificent colonies under favourable conditions (high light intensity). As they can be thinned out easily, they do not threaten to overgrow the invertebrates.

Ulva lactuca, the sea lettuce, which can be found worldwide, usually grows in areas of the coral reef which have a relatively high nutrient content, e. g. in coastal areas or in those which are drained nearly completely at low tide. These are also reef areas where herbivorous animals are hardly ever found. The sea lettuce has a

The figure below shows the life cycle of the filamentous alga *Derbesia marina* (after HOEK, 1978):

At the bottom is a sporophyte with algae filaments (A) and a sporangium (B). In the sporangium the reduction division (meiosis, in which the chromosomes are divided in half) takes place and and male and female zoospores are released (C and D). They grow and become gametophytes (E and F). The gametophytes develop male and female gametes (germ cells G and H), which unite to form a zygote (I), a stage at which the chromosome number is doubled again. The zygote now develops into a sporophyte and the life cycle starts all over again (see also page 287).

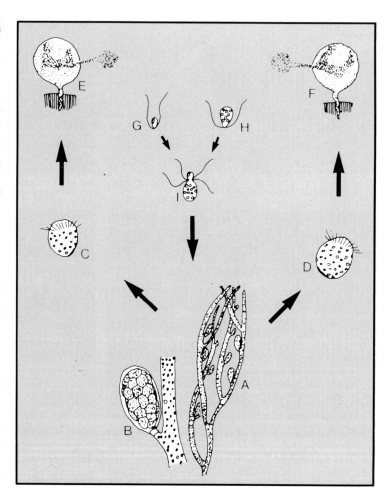

The series of pictures on page 283 (magnification 350x) reveals how the zoospores leave the sporangium:

Picture at the top: three sporangia have developed on a sporophyte. The sporangium in the middle is not yet mature, while the one on the left is nearly so and the one on the right is completely mature. In this last one the cell wall has already been lifted off the spores. The picture below shows the moment when the sporangium bursts. Within a few seconds – next picture – the zoospores spread out, and the sporangium has completely broken up. The zoospores float in the water until they reach a place where they can settle and develop into a gametophyte. Occasionally these gametophytes, which look like small, bright clubs, can be found on live rock – picture at the bottom (magnification 20x).

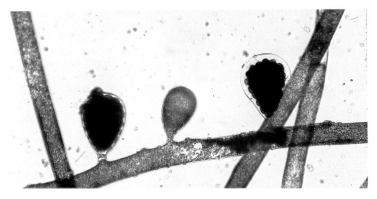

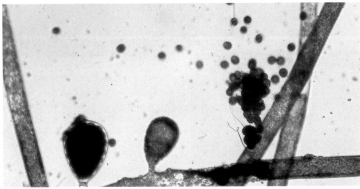

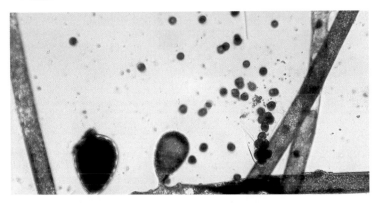

complicated but rather interesting life cycle, as it alternates from a haploid generation of gametophytes to a diploid generation of sporophytes.

While the thalli of *Ulva lactuca* are oval or nearly round, *Ulva fasciata* has leaf-shaped, long and narrow thalli with curly rims. This species can be found quite often at a depth of up to 10 m in tropical waters off coasts which have a high nutrient content.

Ulvaria oxysperma has a thallus consisting of only one layer of cells and is therefore placed in a separare genus. Because of the characteristics of its thallus, this alga is nearly transparent and it only shows the slightest hint of green colour.

The genus *Enteromorpha* is closely related to the genus *Ulvaria*, yet it cannot be mistaken for this or any other species of green algae. Our experience shows that the thalli, which are bright green, hose-shaped (Enteron, gr. = bowels) and folded, grow very well on live rock in a newly set-up aquarium. Usually they disappear a short time after they have appeared. Nevertheless they look very beautiful and impressive during their period of growth. In an aquarium with biological filtration and with little or no protein skimming *Enteromorpha* may develop into bushy turfs that last for long.

Algae of the genus *Enteromorpha* are typically cosmopolitan. They are found in shallow reef zones and very often in estuarine areas, where they grow epiphytically on other algae. *Enteromorpha clathrata* is a very common tropical species.

❷ Order Dasycladales

The order Dasycladales includes ten genera which are all found on tropical coasts. In a coral reef aquarium the tender and beautifully shaped species of the genera *Polyphysa* and *Acetabularia* are most conspicuous.

Polyphysa are small algae of not more than 1 cm height with a little stalk which consists of only one cell with one nucleus and with

Left: Typical growth of *Cymopolia barbata* at the shoreline of Caja de Muertos, Puerto Rico.

Above: The algae of the genus *Polyphysa* are very delicate. The thallus disc contains calcium carbonate, as the white spots clearly show. It is covered with *Derbesia* sp.

Left: *Enteromorpha* sp. often appears on live rock during the early break in period, but disappears again before long. Here this alga (foreground) grows together with filamentous algae of the genus *Bryopsis* (background).

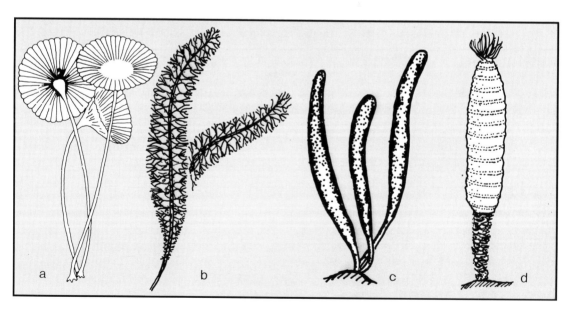

Typical thallus of four different genera in the order Dasycladales.
a: *Acetabularia*; b: *Batophora*; c: *Dasycladus vermicularis*; d: *Neomeris annulata*

a flat, disc-shaped thallus. The thallus disc is supported by ribs which are connected incrustations of calcium carbonate. We have now and then seen the algae grow out of live rocks, but they have never survived for a long time. They are among those algae that may appear in newly set up coral reef aquaria.

Polyphysa can easily be mistaken for *Acetabularia* spp., which are parasol-shaped as well. Algae of the genus *Acetabularia*, however, grow larger and prefer rather calm and shallow water.

The genus *Batophora* is found in calm, shallow lagoons and most frequently in areas with brackish water. These algae usually develop cylindrical thalli, which are up to 10 cm high and contain calcium carbonate. When they reach sexual maturity, they grow brown zoosporangia at the end of their thalli. *Batophora oerstedii* is a common species in the Caribbean.

Dasycladus vermicularis is very similar to *Batophora oerstedii* and is also found throughout the Caribbean. It remains slightly smaller, however, and grows only one zoosporangium at the end of each thallus, two features which distinguish it from *Batophora oerstedii*.

On live rock you can often find some small (up to 2.5 cm), green thalli which obviously contain calcium carbonate. These algae are usually *Neomeris annulata*. LITTLER et al. (1989) report this genus

A multitude of different algae may grow from live rock: In the middle of the picture a typical *Neomeris* sp. can be seen, to the left of it some specimens of a *Polyphysa* sp.; to the left at the very bottom near the margin of the photo we can see a thin, but typical growth of *Cladophoropsis* sp. On the right half of the picture there are various calcareous red algae of the genera *Sporolithon* and *Hydrolithon.*

from the Caribbean, where it is found in depths of up to 30 m. We have also found *Neomeris* however, on live rock that was imported from the Indo-Pacific. Like most of the algae of the order Dasycladales, *Neomeris* spp. do not seem to be able to survive for a longer time in a coral reef aquarium, yet they thrive during the break in period. A rather special alga that occupies the shoreline of the Caribbean is *Cymopolia barbata*. The branching is irregular and dicotomous and the branches are heavily calcified. At the tips of the

branches there are short, bright green filaments arranged in a rosett. We have not yet seen this beautiful plant in the reef aquarium, but it should be perfectly suited especally in an aquarium which simulates the tidal shore.

❸ Order Siphonocladales

Two genera of this order are important for the coral reef aquarium in the first place, *Valonia* and *Ventricaria*. Because of their vesicle-like, spherical form they are called bubble algae. One vesicle con-

Left: In a coral reef aquarium *Ventricaria ventricosa* usually grows in "solitary clusters" that appear somewhere at random, yet it may also develop into large colonies, overgrowing everything. Right: On a reef flat off the Maldives we found *V. ventricosa* on the bottom side of large rocks together with turf algae. Yet we did not find clusters as large as the ones that can grow in aquaria.

Valonia macrophysa develops club-like cells that grow closely together. Usually each cell is about 5 to 20 mm long. This colony developed on live rock.

sists of one cell only, which means that these cells are among the largest cells that exist. Under favourable conditions these algae grow very well and may overgrow large parts of the aquarium. In some aquaria they may grow so fast by vegetative reproduction that they become a pest (BIRKHOLZ, 1986).

Ventricaria ventricosa (often also called *Valonia ventricosa*) de-

The beautiful thallus of *Dictyosphaeria* spp. consists only of one light green layer of cells. Our experience shows that *Dictyosphaeria* only very rarely appear in coral reef aquaria.

velops dark green, round vesicles that usually have a diameter of 1 to 2 cm, but exceptional ones may reach 5 cm. It is the bubble algae that we regularly find in larger amounts in a coral reef aquarium. In the ocean we find it in depths down to 80 m, often growing between other algae or in smaller cavities. It may grow solitary as well as in dense colonies.

Valonia aegagrophila grows at depths of up to 5 m in water that flows gently. It has oval, olive-green thalli. While other bubble algae cling to their substrate with small rhizoids, *Valonia aegagro-*

phila can also lead a non-sessile life.

Valonia macrophysa has long, irregularly shaped thalli which are a dark olive-green in colour. It usually grows in shallow waters in the shadow of other algae, where it may develop large colonies. *Valonia utricularia* has club-shaped cells, which may grow as long as 5 cm. It mostly grows as a creeper and develops balloon-like chains on its substrate.

Among the algae in the order Siphonocladales we also find the very attractive *Dictyospheria* spp., which have a hollow thallus like *Valonia* and *Ventricaria*, but which look brighter green. Their thalli also consist of very large cells, which have, however, grown together, making these algae look somewhat knotty. Their thallus is rather large with a diameter of up to 10 cm. LITTLER et al. (1989) report that the genus *Dictyosphaeria* grows in reef areas where the nutrient content is above average. Yet we found a large number of colonies in a shallow zone that was not rich in nutrients at all. This was on the reef flats of Green Island in the Great Barrier Reef, i.e.

On the reef flat of Green Island in the Great Barrier Reef we found various *Dictyosphaeria* spp. They were fully exposed to the sunlight and grew between calcareous red algae and stony corals of the genus *Turbinaria*.

in a biotope with a large variety of species and a good growth of stony corals.

In some coral reef aquaria we have seen *Dictyosphaeria* growing on live rocks. We find this alga very decorative. Under favourable conditions all the species of the order Siphonocladales may grow explosively and may overgrow large parts of the aquarium. Thus it is of great importance to keep their growth under control.

❹ Order Caulerpales

The order Caulerpales is of great importance from a biological as well as from an aquaristic point of view. It includes 45 genera with more than 400 species.

Filamentous algae of the genera *Bryopsis* and *Derbesia*

In a coral reef aquarium with a high light intensity, strong water movement, and water that has been allowed to age for a few weeks the living conditions for filamentous algae are favourable. Their period of maximum growth begins when the more or less intense growth of the blue-green algae ceases, which will usually be the case after three to six weeks. With a few exceptions filamentous algae belong to the genera *Bryopsis* and *Derbesia*. Both genera are found in marine biotopes all over the world. In Western Europe we find *Bryopsis plumosa* and *Derbesia marina*, which we probably also have in our aquaria, especially if we make use of natural seawater.

The distinctive features of *Bryopsis* spp. is their branched shape, while *Derbesia* spp. have long filaments which do not branch at all. If filamentous algae are allowed to grow freely they will soon overgrow the whole aquarium. It seems that *Bryopsis* sp. may be introduced into the aquarium on live rocks. They are not difficult to control, however, even though most algae-eating fish do not even touch them. *Derbesia* spp., on the contrary, may easily become a nuisance. Their growth rate is so extreme that they may spread a layer of algae over the whole aquarium decoration very fast, killing everything that they cover.

Bryopsis and *Derbesia* spp. have an alternating life-cycle, which changes from a sporophyte, which produces unisexual zoospores, to a gametophyte, which brings forth male and female gametes (see drawing on page 282). In *Derbesia* the sporophyte is formed by the algae filaments (see the three pictures at the top of page 283). The gametophyte is small, green and oval. It often grows between calcareous alge. This stage of the development may be observed quite well through a magnifying glass (see the picture at the bottom of page 283).

In former times aquarists were often convinced that a good growth of filamentous algae was a prerequisite for a healthy marine aquarium. This is utterly wrong!

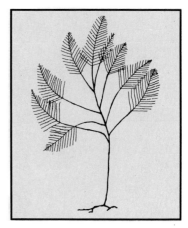

Typical thallus of *Bryopsis*.
(Drawing after Hoek, 1978)

The opposite is true! It is absolutely impossible to maintain a coral reef aquarium successfully if filamentous algae are allowed to grow without restriction. Filamentous algae, when they grow, compete with the symbiotic zooxanthellae and may therefore be indirectly responsible for the death of animals that live in symbiosis with these zooxanthellae. Sessile invertebrates that cannot clean themselves fast enough are overgrown by them and are, in a way, "choked". In addition, many compounds that have been accumulated by the algae are emitted into the water once they die, which is quite common, if the filamentous algae grow heavily. Thus there will be grave changes to the worse in the quality of the aquarium water and in the living conditions of the

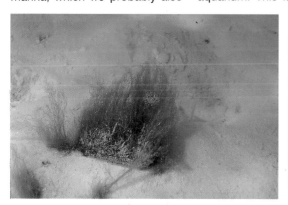

Here *Derbesia* grows on sandy ground in a shallow lagoon off the island of Kuredu, Maldives.

Bryopsis on live rock in an aquarium. The feather-shaped thalli are typical of these filamentous algae.

Most of the surgeonfishes of the genus *Zebrasoma* are good at eating filamentous algae; here *Zebrasoma gemmatum*.   Photo: Dr. D. Brockmann

urs of the blue and UV-A range of the spectrum should be predominant over the yellow and red ranges in the artificial light that is used. In addition to that, algae-eating animals are a must. They should be the first animals to be introduced into the aquarium during the break in period.

If we simplify matters slightly, we may subdivide algae-eating animals into three groups: species that

a) only eat filamentous and other tender algae,

b) eat many species of algae, among them also calcareous algae,

c) are carnivorous and eat algae only as a supplementary diet.

In group a) there are only a few animals that are suitable for a coral reef aquarium. Surgeonfishes of the genus *Zebrasoma* are excellent eaters of filamentous algae and usually do not touch corals and other invertebrates. We have never had any trouble with these fishes in our coral reef aquaria. Even if several specimens are associated in one aquarium they will hardly fight each other. Surgeonfishes do get quite large, however, so that it is impossible to keep more than one fish in a coral reef aquarium with a volume of less than 200 litres.

The surgeonfishes most regularly available in aquarium shops are *Zebrasoma flavescens*, *Z. scopas* and *Z. veliferum*. The very beautifully coloured yellowtail surgeonfish, *Zebrasoma xanthurus* from the Red Sea is rarer. We cannot confirm the reports that claim that the yellowtail surgeonfish also nibbles at corals. In our aquaria it grazed on algae in the same intensive way as do all the other species of surgeonfishes. The surgeonfishes of the genera *Acanthurus*, *Ctenochaeus*, *Paracanthurus* and *Naso* belong to group b). They eat most species of algae, including *Caulerpa* spp. and brown algae, yet they normally do not touch calcareous

aquarium animals. Moreover an aquarium that is overgrown with filamentous algae is not exactly a pretty sight.

We think that the growing of filamentous algae should be avoided completely in a coral reef aquarium. This problem is not easily solved, but it is possible to do so. It is important in the first place that the coral reef aquarium should not be exposed to direct sunlight of a long duration during the break in phase. If it is located close to a window, the aquarium sides have

to be covered against the intense solar radiation. It is also important to add "Kalkwasser" which rises the pH to levels around 8.4 - 8.5 and thereby prevents the pool of phosphate, always present in aquaria, to become active (see pages 227-235). A high nutrient content (especially of nitrate and phosphate) is always dangerous. To keep it as low as possible, effective protein skimming is required. Only unpolluted freshwater should be used for the top-off with "Kalkwasser". Moreover the colo-

If filamentous algae are not kept under control, they may overgrow and kill the calcareous algae which are so very welcome in the reef aquarium.

Calcinus tibicen **is an example of an excellent grazer of short, filamentous growth of algae.**

algae. It is a disadvantage that the larger *Acanthurus* spp. need ample swimming space and are therefore not suitable for aquaria under 300 litres. They often behave so very actively and roughly that they disturb many invertebrates.

If a surgeonfish is already resident in an aquarium, all new surgeonfish added afterwards will (usually) be violently attacked. Many herbivores including the surgeonfish will occasionally nip coral polyps, mistaking them for algae. Moreover the surgeonfish seem to be especially liable to suffer from parasites.

There are also many algae-eating species in the family Blenniidae. Among them is the species which, according to our experience, is the best algae-eater, *Salarias fasciatus*, the jeweled blenny. It is found in a large area and is common in many regions of the Indo-Pacific. Its fabulous qualities as an algae-eater become clear if we consider the fact that four of these blennies can completely rid an overgrown 3000 litre aquarium of most algae within a few weeks. When no algae are left in the aqua-

Among the best algae eaters in the coral reef aquarium are the snails of the genus *Astraea*.

rium there is a danger that these fish may starve to death, because some individuals hardly ever accept substitute foods. Blennies of the genus *Ecsenius* are also very successful as algae-eaters. If the algae growth is insufficient they will accept substitute food quite willingly.

Some mollusks, among them the tropical snails of the genus *Ne-*

Sea-urchins of the genus *Echinometra* are often found in reef zones with profuse algae growth. They not only feed on filamentous algae, but also on calcareous algae and so they should be closely watched if they are kept in a coral reef aquarium.

Surgeonfishes,e.g. *Acanthurus sohal* (left) and tangs, e.g. *Zebrasoma xanthurus* (right), are among the best algae-eating fishes for the coral reef aquarium. While surgeonfishes eat many different species of algae, tangs seem to prefer filamentous algae, e.g. *Derbesia*.

Photos: Dr. D. Brockmann

rita and of the Caribbean genus *Astraea* which are imported quite regularly, only eat small algae. Whereas *Astraea* spp. survive for rather a long time in a coral reef aquarium, *Nerita* spp. do not. If you want good results with them as an algae-eating "task force", you have to keep a larger number. There should be at least 30 to 40 of them in a 200 litre aquarium. A large variety of snails and slugs is introduced into our aquaria on live rocks. Most of them seem to feed on algae exclusively.

Only a few hermit crabs feed only on algae. Unfortunately there are also a lot of predatory species in this group of crustaceans (BAUMEISTER, 1988). It may turn out to be quite difficult to tell the algae-eating species from the predatory ones. However, some species of hermit crabs are excellent algae-grazers. This is indeed true for some Caribbean species like the Red Hermit Crab *Paguristes cadenati*, the Polka-Dot Hermit *Phimochirus operculatus* and the Red-Leg Hermit *Calcinus californiensis*. The Orangeclaw Hermit *Calcinus tibicen* is also excellent, but belongs to the rougher species and grows as big as an inch. In our experience there are no better

grazers of short, dense filamentous algae and turf-algae as these and other herbivorous hermit crabs. The only disadvantage is that they should be kept in large numbers to be really efficient. In a 500 litre tank one can easily keep 50-100 specimens. See SCHEIMER (1994) for an excellent review of this subject.

Cowries of the genus *Cypraea* may be algae-eaters, yet a number of species are "predatory" that also "have a go" at sponges, corals and other types of food they like.

There are also a number of sea urchins that belong to the group of algae-eating animals. *Echinometra* spp. are nice, they are very good at destroying algae, yet they also nibble on calcareous algae. *Diadema* spp., which have long spines, show the same kind of behaviour, but they are more active and move around more freely.

For all animals in groups a) and b) algae are the staple food. They may also take in microorganisms as supplementary food. Normally they do not touch more highly developed animals. Animals belonging to group c) eat not only algae, but also those organisms that we would like to keep in our coral reef aquarium. Most angel-

fishes of the genus *Centropyge*, for example, feed mainly on filamentous algae and the small crustaceans living there, but they also feed on other small animals. Occasionally they attack corals. This may be different from one species to the next as well as from one individual to another. Many of the larger angelfishes of the genera *Pomacanthus*, *Holacanthus*, etc. like to eat algae as well, but they also love to feed on corals, sponges and feather duster worms. This makes them unsuitable for a coral reef aquarium. There are also a number of regulations and laws that restrict the import of these fishes in Europe.

In most coral reef aquaria filamentous algae start to grow more or less heavily in the first six months. As long as this is the case, delicate animals like stony corals, disc or colonial anemones should on no account be introduced into the aquarium because there is no chance for them to survive as long as there are filamentous algae growing.

The necessity to check on filamentous algae and to remove them can take time. Sometimes it takes months before they disappear. When they begin to decline,

Certain starfish are also suitable as the first algae-eaters during the break in period; here we see *Fromia monilis* in its natural habitat off the Maldives.

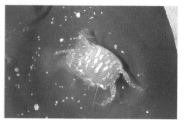

the filamentous algae do not grow as long as before, and their colour becomes lighter. Then the individual growths become smaller. Yet it is astonishing how long they can survive in places with strong water movement and a high light intensity. When the filamentous algae have vanished, other kinds of species begin to grow, especially if the aquarium has been decorated with live rock.

Various genera

Chlorodesmis fastigiata is another filamentous alga which is often found on the coral reef, but only rarely in the aquarium. The only place where we could see that it was successfully kept in an aquarium was in "The Great Barrier Reef Aquarium" in Townsville, Australia. On a reef they can be made out as beautiful green spots of colour. *Caphyra rotundifrons*, a small crab, lives between the green thalli of this alga all of its life and has adopted the same green colour. In English *Chlorodesmis fastigiata* is called "turtle weed" because it is said to be eaten by turtles. We do not know if this is so. It is certain, however, that unlike other filamentous algae, it is not eaten by herbivores in the reef. The reason may be that this alga contains a toxic substance.

Occasionally we find *Codium* spp. on offer in the aquarium shops. In the Indo-Pacific region *Codium spongiosum* grows on reef flats and reef edges, often on the bottom of large blocks of live rock. These and many others of the nearly 50 tropical species are very similar to our native *Codium fragile*. Although *Codium* spp. occasionally can grow very good in the reef aquarium, they must in general be regarded as difficult to keep. The shapes that *Codium* spp. develop are very different. There are species that develop as creeping algae beds, others that grow as large hollow balls and yet others develop into branched bush-shaped colonies of heights of up to 1 m. All species have a spongy, rubbery tissue.

Cladophoropsis spp. however, keep for a long time. They grow into dense, dark green colonies with rather stiff algae filaments. *Cladophoropsis* spp. are often found in the tidal zone and on tropical coasts at a depth of up 5 metres. They are usually found on live rocks. In coral reef aquaria they thrive under the high light intensity of HQI-light and grow for a long time in a limited space.

In many lagoons or in other places of the reef where sediments accumulate, we will find the interesting and beautiful green algae of the genera *Avrainvillea*, *Udotea*, *Penicillus* and *Rhipocephalus*, of which we would like to present a number of species in the following passages.

The genus *Avrainvillea* includes

Two *Codium* spp. growing side by side on a live rock in the aquarium of P. Findeisen, Witten, Germany.

Cladophoropsis sp. can grow for a long time in a limited area in a coral reef aquarium.

rather large algae with thalli of 10 to 30 cm in diametre. They have longer stalks on which disc-shaped or club-shaped thalli can be found.

The genus *Udotea* includes 15 species, which are all found in tropical or subtropical marine zones. On the reef these algae which accumulate calcium carbonate often grow in the shadow of corals. In the Great Barrier Reef we mostly found them at depths of more than 10 m, yet sometimes also in shallow water, always, however, in places with low mean light intensity. On live rock *Udotea* algae are very common.

Udotea cyathiformis (page 295) has a beautiful, cuplike shape and grows to a maximum height of 15 cm, whereas the more common *U. flabellum* (page 294) grows

with a fanlike shape and up to 20 cm. Both species only fix small amounts of calcium ions from the water. The bright green *U. occidentalis* is able to fix larger amounts. This species can be identi-

fied easily by the numerous small thalli which grow out of the centre of one large thallus. It is found in depths of up to 40 m. Another species, *U. wilsoni* grows in shallow water instead, often together with

The typical appearance of *Avrainvillea* sp., as seen in the heavily lighted coral reef aquarium of D. Kornfeld, Bielefeld, Germany.

This finger-shaped alga, which grows up to 20 cm, may perhaps be *Tydemania expeditionis.* It is very common off the Maldives.

New shoots on a *Udotea flabellum.*
Photo: W.A. Tomey

eel grass (Zosteraceae).

Penicillus spp. have the form of a whip or of a shaving brush. There have been occasional reports that they have been kept successfully in aquaria. They grow very fast, but the upright part of the algae only lives about two weeks, then it begins to fall apart. New algae then spring up from the adjacent sand, connected to the parent specimen by filaments growing from the basis buried in the sand. The juveniles grow like mushrooms, up to several inches per day when they are in bright light. Their normal habitat is shallow sandy seagrass beds that are heavily illuminated. Most aquarists give up on *Penicillus* and throw it away when they see that the thallus fall apart. One should, however, be patient as new algae normally develop.

There are five species in the genus *Penicillus* which all grow in

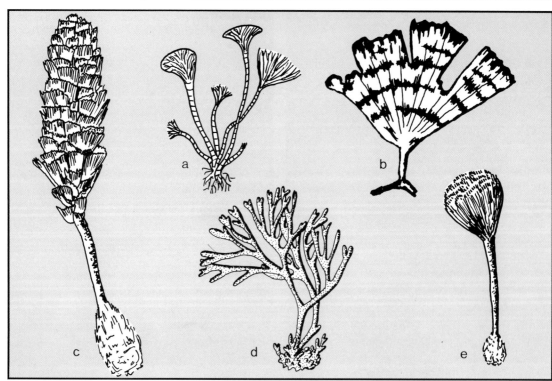

The shapes of the thalli of various genera of the order Caulerpales
a: *Avrainvillea*; b: *Udotea*; c: *Rhipocephalus*; d: *Codium*; e: *Penicillus*

Udotea cyathiformis on sandy ground at a depth of only 2 m off Bonaire in the Caribbean.

Penicillus capitatus growing beautifully in an aquarium in Miami, Florida.

the sand and hold on to it with a bulb-shaped anchoring organ. *Penicillus capitatus* is found in shallow lagoons, which are muddy or rich in sediments. It has a stalk of 5 to 10 cm length which is incrustated with calcium carbonate and which carries the brushlike thallus. *P. dumetosus* and *P. pyriformis* have a shorter, thicker stalk and a dark green thallus.

The genus *Rhipocephalus* has an intermediate position between the genera *Udotea* and *Penicillus*. In this genus the thallus consists of flat plates which sit tightly packed on a stalk. These algae mainly live on sandy ground, some species as deep down as 40 m.

Green calcareous algae of the genus *Halimeda*

In the coral reef aquarium green calcareous algae of the genus *Halimeda*, of which we know at least 25 species, are very decorative. In the reef they are very common. Scientists estimate that *Halimeda*-like calcareous algae first appeared as far back as the Triasssic, i.e. 225 million years ago. In many regions of the earth we find geological formations that were completely produced by the calcareous algae of former epochs. In the Great Barrier Reef there is a zone of sandbanks behind the reefs which is the result of the growth of

Halimeda algae during the last 10000 years. The layers of the *Halimeda* sediments are between 2 and 20 m thick. This shows how important the role of these calcareous algae was and still is in the formation of sediments in the coral reef (FLÜGEL, 1989; MARSHALL & DAVIS, 1989).

If you dive on a coral reef it does not take long before you notice the first *Halimeda*. Very often you see them on steep reef slopes where they are protected against intense sunlight. Some species also grow in dense clusters in the intense solar radiation of the shallow reef flat zone. Large areas of the bottom of lagoons may also

Halimeda sp. in the aquarium.

Photo: W. A. Tomey

be covered with green calcareous algae. Some species, e.g. *Halimeda copiosa*, *H. cryptica* and *H. gracilis* from the Caribbean are found there as deep down as 150 m. Most of the species, however, grow at depths between 0 and 30 m (see drawing on page 298).

Halimeda spp. are very robust and not easily harmed by algae-eating animals. Only a few species of fish feed on them. The reason for this is that *Halimeda* sp. excrete the toxic metabolites Halimedatrial and Halimedatetraacetat (PAUL & VAN ALSTYNE, 1988). We find this kind of chemical defence in many other algae, but also in sponges, corals and other reef organisms. One should always take into account that the excretion of these metabolic substances may cause problems in the coral reef aquarium.

The thalli of the *Halimeda* spp. are divided into segments which have the shape of a kidney or a heart and which are of different size. The segments are connected by a sort of tube-like joint. Whether these joints can be moved or whether they are rigid is a feature that serves to distinguish species from each other. As a rule, most of the species are difficult to tell apart by their outward appearance. Some, however, have an appearance which is very different from that of most of the others. This is true, e.g. for *Halimeda monila*, whose segments are almost cylindrical. *H. lacrimosa*, in which the segments have the shape of a drop (lacrima, lat. = tear) is also unusual in appearance.

If live rocks are used to decorate a coral reef aquarium it is rather certain that green calcareous algae will start to grow in one place or the other. Especially in the first year often large colonies develop. Later their growth usually decreases but it may increase again afterwards from time to time. The species most often kept in coral reef aquaria are *Halimeda opuntia*, *H. incrassata* and *H. tuna*. These three species are mostly found in the shallow waters of the coral reef and are therefore also imported on live rocks.

Above: In the deeper regions of a coral reef, like here at "China wall" in the North Boomerang reef in the Coral Sea, the luxuriant growth of *Halimeda* and other green algae may be very impressive; the sponge in the middle of the picture is a *Cinachyra* sp. Below: *Halimeda opuntia* is a green calcareous alga which is quite common on the reef. It also grows in shallow water zones in full sunlight, like here in a lagoon off the Maldives.

H. incrassata.   Underwater photo: O. Gremblewski-Strate.

The thalli of *Halimeda* consist of clearly marked off segments. At the tips of the old segments new, small ones grow.

ty for *Halimeda*, they may grow so intensely that it becomes necessary to thin out the colony from time to time so that the invertebrates aren't overgrown. On the other hand it will hardly be possible to keep *Halimeda* spp. in aquarium water that is rich in nitrate and phosphate. At the beginning of the 70's we were often told that it was completely out of the question to keep *Halimeda* in the aquarium. Today this statement has been proven to be false, as it is no problem at all to keep these beautiful algae in a coral reef aquarium if the advice given in this series of books is followed consequently. This is another proof for the enormous progress that marine aquaristics have made during the last 20 years!

Halimeda opuntia has small segments which usually have a diameter of 5 mm. It develops into a dense colony which spreads out from several points where it is anchored to the substrate. It grows so densely that its threads get matted. At the single segments you can only just see three lobes and three ribs that run lengthwise. In *H. incrassata* three lobes are clearly to be seen. The bottom segments of the thallus may be almost cylindrical. The segments of *H. tuna* are much larger than those of the other two species and have a diameter of 1.2 to 1.5 cm. Their shape is triangular or disc-like. In all three species the joints can be moved and there are no calcium deposits.

If there are enough calcium ions available in the coral reef aquarium, which is an absolute necessi-

Like other green algae as well, *Halimeda* spp. reproduce sexually at certain intervals. At that stage gametophytes (gametangia), which are another species-distinguishing feature, grow on the outside of the segments. The nutrients that are needed for this process are extracted by the gametangia from the original plant, which causes it to die. In their natural environment these gametan-

Distribution of *Halimeda* spp. in the reef, shown at the example of a reef off Grand Cayman, West Indies. (Drawing after ROBERTS & MACINTYRE, 1988).

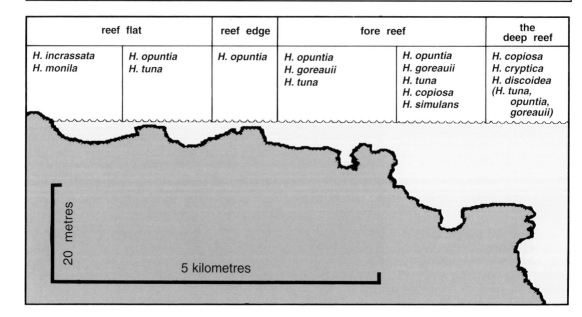

reef flat		reef edge	fore reef		the deep reef
H. incrassata H. monila	H. opuntia H. tuna	H. opuntia	H. opuntia H. goreauii H. tuna	H. opuntia H. goreauii H. tuna H. copiosa H. simulans	H. copiosa H. cryptica H. discoidea (H. tuna, opuntia, goreauii)

20 metres

5 kilometres

Halimeda tuna or *H. discoidea*; both species have big segments but *H. discoidea* is the most common of the two species in aquaria.

gia start growing at certain times of the year. It is even possible that the exact point in time is determined by the phases of the moon. It has been shown that species which easily reproduce asexually (vegetatively), develop gametangia less often than those whose asexual reproduction is less intense. *Halimeda tuna* is a species in which asexual reproduction is not very significant (more information on sexual reproduction can be found in DREW & ABEL, 1988b). In the coral reef aquarium sexual reproduction and the growing of gametangia are rather rare events.

Caulerpa

The marine algae best known among aquarists are doubtlessly the green macroalgae of the genus *Caulerpa*. They have been kept in aquaria since the beginning of marine aquaristics. There are about 75 species altogether, which all live in tropical or subtropical seas. Some species grow on muddy ground in waters that are rich in nutrients, others prefer a rock substrate and waters with a low amount of dissolved nutrients. *Caulerpa* spp. may be introduced into the coral reef aquarium with live rock, but they may also be bought separately in aquarium shops.

Probably the most common *Caulerpa* species in marine aquaristics is *C. prolifera*. In its natural environment it often grows on muddy ground and it is found worldwide in tropical as well as in subtropical areas. In aquaria with

Sometimes the green calcareous algae reproduce sexually in the aquarium. The plant then forms sexual organs (gametangia) and loses the pigmentation. After completing the sexual activity the original plant dies. The picture in the middle shows an overview of a spawing *Halimeda*, while the picture to the right shows the gametangia in close up (magnification 18x).

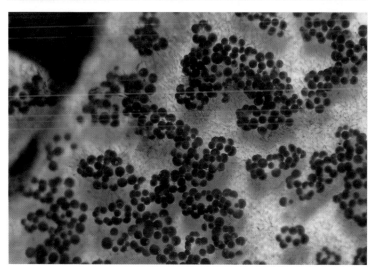

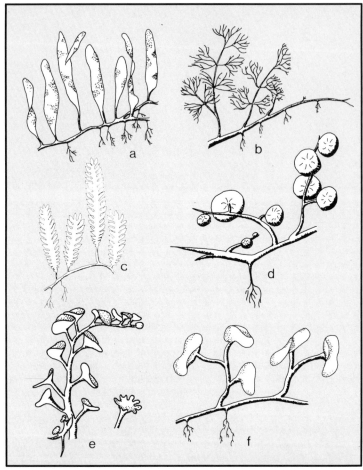

Caulerpa nummularia   Photo: W.A. Tomey

a high light intensity it will not grow very well, but it will do fine under fluorescent tubes. *Caulerpa prolifera* would be ideal to be used in an algae filter (see page 255) if it were not for the following quality, which disqualifies it for this purpose: Occasionally little yellow spots appear on its thallus, which indicate that gametes are produced and thus that sexual reproduction is taking place. When the gametocytes are fully developed the majority of the plant dies and decays. As only a small part of the plant tissue will survive, the death and decay of the larger part poses a heavy threat to the aquarium milieu. Sexual reproduction takes place in very much the same way in many other *Caulerpa* spp.

Caulerpa racemosa is also among the more popular species in marine aquaristics. It is often found in coral reefs in tropical and subtropical areas all over the world. Usually *Caulerpa racemosa* has a thallus that consists of many "spheres", yet it grows in very variable forms and there are so many that it is difficult to obtain a general idea of them. Perhaps many of the forms that are classed with *Caulerpa racemosa* are geographical races or separate species. In the aquarium *Caulerpa racemosa* is usually easy to keep. We think that a limited amount of this species looks very decorative and natural in a coral reef aquarium.

Caulerpa peltata is considered to be a separate species by many authors, yet others, like LITTLER et al. (1989) classify it with *C. racemosa*. The distinctive feature of this species is, that the "spheres" of the thallus are flattened. *C. racemosa* and *C. peltata* – if we regard it as a separate species – may be introduced into the aquarium with live rocks.

Caulerpa nummularia is also regarded as an independent species even though its outward appearance is very similar to that of *C. peltata*. One special characteristic of this species are the phylloids that it develops, which are different in shape from the normal thallus.

Caulerpa sertularioides   Photos: W.A. Tomey   *Caulerpa scalpelliformis*

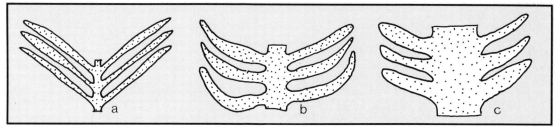

Segment shapes of a: *Caulerpa sertularioides*, **b:** *C. taxifolia* **and c:** *C. scalpelliformis.*

Caulerpa sertularioides, C. taxifolia, C. scalpelliformis and *C. mexicana* all have a feathered thallus with the segments differing in length from one species to the other. *C. serrulata* may easily be recognized from the serrated thalli. All the species mentioned here may be introduced on live rocks. Most of the *Caulerpa* spp. make higher demands on the quality of the aquarium water than does *Caulerpa prolifera*.

Many species of *Caulerpa* may also be found in the coral reef. Some grow in cracks in the reef or in depressions, others prefer small stones or sandy bottom to settle on. In the coral reef aquarium a limited growth of *Caulerpa* is acceptable. As long as they do not dominate the overall impression their decorative effect may be extraordinary. It is a disadvantage, however, that they are very difficult to remove once they have established themselves in an aquarium. Even after they have been thinned out, new plants can grow again from tiny fragments.

Two varieties of *Caulerpa serrulatu.*   Photos: W.A. Tomey

Caulerpa racemosa in the aquarium.   Photo: W.A. Tomey

Moreover we should always keep in mind that any *Caulerpa* that grow in profusion may become competitors for zooxanthellae in very much the same way as we have described it for filamentous algae.

Caulerpa spp. may also emit toxic substances, e.g. "Caulerpin". These are substances which originally serve the purpose to defend the algae in the reef against competing organisms.

⑤ Order Cladophorales

The order Cladophorales includes a number of species in the genus *Chaetomorpha*, whose outward appearance reminds us of entangled nylon threads. The name of the genus means "with brushlike shape".

In their natural surroundings we find these algae in zones with shallow water rich in nutrients, where they grow in seagrass beds

unattached to the ground (LITTLER et al., 1989). The filaments consist of short, cylindrical cells. They have a brushlike shape, which gives these algae their characteristic appearance.

ROUND (1973) remarks that the outer layer of cells of the thallus consists of incrustated material that is similar to proteins. This would mean that these algae take in proteins from the water to make them available for their own metabolism.

Chaetomorpha linum is bright green and is found in brackish water whereas *C. crassa* is dark green and grows epiphytically on other algae in shallow water. The last species is similar to the one that is occasionally introduced into the coral reef aquarium on live rock. Yet *Chaetomorpha* are only rarely kept in aquaria (we have only now and then seen thickly growing beds of them). If these green algae are given a chance to develop a limited colony, they can look very decorative.

Division
Heterokontophyta

Class Phaeophyceaa
Brown algae

The growth of brown algae depends on the constant and sometimes abundant availability of nutrients, like nitrogen and phosphorus, and, last but not least the trace element iodine. In natural surroundings many brown algae contain a concentration of iodine which 20000 times higher than that of the seawater they live in. Because of this in former times brown algae were used as a raw material for the production of iodine. Other major and trace elements are also stored in such enormous amounts in algae. In aquarium water the concentration of iodine decreases rapidly with the growth of the algae, so that it becomes absolutely essential to add iodine to the water if you want

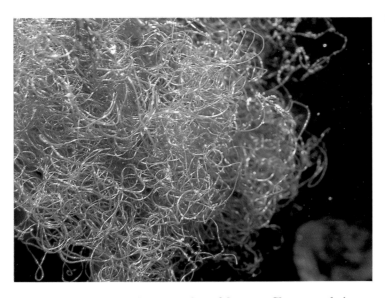

The outward appearance of the green algae of the genus *Chaetomorpha* is very characteristic. They can hardly be mistaken for other algae.

Caulerpa racemosa off Bequia, Caribbean. Underwater photo: O. Gremblewski-Strate

These *Halimeda* tufts look like little trees. They have anchored on shells or pieces of dead coral under the sand.
Underwater photo: G. Bertholdt

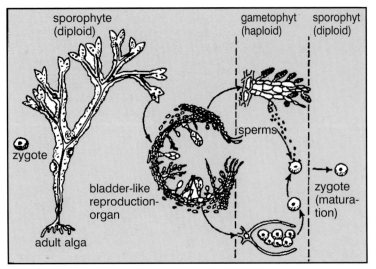

| sporophyte (diploid) | gametophyt (haploid) | sporophyt (diploid) |

zygote

bladder-like reproduction-organ

adult alga

sperms

zygote (maturation)

Diploidic-reproduction in the genus *Fucus*.
(Drawing after WALLACE et al., 1986)

the algae to continue growing. This can be done simply by adding potassium iodide (KI, see page 237). If nutrients and iodine are constantly available, a large number of brown algae will thrive.

As the coral reef aquarium in principle should be a system that contains a low amount of nutrients (nitrogen and phosphorous compounds), we will not introduce more nutrients into it beyond those which get there by feeding and by the metabolic activities of the organisms. As a consequence most brown algae only thrive in an aquarium newly set up with live rock. In a coral reef aquarium with an effective protein skimming system the growth of the leafy brown or red algae will decrease while at the same time the calcareous algae that remain low will spread. In the first years, however, we will again and again see a lot of brown algae that grow out of the live rocks. They are part of the algal flora that appears successively in the course of the development of a coral reef aquarium.

All brown algae are multicellular and – except for four or five freshwater species – they are marine. About 1500 species have been described altogether. Many of them have large, leaflike thalli and may grow to lengths of several metres. In their cells carbohydrates are deposited, among others laminarin and mannitol, as well as

polysaccharides, among them algin, (a substance that is used in the production of icecream). Brown algae are brown because the brown pigment, fucoxanthin, overlies the green one, chlorophyll. Fucoxanthin belongs to the group of pigments called xanthophylls.

The reproduction of the brown algae is very complicated and in most cases alternates between the asexual sporophyte and the sexual gametophyte. There are three main types of reproduction, which are well worth a closer look.

a) Regular alternation of isomorphic generations

The sporophyte and the gametophyte are morphologically identical. There are two types of reproductive organs, which either produce haploid (containing only a single set of chromosomes) or diploid (containing two sets of chromosomes) spores or gametangia, which on their part can produce gametes. The genus *Dictyota* is an example of a brown alga with a regular alternation of isomorphic generations.

b) Regular alternation of heteromorphic generations

The sporophyte is large and dominating, the gametophyte is microscopically small. The sporophyte

may grow to heights of several metres, while male or female gametes develop in the small generation of unisexual gametophytes. The large *Laminaria* spp. of our northern coastal waters are among the brown algae with a regular alternation of heteromorphic generations.

c) Diploidy

The species with this type of reproduction do not have alternation of generations nor asexual reproduction by spores. The sex organs develop in special bladders on the thallus. These bladders should not be confused with buoying organs which can be seen quite clearly in the aquarium in *Sargassum* spp. (see photo on page 307). Brown algae of the genus *Fucus* that we find along the coasts of Northern Europe belongs to this group as well.

❶ Order Dictyotales

Dictyota dichotoma, which can be found almost worldwide, is a typical representative of this order. This alga often grows out of live rock. It can grow so abundantly that it may become necessary to thin it out, which, fortunately, is not too much of a problem. The reproduction of *Dictyota dichotoma* is a most typical example of the regular alternation of isomorphic generations in brown algae. This is all the more reason to observe this alga carefully in the aquarium.

One of the most beautiful representatives of the genus *Dictyota* is *D. bartayresii*, which is quite common in the reef. It has a blue fluorescent thallus and y-shaped, characteristic ends, which is typical of many *Dictyota* spp. The yellow-brown *D. ciliolata* has a slightly spiral-shaped thallus with a dentate edge. Most of the species grow up to 15 or 20 cm high.

The genus *Dictyopteris* includes species which may easily be mistaken for *Dictyota*. Their thal-

Small, but very beautiful colonies of *Dictyota* sp. can often be found off the Maldives at a depth of about 15 m. This colony grows on a red sponge.

lus has a slightly thickened "midrib", which helps to identify them.

Stypopodium zonale has a very characteristic appearance and can hardly be confused with any other algae. Its thallus is fan-shaped, slightly curly, with a fluorescent yellow-brown colour and a structure of transverse ribs made of delicate, transparent, hairy forms.

The appearance of the genus *Padina* is quite similar. These species often grow from live rock. *Padina* spp. are the only brown algae that deposit calcium ions from the water. Even though these algae contain only a small amount of calcium carbonate, you can still feel it with your fingers if you touch them. The thallus usually shows white transverse stripes, which are caused by the calcium carbonate deposits.

A similar ruffle-edged brown alga called *Lobophora variegata* is also introduced into the coral reef aquarium on live rock. It may develop into dense, sometimes magnificent colonies. As the name of this species already tells us, it is quite variable. In the sea this alga usually grows in zones of calm, shallow water, where not too many herbivores are found. *Lobophora variegata* may easily be recognised by its undulating thallus, which has long hairy appendices.

Stypopodium zonale at a depth of 15 m off Bonaire, Caribbean.
Underwater photo: O. Gremblewski-Strate.

A *Padina* sp. in the aquarium. *Padina* spp. are the only brown algae that store calcium carbonate.

❷ Order Fucales

The best known brown algae are in the genus *Sargassum*. They are well known as Sargassum weed, as there are large, free-floating masses of these algae in the Sargasso Sea of the Western Atlantic. The majority of the *Sargassum* spp. however are sessile, i.e growing on a substrate. The floating as well as the sessile species have air bladders, which are a promi-

Above: This *Padina* sp. grows at a depth of 10 m at the outer reef near the island of Kuredu, Maldives.

nent characteristic of this genus. *Sargassum* spp. occasionally appear on live rocks, yet they usually disappear as soon as the contents of algae nutrients in the aquarium water decreases.

In the order Fucales we also

Brown algae of the genus *Lobophora* may grow from live rocks in the aquarium and may develop into dense colonies. These brown algae are easily identified by their hairy thalli.

Sargassum spp. are often found on live rocks. They may grow quite large in the aquarium. This picture shows a *Sargassum* sp. in an aquarium at "Biotop-Aquaristik", St. Augustin-Hangelar, Germany.

find the beautiful genus *Turbinaria*. We must take care not to confuse it with the coral genus *Turbinaria*. The identity of these two generic names results from the fact that the two genera belong to two different systems of nomenclature, one to the zoological, the other to the botanical nomenclature. This identity of names could very well have been avoided if zoologists and botanists had cooperated more closely, which would have been all the more important because marine organisms are concerned in both cases.

Turbinaria are the most common brown algae in the coral reefs of the Indo-Pacific and they are used by the people there as food, either fresh or preserved, or as fertilizer. In the Maldives we found this brown alga at a high light intensity in a shallow lagoon, yet we have never seen it in an aquarium.

Division
Rhodophyta

Red algae

Red algae are among those algae that can be found even in the depths of the sea, i.e. as deep down as 280 m. They contain the pigments r-Phycoerythrin and r-Phycocyanin, which give them their red hue. They also enable these algae to photosynthesize with dim light. Moreover, while they lack chlorophyll b we also find chlorophyll a in these red algae. Altogether there are more than 4000 species in 600 genera

These very interesting brown algae of the genus *Turbinaria* can be seen in the shallow waters of coral reefs. We have, however, never seen them in a coral reef aquarium.

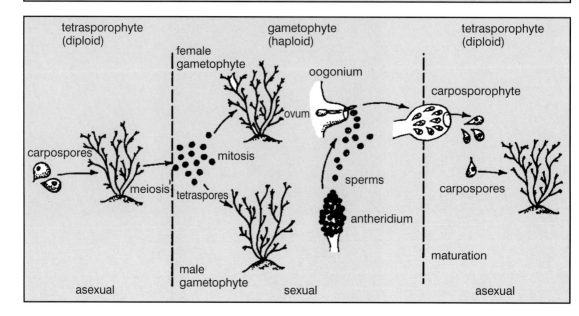

that have been described, nearly all of them marine – the same as with the brown algae.

The reproduction of the red algae is a very complex process in which usually three generations alternate. The basic stages of this process can be described as follows: The gametophyte (original plant) has male and female gametangia. The sperms (male gametes) are produced in antheridia. The gametangia that produce female germ cells, ova, are called oogonia. The ova, egg cells, are fertilized in the oogonium, which often develops into a sort of container or cavity on the gametophyte. The fertilized egg cell (zygote) here develops into a carposporophyte which is hardly visible and lives as a parasitic plant on the original plant. The carposporophyte then develops spores which grow and become tetrasporophytes, which resemble the original plant. These tetrasporophytes, however, develop sporangia and spores with reduction division (meiosis). These spores, from which a new generation of gametophytes grows, are called tetraspores.

This interesting and very com-

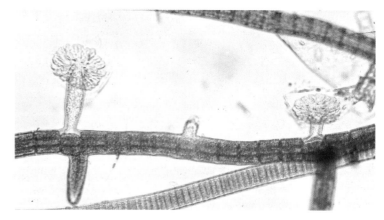

Carposporophytes live a parasitic life on the thallus of the original plant (magnification 560x).

plex life history proves that red algae are among the most highly developed algae.

❶ Order Bangiales

Except for their red colour *Porphyra* spp. resemble the green algae of the genus *Ulva*. Their thallus usually consists of only one layer of cells and is folded along the edges. Because of their dark red colour these algae are also called "purple algae". They only grow during certain periods of the year, yet they may be quite durable. A

lot of research has been done on *Porphyra tenera*, because this species is used as food in Japan.

❷ Order Gelidiales

In this order we find a typical genus of turf algae, which is always found on live rock. If we turn live rocks around, we see numerous turf algae in places where they cannot be reached by algae-ea-

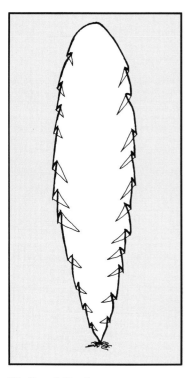

Thallus of *Porphyra*.

ting fishes. There are nearly always representatives of the genus *Gelidium* among these turf algae. Their thallus is dark red. Narrow branches grow from their rhizoids that creep on and cling to the rocks.

❸ Order Nemaliales

In this order we find beautiful red algae, which grow rather large and branch out strongly. The genus *Liagora* includes a number of species in which a certain amount of calcium carbonate is deposited, so that the thallus has a slightly whitish colour. This is also the case with some species of the most decorative genus *Galaxaura*.

The thallus of *Galaxaura marginata*, which is one of the most beautiful red algae that we know, also contains a certain amount of calcium carbonate. Only once, in the aquarium store H. Schmidt, Lünen, Germany, have we ever seen a species of the genus *Galaxaura* (?) growing in an aquarium. Many *Galaxaura* spp. have a small

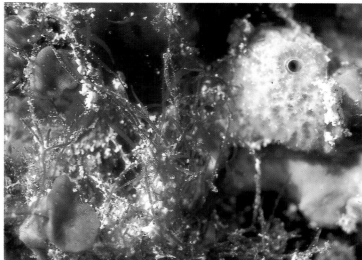

One of the most common turf algae appearing on live rocks from the genus *Gelidium* (magnification 3x).

hole at the foot of each branch, which is a typical characteristic of this genus. The thallus of some species, e.g. *Galaxaura subverticillata*, is also densely covered with hairy filaments.

❹ Order Ceramiales

In this order there are many red algae with a rather thin and ramified thallus. *Ceramium*, in which the tip of each branch of the thallus has the form of a pair of hooked pincers, is the genus that is best known. For the aquarist it is hardly possible to tell the numerous species of this genus apart. In their natural surroundings *Ceramium* spp. often grow in tide pools or as epiphytes on live rock. They are often introduced into our aquaria on these rocks.

Among the many other genera

Many algae secrete slimy substances that may have toxic effects on other organisms. This macro photo of a red alga from the Great Barrier Reef shows the secretion quite clearly.

Galaxaura marginata (?) to the left: off Bonaire in the Caribbean (underwater photo: O. Gremblewski-Strate) and to the right near the island of Kuredu, Maldives, both at a depth of 15m.

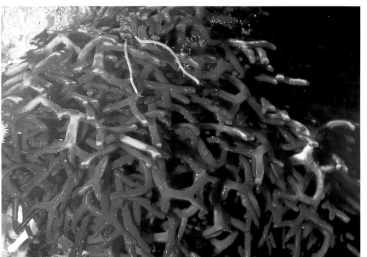

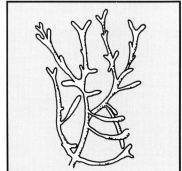

Thallus of *Liagora*.

Above: We saw this beautiful *Galaxaura* (?) in a display aquarium of the store Zoohaus H. Schmidt, Lünen, Germany.

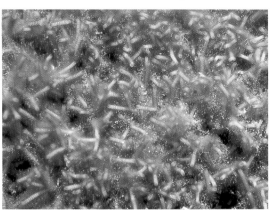

Above: *Galaxaura subverticillata* may easily be recognized by its hairy thallus and its very dense, matted growth. We found the colony to the left on the underside of a boulder on a reef flat off the Maldives, whereas the colony to the right grew on a reef slope at a depth of about 15 m.

of this order *Martensia* is especially remarkable. *Martensia pavonia* is found in up to 30 m depth in the Caribbean. It has a unique thallus which is divided into two alternating types of zones. Every other zone is composed of a structure one layer of cells wide and shaped like a mesh of holes, an appearance we also find in the freshwater plant *Aponogeton madagascariensis*. The other zones of the thallus are a solid membranous structure several cell layers thick.

In a coral reef aquarium we almost always find representatives of the order Ceramiales. They grow together epiphytically with red calcareous algae. The algae filaments are often very thin and delicate so that it takes a magnifying glass to notice these beautiful appearances. These red algae are a good example that shows that a thriving coral reef aquarium always contains an important algal flora.

If we look at small live rocks with a good growth of calcareous algae, here *Mesophyllum* sp., through a binocular magnifying lens, we can see at once the filamentous red algae of the order Ceramiales, which grow epiphytically (picture above, magnification 30x). If we do not keep these threadlike algae under control they may grow rampant and become a nuisance. Here (picture below) they grow together with a bush of *Ochtodes* red algae, which often grow out of live rocks.

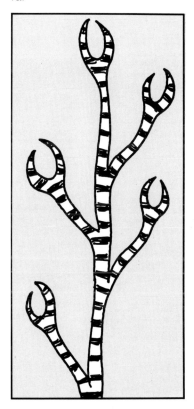

A thallus of *Ceramium* with the typical pincerlike tips (natural size about 5 mm).

⑤ Order Gigartinales

In the order Gigartinales there are two genera which we often find in coral reef aquaria, *Hypnea* and *Eucheuma*. The species which are most common in the aquarium have rather thin, slightly stiffened thalli. The two genera are rather difficult to tell apart, but the thallus of *Eucheuma* has a lot of protecti-ve, thorn-like structures, which make it look prickly.

Eucheuma is very common in the central area of the Indo-Pacific. About 20 species are found there, whereas there are only a few in the Caribbean and none at all in tropical West Africa. In some countries *Eucheuma* spp. are used to produce an aphrodisiac drink (an agent exciting sexual desire). They are also used as components in the production of many food and dairy products.

In this order we also find beautiful, rather exotic looking red algae in the genus *Gracilaria*. Most of these have a branched thallus and they are often red or brownish in colour. In the sea these red algae usually cling to coral rocks, on which they grow in shallow water.

❻ Order Cryptonemiales

One of the most common red algae on live rocks belongs to the genus *Halymenia*. Its thallus is mostly bright red and more or less lobed. There are numerous species in this genus. The one in the picture on page 313 grew beautifully in an aquarium with biological filtration, but it disappeared when a protein skimmer was added. In the genus *Ochtodes* we find magnificent species with marvellously iridescent colour – everything from blue to violet on a red background. If these algae are taken out of the water, they lose their beautiful colours

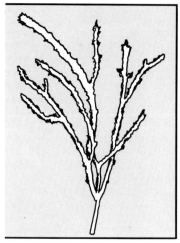

Above: Thallus of *Euchema*.
Left: Thallus of *Hypnea*.

and look brown. *Acanthophora spicifera* looks similar to *Ochtodes*, but is highly variable in colour. In our aquarium these algae grew from live rocks which had been placed directly under the HQI-lamp. They vanished, however, as fast as they had appeared.

❼ Red calcareous algae

Among the red algae there are many species that store larger amounts of calcium carbonate in their tissue: the red calcareous algae. They belong to several different genera, yet they have one

A beautiful colony of a *Halymenia* sp. in an aquarium with a low light intensity in the zoo in Bochum, Germany.

main characteristic: the structure of the calcium incrustations in their thallus. Aquarists will probably give up hope before long if they start trying to understand the systematics of this group of algae. This is why we will not try to arrange them in systematic groups here. More information about these taxonomic problems can be found in WOELKERLING (1988).

Some years ago making calcareous algae grow in a marine aquarium was still thought to be impossible. Only when modern technology and the latest findings in filtration methods and water processing were applied, and when, as the most crucial factor, live rocks were imported, it became possible to cultivate these extraordinarily important algae. Thus another fundamental type of orga-

This *Halymenia* sp. grew in an aquarium with biological filtration, yet it died, when a protein skimmer was added.

Above: Sometimes *Ochtodes* may display a magnificent purple colour. This contrasts beautifully with the yellow colonial anemones.

Sometimes we observe that an extraordinarily large bush of *Acanthophora spicifera* grows from live rock. These red algae prefer a high light intensity and grow extremely fast.

nism of the coral reef ecosystem could become a beneficial component of coral reef aquaria.

With the help of red calcareous algae we are able to create an aquarium decoration that gives a very natural impression of unity because it is caked together gradually by the growth of the algae. The hardening of the rocks is an important function of the red calcareous algae in the aquarium as well as on the reef. This process gives stability to the structure of the reef. The crucial importance of the red calcareous algae has only been realized recently. In some

In a coral reef aquarium different calcareous algae will certainly grow after a while.

reefs red calcareous algae may form crests, so-called "algal ridges", which protect the fauna behind them against heavy seas. There are some reefs which have been built up solely by calcareous algae. Red calcareous algae include only marine species. Most of them are cosmopolitan and thus can be found in all tropical seas.

To achieve a good growth of calcareous algae in a coral reef aquarium, it has to be ideally buffered with a regular addition of cal-

Beautiful colonies of two branching red calcareous algae on live rock: *Amphiroa* (left) and *Jania* (right).

cium ions and a carbonate hardness of around 8 °KH. This can be guaranteed best if "Kalkwasser" is added regularly (see pages 227 - 235). The growth of calcareous algae is also supported by a stable pH of not more than 8,5 (most easily achieved by an automatic CO_2- system). It is moreover important to realize that most red calcareous algae (especially those that do not branch out, but grow crustlike on their substrate) grow best at a moderate light intensity (along the sides of the aquarium or in the half-shade of

Colony of a crustlike red calcareous alga of the genus *Mesophyllum*.

In an exposed place in Flinders Reef in the Coral Sea we can find beautiful soft corals, gorgonians (the yellow gorgonian is *Isis hippuris*) and hermatypic stony corals on a reef platform. Everywhere between them there are red calcareous algae of the genera *Spongites* and *Lithophyllum*. They connect the pieces of coral rock and give the reef a stable structure. Red calcareous algae may also be described as "reef-hardening organisms".

overhanging pieces of rock in the bottom area of the aquarium). Our experience shows that they do not grow well under the direct light of HQI-lamp and grow more slowly there than in dim light. This corresponds to the natural way of life of red calcareous algae. Many species can even prevail in very dim light. Some have been found as deep down as 250 m, where the light intensity is extremely low, yet most of them inhabit areas that are not as deep as that.

There are two different types of shape that we find in red calcareous algae:

a) erect and branched,

b) creeping and crustlike.

Both types can also be found in coral reef aquaria. They reproduce either asexually by spores, which grow in inner sporangia, or sexually by germ cells from conceptacles (cavities) in the thallus. Conceptacles and sporangia can only be seen through a magnifying glass.

In a coral reef aquarium we realize nevertheless before long that the red calcareous algae reproduce. On the panes of a healthy aquarium we always find small red rings, which show us quite clearly that new colonies establish themselves. Nowadays we have to remove red calcareous algae from the panes of our aquaria as regularly as we had to do with filamentous algae in former times!

The genus *Jania* can be distinguished rather easily from other calcareous algae that grow in brushlike shapes. *Jania* spp. have segments which do not contain calcium carbonate, thus making the thallus flexible. The thallus and its branches are very thin. *Jania rubens* grows erect, its branches

form acute angles, and colonies may grow up to 6 cm high. In *Jania adherens*, another very common species, the angles between the branches are much wider so that these colonies grow broader rather than taller.

The genus *Neogoniolithon* also grows in a branched shape, yet it lacks the flexible segments between the branches. The branches are not always arranged as delicately, and may give an impression of coarseness compared to *Jania*.

The branches of *Neogoniolithon strictum* are up to 5 mm thick and have a lightly violet colour. In its natural surroundings this red calcareous alga often grows together with seaweeds along the coast and can be found growing freely on the bottom.

Neogoniolithon spectabile has such massive branches, that they do not look like branches, but rather like lumps. It develops into

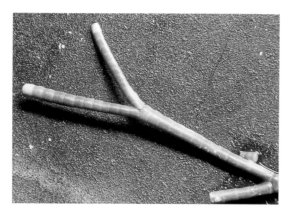 

Branching red calcareous algae may have round (left) or more flattened (right) thalli. The "joints" at a branching point may be more or less flexible, depending on how much calcium carbonate is deposited in them.

hard, lumpy, dark violet elevations on a firm substrate.

We find some of the most beautiful branched calcareous algae in the genus *Amphiroa*, which is very common in the Caribbean. Their thallus is often violet or reddish and develops thick ramifications with very flexible segments between the branches.

Amphiroa fragilissima has distinct thickenings on its segments, while *A. tribulus* has flattened branches. *A. brasiliana* has a splendid violet colour, grows more thickly, brushlike and not very high, and has a very hard thallus which is encrusted with calcium carbonate. *A. rigida* has cylindrical branches, in which the segments are only moderately flexible and have no thickenings. It grows in shallow water.

The genus *Lithophyllum*, which is among the especially robust calcareous algae, shows a crust-to lumplike shape. These algae store so much calcium carbonate that their thallus is as hard as rock, (lithos, gr. = stone and phyllon, gr. = leaf). In the reef these calcareous algae grow in zones that are extremely exposed to heavy seas, which explains their sturdy structure. Only rarely are live rocks collected in these zones so that *Lithophyllum* spp. are not so common in coral reef aquaria. In an aquarium they will certainly not grow in their typical shape, as they are not exposed to the extreme conditions of their natural surroundings.

Mesophyllum spp., which are tile-shaped, are very often found in coral reef aquaria. Under favour-

able conditions magnificent colonies may develop. Colonies of this size and beauty can only rarely be seen in the sea, because they are continuously grazed on by certain herbivores, e.g. sea urchins. Such herbivores should not be introduced into coral reef aquaria in which these calcareous algae are supposed to grow. A thin white band along the edge of the thallus is a sure sign that the *Mesophyllum* are growing.

Sporadically we have found calcareous algae of the genus *Titanoderma* in coral reef aquaria. The species in this genus have a typical violet colour with grey areas. These areas result from surface cells that have been cast off. They are supposed to protect the algae against epiphytes which would otherwise overgrow them.

The thalli of *Amphiroa* spp. may be very decorative. In the picture to the left an *Amphiroa* sp. grows around a soft coral of the species *Sinularia dura*. The picture to the right shows a tightly-packed growing colony of an *Amphiroa* sp. The colony only covered an area of 12 x 18 mm.

The beautiful dark red to chestnut brown calcareous algae of the genus *Peyssonnelia* are among the red calcareous algae that can do with a low light intensity. In a reef near the island of Kuredu, Maldives, we found them on the underside of a rock boulder.

Also found encrusting the rocks and walls of aquariums sometimes, *Peyssonnelia* spp. are very beautiful and have an intense dark red colour. In their natural surroundings they are found from the water surface down to depths of 200 m. In an aquarium we found one red calcareous alga which probably belongs to this genus. It was one of the first red calcareous algae that developed in a newly set up coral reef aquarium. Unfortunately it often seems to disappear only a short time after it has appeared or it is overgrown by *Mesophyllum* spp.

The genus *Spongites* (synonym *Porolithon*) is among the most common calcareous algae of the reef, where it grows on less

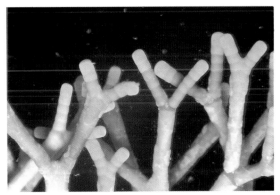

The intensity of the light has great influence on the shape of the thallus of the genus *Amphiroa* (left): thallus under (a) light of high intensity and (b) low intensity. The shape of the "joints" (right) of branching red calcareous algae is often a quality that characterizes species or genera.

exposed reef edges and develops as a low, calcareous coating with violet colour. In the Caribbean *Spongites pachiderma* is very common and one of the more important reef-building organisms. *S. onkodes* is very often found in the Indo-Pacific and most often on the leeward side of exposed reefs, where *Paragoniolithon conicum* also grows. This is a low, crustlike calcareous alga and another important organism that helps to stabilize the structure of the reef. Red calcareous algae also harden live rock and other materials in the coral reef aquarium, which serves to stabilize the decoration.

If live rocks are used as decoration of a coral reef aquarium beautiful colonies of red calcareous algae of the genus *Mesophyllum* may develop on them after some time.

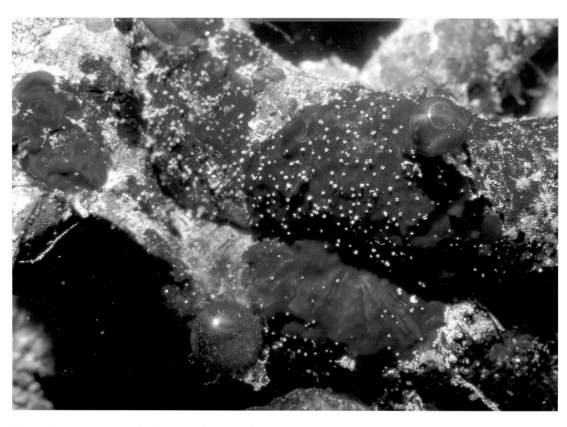

In a coral reef aquarium red calcareous algae grow best only in areas with a low light intensity. This *Peyssonnelia* was growing on the bottom of a small cave.

Most of the more than 1000 dinoflagellates that we know are single-celled and microscopically small. Along the northern coasts of Europe there is an algal bloom of dinoflagellates regularly late in summer and in autumn, so that the water turns dark brown. Such an explosive increase of algae is also very common in tropical areas, but not on coral reefs because water conditions are stable there. Larger amounts of nutrients are usually not added, and the conditions are regarded as nutrient poor.

In a coral reef aquarium a higher nutrient content may easily lead to an increase in the growth of algae. This will usually be noticed first on the front pane, on which a yellow green algae coating will grow. If you look at this algae coating through a microscope, you will find various diatoms and a heavy growth of dinoflagellates (see page 275 at the bottom). Sometimes a filamentous growth of flagellates resembling that of the blue-green algae can colonize the reef aquarium.

It may seem strange, but it is just a tiny dinoflagellate that is mainly responsible for the existence of the coral reefs. Without it there would not be any coral reefs!

Zooxanthellae

The fluorescent colours of corals are caused by the many UV-protecting pigments produced by the animal (see chapter 8). Most corals are, however, brownish. In most cases it is an alga that lives in the endoderm of the coral (see picture below) which is responsible for these shades. It is the dinoflagellate *Gymnodinium microadriaticum* (some authors place this species in the monotypical genus *Symbiodinium*). These dinoflagel-

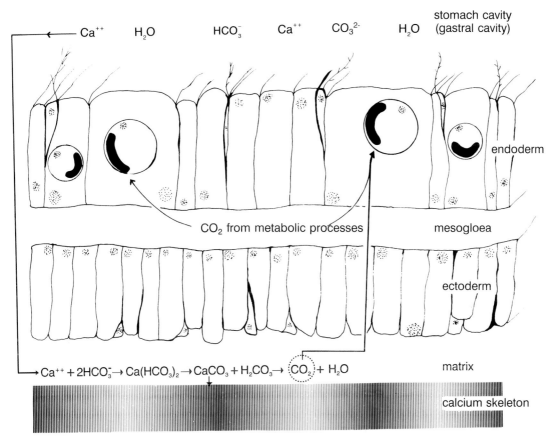

Diagram of the calcium carbonate synthesis in cnidarians: the zooxanthellae are shown as spheres in the endoderm. In the stomach cavity of the animal there is seawater which contains calcium ions and carbonates among other substances. The calcium synthesis takes place in the matrix between the ectoderm and the calcium skeleton. When the zooxanthellae take CO_2 from the calcium bicarbonate, calcium carbonate ($CaCO_3$) in the form of aragonite is precipitated. Some CO_2 that is used by the zooxanthellae is also produced by the metabolism of the host.

(**Drawing after** Schuhmacher, **1982**).

lates, which are algae, are called zooxanthellae.

When the symbiotic relationship between the zooxanthellae and the coral polyps was discovered around 1930, it soon became clear that this was the most important discovery this century in the research on coral reefs. Since then a lot of scientific treatments on the biology of the zooxanthellae have been published, yet their overall importance for the life history of the corals has not been fully appreciated. Many scientists

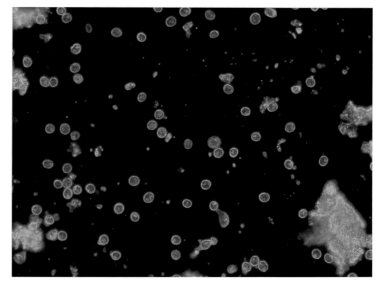

The tiny algae *Gymnodinium microadriaticum* are of crucial importance for the existence of the coral reefs; here in the tissue of the blue coral, *Heliopora coerulea* (magnification 560x).

have done research on these symbiotic algae. Among them T. F. GOREAU and L. MUSCATINE are perhaps two of the most prominent ones. The results of the work on the importance of calcium fixation in hermatypic corals in the fifties and sixties were revolutionary.

The number of zooxanthellae in coral tissue can be very high – up to 1 million algae per cubic centimetre. Even the larvae of many corals already contain zooxan-

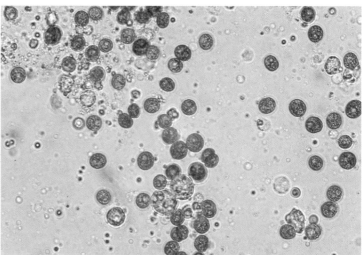

If we look at a slide preparation of the tissue of the stony coral *Euphyllia ancora* through a microscope, the zooxanthellae are clearly visible (magnification 1100x).

thellae. 7400 zooxanthellae were found in the larva of a *Porites* stony coral 1 mm long.

The life of the corals in the milieu of the coral reef with its low amount of nutrients depends highly on the symbiosis with these zooxanthellae. They are – like all plants – primary producers in the coral reef and provide oxygen and organic compounds rich in energy by photosynthesis using the carbon dioxide in the water. The light of the sun provides the energy for this process.

If a phase-contrast is used the zooxanthellae may be seen even more clearly (magnification 1100x).

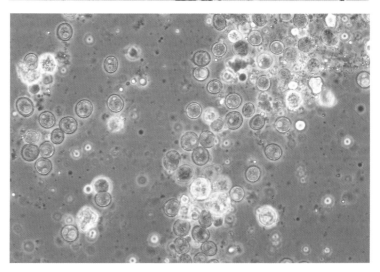

The intensity of the light affects corals greatly. The species on reef flats are flooded with light with a high portion of ultraviolet radiation. They have zooxanthellae that differ morphologically from those that we find in corals that are exposed to less light, and it is now known that different strains of zooxanthellae adapted to different conditions exist among corals.

Under intense solar radiation the amount of symbiotic algae is decreased while the amount of UV-protective pigments is increased (see chapter 8). The zooxanthellae also show several adaptations to weaker light. In order to optimize the fixation of carbon in deeper waters and in shade, the zooxanthellae change the content of pigments (chlorophyll a, chlorophyll c2 and peridinin) as well as the activity of enzymes. See in particular MUSCATINE (1990), DUNLAP & CHALKER (1986), MOHAN (1990), and SHIBATA (1969).

The compounds rich in energy produced by the zooxanthellae are glucose, glycerine, amino acids and organic phosphates. Extensive research, in the field as well as in the laboratory, has shown that some of these compounds are transferred from the cells of the algae to the cells of the host animal. Most prominent among these compounds are glucose, alanine, glycine and glycerol (MUSCATINE, 1973). This phenomenon, called translocation, is an important reason why such a large biomass like the corals in a coral reef are able to exist in an environment that has such a low nutrient content.

There are differences from one species to the next in the degree to which translocation can meet the energy demand of its host colony. VERON (1986) reports that up to 98 % of the nutrient demand is met by translocation. MUSCATINE et al. (1981) found that in *Pocillopora damicornis* and *Fungia scutaria* in Hawaiian reefs 63 to 69 % of the energy demand was met that way. In *Pocillopora eydouxi* the degree to which this happens is variable, as DAVIS (1984) reports. Under favourable conditions 90 % of the

A bunch of dead zooxanthellae are expelled from a polyp of the stony coral *Euphyllia divisa.*

demand were met, yet the average value was 51 %. DAVIS also adds that the average value of 40 % that is often quoted is slightly too low.

Like all plants zooxanthellae need nutrients, especially nitrogen and phosphorus. Readings taken in the Great Barrier Reef showed concentrations of these substances as nitrate (0.002 mg/l) and as phosphate (0.016 mg/l) (FURNAS et al., 1990). This concentration is so low that it is not sufficient, at least theoretically, to keep the ecosystem alive. Nitrogen and phosphorus are in short supply in the coral reef and are

therefore limiting factors for the growth of the algae. How do zooxanthellae solve this problem? Probably in two ways: On the one hand the low concentrations of the nutrients dissolved in the seawater (in the first place ammonium, nitrite, nitrate, phosphate and carbon dioxide) are taken in directly from the water – through the cell tissue of the host animal. On the other hand the substances are recycled, i.e. they are used several times. First they are transferred to the algae which make use of them for photosynthesis and respiration. Thus they become part of the organic compounds rich in energy that are now transferred back to the host. The host burns these nutrients thus gaining the energy it needs to survive. At the same time it produces metabolic wastes which contain valuable algae nutrients. These are not excreted into the surroundings, but are utilized in part or completely by the zooxanthellae. Thus the process of re-cycling is complete, a great example of how two organisms can survive by symbiosis in surroundings devoid of nutrients.

Zooxanthellae are of great importance for hermatypic stony corals and other reef-building organisms for another reason. Stony corals build their skeleton from calcium carbonate ($CaCO_3$). Calcium ions are available in the water as calcium hydrogen carbonate ($Ca(HCO_3)_2$), which is balanced with calcium carbonate and carbon dioxide:

$$Ca^{2+} + 2HCO_3^- \leftrightarrow CaCO_3 + H_2CO_3 \leftrightarrow CO_2 + H_2O$$

According to the Law of Chemical Equilibrium we find a certain relation between the mass of the various compounds that are chemically balanced. By meeting their demand of CO_2 the zooxanthellae shift the balance to the right. The calcium carbonate ($CaCO_3$) in the formula above is precipitated in its crystalline form aragonite, which the corals use to build their skele-

Life cycle of the zooxanthellae *Gymnodinium microadriaticum*: 1, 2 and 3 show different stages in the growth of the algae cells. In stage 3 they divide, so that cells develop that are physiologically young (1) and old (2). The oldest cells are expelled by the host coral. In addition to normal daughter cells, sporangia can grow that develop motile zoospores. Thus the alga can spread to other coral colonies. Zooxanthellae may also reproduce sexually. A normal cell undergoes a reduction division (7) and develops gametes with a haploid set of chromosomes (8). These motile gametes (9) unite to form a normal algal cell (k = chloroplast and n = nucleus. (Drawing after TAYLOR, 1969)

ton (see also the drawing on page 319).

SIMKISS (1964a and b) points out that phosphate disturbs the building up of the coral skeleton. The fact that zooxanthellae consume phosphate helps to improve the ability of the corals to build up their skeleton.

The increased fixation of calcium only takes place when light is available, i.e. during the photosynthesis of the zooxanthellae. The light intensity has to be high enough to penetrate the outer layers of the tissue of the host. The spectral structure of the available light is also important (see chapter 8).

Zooxanthellae contain a lot of pigments and their absorbing capacity is nearly total. Of the carotenoids Perinidin, Neoperinidin, Dinoxanthin and Diadinoxanthin are present. Moreover xanthophylls and chlorophyll a as well as small amounts of chlorophyll c2 are found. Zooxanthellae not only pro-

duce sugar compounds and amino acids, but also fat and fatty acids with the help of a specific light-dependent reaction. They can also store fatty substances. About 40 % of the dry substance of a coral colony consists of fat that is used as a food reserve.

The drawing below shows the life cycle of the zooxanthellae. It shows that after some time they reach a stage at which the hosts get rid of them. We can observe this process when at certain intervals brown masses are excreted from the mouths of the animals (see page 321).

Most of the corals from shallow water zones have zooxanthellae. When we buy these corals we have to check carefully if these zooxanthellae are alive. If colonies of species that usually have bright colours look pale or even white, the reason may be that the zooxanthellae have died already. If the colonies look beautifully coloured and fluorescent, we may sa-

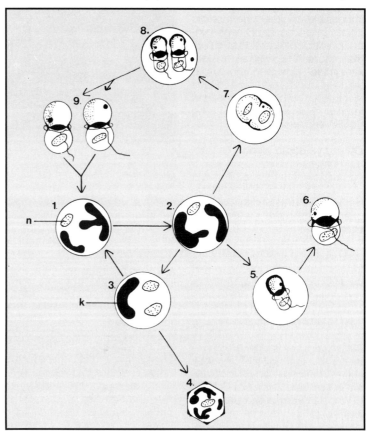

Not just corals, other reef organisms as well live in a symbiotic relationship with zooxanthellae; here a giant clam, *Tridacna crocea* in a coral reef aquarium.

Photo: Dr. D. Brockmann

fely assume that the zooxanthellae are alive. If we introduce a healthy stony coral into an aquarium that is lighted by HQI-light and has good water quality, thus providing healthy surroundings, most corals will develop beautiful colours before long. If they have previously been kept at a lower light intensity they have to be adapted to HQI-light gradually.

We think that hermatypic stony corals are among the most interesting organisms that can be kept in a coral reef aquarium. If we are successful in making them thrive or perhaps even reproduce, we may witness one of the most fascinating phenomena of the coral reef – the fixation of calcium. One of the main reasons why people thought for a long time that it was impossible to keep hermatypic corals in an aquarium was probably a lack of knowledge about the important function of the zooxanthellae. However, the knowledge about the zooxanthellae is increasing, but still there is a lot to learn and new results are being published every year.

Other symbiotic algae

Apart from cnidarians other organisms in the reef are known to live in a symbiotic relationship with algae. Among them are the giant clams of the family Tridacnidae, which most aquarists know quite well. These clams have zooxanthellae very similar to those that we find in corals. *Gymnodinium microadriaticum* is not the only alga that leads a symbiotic life.

Among the sponges (Porifera)

The colonial sea squirt *Didemnum molle* contains unique symbiotic algae belonging to the genus *Prochloron*. The algae are responsible for the intense green colour inside the colony.

Photo: L. Newman and A. Flowers

there are several species that contain symbiotic blue-green algae (Cyanophyta, see also page 277). Some sponges get some 50-75% of their energy budget from blue-green symbionts. These species are normally found on the reef slope, but can also occur in very shallow water and are named "autothropic" sponges. The common *Carteriospongia 'foliascens* is a good excample of such a sponge. Other sponges are mixothropic (auto-heterothropic) and rely to a medium- or minor extent on the activity of their symbionts. When we examined the tissue of the commonly imported autothroph sponge, *Collospongia auris* we found small blue-green algae of an as yet unknown species. We will return to the sponges in detail in volume 3 in this series of books.

The symbiotic algae of certain ascidians, e.g. *Didemnum molle* from the family Didemnidae, are even more interesting. In the cloacal cavity of the zooids we find algae from the genus *Prochloron*. Although the algae are not endoparasites like the zooxanthellae, they take part in the nutrition of the host. *Prochloron* are not found anywhere else in the nature and show similarities both with green and blue-green algae. The algae are classified in a new division - Prochlorophyta, although some scientists think they are true blue-greens.

This sponge (above), *Collospongia auris*, is now and then introduced into our coral reef aquaria on live rocks. A microscopic examination of the tissue revealed small symbiotic blue-green algae (below). The brown mass to the right of the picture is the mashed sponge tissue, while the algae can be seen as tiny blue dots to the left (magnification 560x).

algae. In such an aquarium the algae would dominate and the fish and invertebrates would be of secondary importance only. For such an algae aquarium we would probably prefer the "biological system", which induces a higher nutrient content of the aquarium water.

Résumé

The variety of algae is almost unbelievable. In this chapter we could only deal with some genera and species very briefly. We think, however, that apart from the zooxanthellae only red calcareous algae should be kept dominant in a coral reef aquarium. Other algae should only be allowed to grow in small patches.

Marine aquarists that have a special interest in algae may of course set up an aquarium only for

Further reading

Algae in general

BECKER, 1982; DRING, 1982; KSIENSYK, 1982; HOEK, 1984; ROUND, 1973; LÜNING, 1985.

Algae on the reef

BOROWITZKA & LARKUM, 1986; GOREAU, 1961, 1963; HILLIS- COLINVAUX, 1986; SCHREWE, 1996; LITTLER et al., 1989; MARSHALL, 1996; ROBERTS & MACINTYRE, 1988.

Calcareous algae

WRAY, 1977; WOELKERLING, 1988.

Diatoms

AMIR, 1982.

Slime algae (Blue-green algae)

AMIR, 1987; CARR & WHITTON, 1993; Editors of "Das Aquarium", 1981; DEURING, 1982; FOGG et al., 1973; HEINZ, 1983a; HUSTER, 1985; THEUNS, 1985, 1986; KNOP, 1987; WILKENS, 1985b.

Filamentous algae

WILKENS, 1985a.

Algae-eating animals

HEINZ, 1983b.

Zooxanthellae

BUCHSBAUM & MUSCATINE 1971; KREMER, 1985; NILSEN, 1983; SCHUHMACHER, 1976; STEEL, 1975, 1976; STEEL & GOREAU, 1977; MUSCATINE, 1990; TAYLOR, 1968, 1969, 1973; TRENCH, 1971; WEBB & WIEBE, 1978, YAMAZATO, 1970; YONGE, 1936, 1968; YONGE & NICHOLS, 1931.

Pocillopora eydouxi in the waters of Kailua-Kona, Hawaii.   Underwater photo: Dr. D. Brockmann

Pseudanthias squamipinnis   Photo: G. Spies

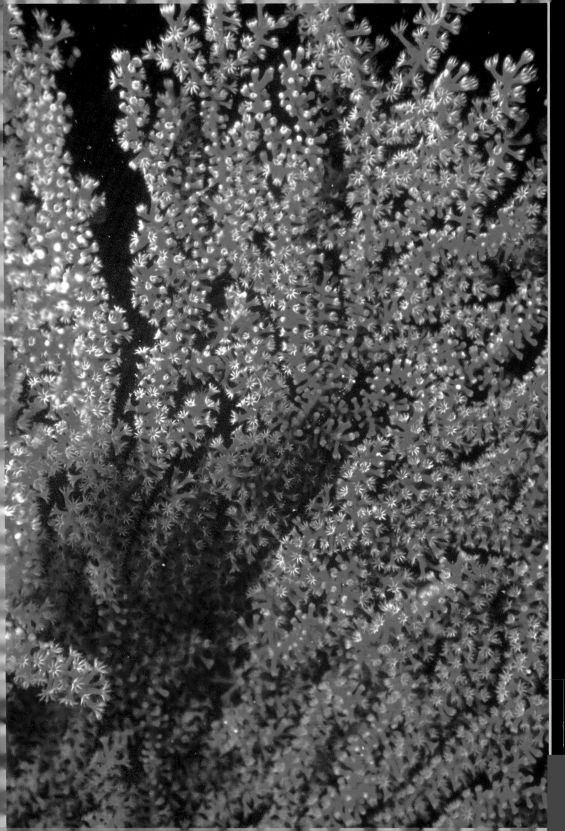

Chapter 14

Marine Aquaristics and Nature Conservation

During the last several years there has been a lot of criticism of what is described as the over-exploitation of natural resources by the trade in aquarium fishes. This criticism turned even harsher when it became more widely known that in the Philippines aquarium fish were caught with the help of cyanide. In this chapter we will deal with some aspects of this criticism and summarize some points of view that stress the important role of aquaristics and the merits of aquarists in the conservation of nature and the stimulation of the love of nature.

Above: Angelfish *Pomacanthus imperator* in its natural surrounding.   Underwater photo: Dr. A. Spreinat

Left: Coral reefs are very sensitive ecosystems. Here a gorgonian in the lagoon of Madang, Papua New Guinea.
Underwater photo: Dr. D. Brockmann

Traditionally most of the coral fish were caught with handnets by divers. When competition increased between the catchers who supplied the export companies with fish, people started experimenting with anaesthetics to get hold of the fish more easily. Different chemical substances were tried out, among which "Rotenone" and "sodium cyanide" had the strongest toxic effects (KVALVÅGNÆS, 1982).

Catching coral fish with the help of cyanide is most common in the Philippines (ROBINSON, 1983-1985), but it is also a widely used method in Indonesia (KVALVÅGNÆS, 1982). According to information we received from this author (personal communication) cyanide catching is also known to be used in eastern Malaysia. He supposes that this method is equally, though not widely used in other states in South East Asia. KVALVÅGNÆS holds the opinion that cyanide catching is not practised to a large extent in other parts of the world, and that it is not used at all in Hawaii, the Caribbean nor in the Red Sea.

Fish that have been anaesthetized with cyanide seem to be perfectly healthy when they are put into a tank with fresh seawater after they have been caught. However, this is not the case! Cyanide poisoning destroys large parts of the enzyme system, and the digestive organs in particular. Fatal harm is done to these fish and they are usually doomed. Not just the fish caught are harmed, the same also happens to the fish, corals and all other animals that remain on the reef. The negative effects on the corals are not as bad, however, as some people claim. Those kinds of corals that serve as hiding places or spawning sites for coral fishes are particularly affected by the cyanide. Quite obviously these are the places to which the cyanide is applied directly by the divers. On the whole dynamite fishing and the great amount of sediment washed out on reefs because of land erosion as a consequence of clearing large areas of woodland are much more detrimental to the corals (McALLISTER, 1988).

Divers that use cyanide put their health and life at risk. ROBINSON (personal communication) tells us about serious illnesses among the population of fishing ports in the Philippines which may be attributed to cyanide poisoning. KVALVÅGNÆS (personal communication) observed four deaths of fishermen who had used cyanide in Indonesia within a short period of time.

Cyanide fishing is not just a problem for nature and the fishermen, but it is highly problematic for the pet trade as well. Fish caught with cyanide may continue to live for a period of some weeks or even to up several months. So the duration of the transport is the decisive factors that determines where the fish die, in the aquaria of the exporting firm, at the wholesaler's, the aquarium shop or in the aquarist's tank. When people found out at the end of the seventies why the fish kept dying, reputable firms stopped dealing with those who had caught their fish with cyanide – if they could find out about it.

Today the major exporting firms in Indonesia take care that divers who use cyanide are excluded from business KVALVÅGNÆS (personal communication). The problem is, however, that divers may have made high profits already before exporters find out about their nasty methods.

In the Philippines exporters themselves were often involved in these methods, so that most of the fish from there were caught with cyanide. Official certificates were issued, saying that certain exporting firms were selling only fish free of the poison. Yet the validity of these certificates was most doubtful, as even state officials and politicians were involved with cyanide catching during the period of the corrupt Marcos regime (RoBINSON, personal communication). The organisation "International Marine-Life Alliance" (IMA), which resides in Hingham, Massachusetts, USA, taught and trained fishermen in its education campaigns to stop them from using poison and to make them use hand nets instead. After this training the fishermen were as successful in catching the fish or even more so than before, when they had used poison (ROBINSON, personal communication).

Without the support of the state the work of the IMA was to no avail. After the assumption of power by Corazon Aquino, the situation improved greatly, as the IMA points out. McALLISTER (1988) reports on the "First Asian Fisheries Forum", where a number of Philippine scientists and state officials, among them the Secretary of State for Agriculture and Food, Ramon Mitra jr, severely criticised cyanide fishing. Other positive results of this forum are revealed by the following quotations from the article in question:

"We read in newspapers of the seizure of hundreds of pounds of cyanide intended for catching aquarium fishes."

"... the government caught a 100-foot ship with over twenty 50-kilogram barrels of cyanide intended for lapu lapu (grouper) food fishing."

"... near Bolinao ... I saw and photographed aquarium fish collectors (previously trained by Steve Robinson) catching coral fishes. The collectors were very effective ... So it is clear that nets are an efficient and economical method of catching aquarium fish."

"He (Minister Ramon Mitra jr.) ended by giving us firm written approval for the IMA's program to train fishermen to use small fine-meshed nets instead of cyanide for catching aquarium fishes."

"Support from the industry is growing. In the Philippines aquarium

For our coral reef aquaria we want healthy fish that have not been harmed by poison: above a goby of the genus *Crypto-centrus* (photo: J. Frische); below: the Maldives anemonefish *Amphiprion nigripes* protecting its brood (underwater photo: Dr. D. Brockmann).

Not only fishes are harmed by cyanide, but also invertebrates, especially delicate animals like symbiotic shrimps, – *Periclimenes yucatanicus* above, *Thor amboinensis* below – or tube-worms – two beautiful species from the family Sabellidae are shown to the right.

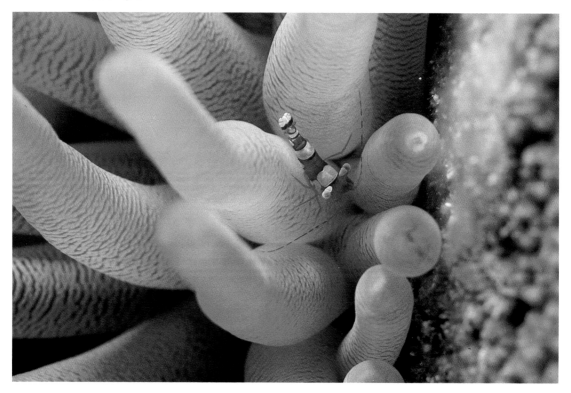

and his associates were early supporters of the netsman program. Manuela flew to the United States to purchase nets."

"Following negotiations with IMA president Pratt, ... the Assistant Minister of Agriculture and Food, Phillip Ella Juico, and exporter Richard Ty, president of the Philippine Tropical Fish Exporters Association, a three-way accord was signed on developing, staffing, financing and undertaking a pilot netsman project in Pagbilao."

Catching coral fish with dynamite

The method of catching fish by exploding dynamite under water is well known. Most of the countries (all of them?) where coral reefs are found have banned dynamite fishing by now. Nevertheless this method is still widely used illegally.

LANDNER (1985) writes:
"Use of explosives to catch fish, though illegal, is rampant in many coral reef areas. The explosives not only kill the larval, juvenile and adult fish together with other marine organisms of no commercial value, but also destroy the reefs, which provide the ecological basis for the very resource that is being exploited. The reefs, once damaged by explosives, might not always recover to their original state, as they might be overgrown by algae resulting in a deflected climax, as is often observed."

RECK (1991) writes about Sri Lanka:
"I saw fishermen catching fish with dynamite. Without exception all the fish that had been swimming peacefully near the zone of the detonation earlier, adult fish or juveniles, were now floating on the surface."

Dynamate fishing can destroy life in coral reefs completely.   Underwater photo: Dr. D. Brockmann

So dynamite fishing is still widely used to catch food fish. Yet now and then also the pet fish trade is accused of being involved with this catching method. In our opinion it is absolutely impossible that fish caught by dynamiting could still be in an acceptable condition to be sold as aquarium fish. This opinion is supported by KVALVÅG-NÆS (personal communication), who moreover firmly denies that aquarium fish are ever caught with dynamite.

Over-exploitation of coral reefs

Fishing can of course, whatever its purpose may be, lead to over-exploitation of the populations of targetted species. The more effec-

tive a fishing method is, the greater is the danger of wiping out the populations of certain species in a certain area. Fisheries in the northern Atlantic is an all too typical example. If populations are decimated in one area, however, there is still a chance that they may recover, if the populations are sensibly managed.

It is a much greater threat to species if they are endangered by the pollution and destruction of their habitats, e.g. by building operations or environmental disasters. So far catastrophes of this kind have not happened to marine species on a large scale. Yet examples of freshwater fishes to which they happened are only too well known. During the last fifty years at least five fish species have been wiped out in the Death Valley in California, because of grave changes that affected their habitat (SOLTZ & NAIMAN, 1978). We would like to stress here that none of the Death Valley species were commercially available in the aquarium trade.

The opinions of scientists are divided on the question of how many coral fish may safely be taken from a coral reef without endangering the whole population. Yet there are people who insist that there is an unbroken chain of evidence that enormous damage is done to coral reefs. Such allegations cannot be taken without a word of protest.

There is no doubt about the fact that coral reefs are very productive biological systems as compared to other regions of the sea.

BARNES (1980) writes:
"... coral reefs are one of the most productive marine environments."

LANDNER (1985) states: "... coral reefs have a very high biological productivity... As a matter of fact, coral reefs have been considered as being the most productive of all natural ecosystems on earth ..." and "An important aspect of the high productivity of a coral reef is its

In the reef divers may encounter shoals of innumerable individuals, here a shoal of sweepers.

Underwater photo: G. Spies

abundant fish life: It has been estimated that the standing stock of reef fishes, in some instances, may be as high as 5 to 15 times that of the highly productive North Atlantic fishing grounds. The potential fish yield of coral reefs could, according to some estimates,

be around 40-50 kg/hectar/year. Another estimate for reefs in the Philippines, came to figures as high as 80-140 kg/hectar/year... one can imagine how valuable the coral reefs may be to the fisheries industries of tropical maritime nations that have coral reefs."

Such a high degree of productivity also implies that the reproduction rate of the individual species is quite high, whereas at the same time the natural mortality during the development from the egg to the adult fish is enormous. (Of course this holds true as well for the

Coral reefs are the most productive ocean areas. If the people who catch coral fishes for the aquarium are under control of an authority and act in a responsible way there is no danger of overfishing.

Underwater photos: E. Svensen (to the left), Dr. D. Brockmann (above)

A dead giant clam *Tridacna maxima* in a coral reef off the Maldives. It is estimated that several million giant clames have been killed since 1960 alone at the northern part of the Great Barrier Reef, Australia, to obtain the adductor muscles which are sold in Asia as a delicacy (BROCKMANN, 1992, and references therein). This clam was probably killed by disease or a natural predator.
Underwater photo: Dr. D. Brockmann

ted is extremely low as compared to the amount of food fish caught from the reef. In 1977 coral reef fishing in Indonesia yielded 2,300 tons of food fish, but only 35 tons of aquarium fish (RAHARDJO, 1984). The survey of the food fishes of the western Indian Ocean in FISCHER & BIANCHI (1984) (published by the FAO, Food and Agricultural Organization of the United Nations) mentions a large number of coral reef fishes. Many species that are popular as aquarium fishes, are included here among the food fish that are commercially exploited. Unfortunately there are no statistics on the fishing quota added here.

Dangers to coral reefs

most common aquarium fish.) WILLIAMS et al. (1986) write about this: "There is evidence that fewer than one recruit is returned for every 100 thousand to 1 million eggs cast into the sea."

A heavy decline of a population caused by fishing or by any other kind of death of the fish results in increased reproduction rates! To corroborate this we would like to quote an example from BOHNSACK (1983): "In January 1977, a record breaking cold spell caused fish kills at Big Pine Key, Florida. Census data collected before and after the cold spell... showed a significant drop in mean number of reef fish species and individuals... During the summer of 1977, a significantly smaller mean fish size and a significantly greater mean number of species and individuals were observed... Contrary to some theoretical predictions, results suggest reef communities are highly resilient to some regional disturbance."

There has been research into the natural mortality of many coral reef fishes in places where no fish were caught. The study of ALDENHOVE (1986) on the bicolor angelfish, *Centropyge bicolor*, which is

a popular aquarium fish, may be quoted here as an example. Research was carried out on the populations of Australia's Great Barrier Reef. The mortality rate of adult, sexually mature individuals during a period of three and a half years at four different localities was 50%, 77%, 79%, and 93.5% respectively. With immature individuals the mortality rate during a period of two years at the same four localities was 31%, 23%. 12.5% and 0.0% per 2.2 months – in other words: the reproduction rate is very high.

In his study of the situation in Hawaii TAYLOR (1978) claims that it is highly unlikely that the catching of reef fishes for aquarium purposes could pose a threat to the populations. He writes: "The probability that one or more species of fish may be endangered in Hawaii by the concentrated fishing of aquarium collectors is extremely low. The recruitment rate of the most frequently collected fishes is very high. In addition, collecting techniques are so labour-intensive that it is impractical and inefficient to collect all of the individuals of a particular species in a limited area."

Finally it may be added that the quantity of aquarium fish collec-

We thoroughly dislike the common habit of drying and bleaching corals to trade them as souvenirs or as decorations for aquaria. Even if perhaps no real harm is done by this, we think that the "slaughter" of corals for this kind of purpose is absolutely futile. Dead coral skeletons are not interesting for use in modern coral reef aquaria anyway.

Live stony corals and live rocks are of much greater importance for contemporary marine aquaristics. Now that we have found out so much more about the requirements of many coral species, they can be kept in aquaria with great success. Growth and reproduction in corals is now the rule, rather than the exception. As the stony corals are the "builders of the reef", it is unconditionally necessary to examine scientifically any kind of exploitation of these animals. Most of the countries where coral reefs are found have by now passed laws that regulate the trade with them. Moreover all stony corals are protected by the CITES (Convention on International Trade in Endangered Species of Wild

Aquarists do not use great amounts of corals for the decoration of their coral reef aquaria. The overexploitation of the coral reefs must be blamed on others – here a boat in the Maldives is loaded to the top with corals and live rocks which are used in the construction of houses.

Flora and Fauna). Importers from countries that have joined CITES must have export licenses (CITES certificates) made out by appropriate authorities of the exporting countries. These papers certify that the export of the corals does not endanger in any way the populations of these animals in their natural surroundings. Moreover the amounts of corals, live rock and coral sand which are taken from the reefs for aquaristic purposes are minimal compared to the amounts taken for other commercial purposes like the building of houses and roads, or lime burning.

Under the heading "Threats of Coral Reefs" SCHUHMACHER (1982) mentions a number of factors which he considers present dangers to the reefs:

- Pollution (introduction of nutrients) from households and centres of tourism cause increasing growth of algae, which then compete with and overgrow the corals. This can clearly be observed off Eilat and Aquaba in the Red Sea and in the Kaneohe-Bay, Hawaii.

- Oil spills causes great harm to corals and other sessile organisms. Coral reefs near large ports are continually exposed to oil pol-

Building an airport in the middle of nowhere! The Maldives are a perfect example of how tourism directly and indirectly affects the coral reefs. In order to get the necessary area for an airport, artificial land has been created from coral rock. Can you imagine how many aquaria could have been decorated by the rock used to build this single runway alone? Still it is the aquarium industry who gets the blame for exploiting live rock! But of course, tourism also provides necessary income.   Photo: K. Nagy

considerably the chances of the species there to regenerate their populations.

- Sports divers cause destruction when they try to anchor their boats, thus ploughing through the bottom of the coral reef, breaking off pieces of coral colonies or damaging them otherwise. Other tourist activities like wandering across the reef at low tide can cause considerable damage as well. Studies of the surrounding area of a large centre for tourism at the Great Barrier Reef show that the amount of coral material destroyed every year by such activities exceeds the amount of material added to the reef by the growth of the corals.

Even though it is forbidden, corals are removed from the reefs in Sri Lanka as well to produce building materials for the construction of houses (above) and roads. The heaps of coral rubble along the roadsides (below) bear witness to the extent of this overexploitation. Parts of the reefs are damaged so severely that unchecked breakers can devastate the coast at times of rough sea.

Photos: K. Reck

- Soil erosion caused by e.g. construction sites, may lead to the deposition of mud. Sediment layers off Hawaii have grown as thick as 1.6 m during a period of only 40 years.

SCHUHMACHER does not refer to aquaristics in this connection, LANDNER, however, writes: "It is anticipated that this trade will further increase, which may lead to overexploitation of this particular resource."

In his paper "Human activities causing reef degradation" LANDNER does not mention aquaristics, but he refers to the following harmful influences instead:

- commercialised coral mining,
- dynamite fishing,
- tourist activities like diving and snorkelling,
- soil erosion caused by the destruction of forests and by adverse or incorrect agricultural methods used,
- the dumping of sewage and coolants,
- oil pollution,
- the selective catching of key organisms in the food chain and
- excavation work and building activities which cause sedimentation.

lution. This causes growth disorders and reduces fertility in the corals. Delicate species are often completely eliminated.

- In spite of the fact that dynamite fishing is forbidden, it is a widely used method, nevertheless. The immense increase of the human population is the reason why conventional fishing methods cannot meet the demand for food fish. The yields in dynamite fishing are high, yet the numbers of fish that thus are killed without being used are much higher. Its harmful influence on the structure of the reef in general at the same time reduces

In Germany angelfishes may not be offered for sale. This is definately not logical, because they are not threatened in their natural surroundings and not difficult to keep in an aquarium. The blue-face angelfish, *Pomacanthus xanthometopon* is one of the more delicate ones and should only be imported at a size smaller than 10 to 15 cm.

Death rate of animals in the aquarium trade

Many authors report incredibly high losses in the trade with coral reef animals, especially in transit. Allegations that 30 to 40 % of the fish in a consignment die are not at all uncommon. Such a high death rate may occur on rare occasions, e.g. if flights are delayed or cancelled (virtually all shipments of aquarium fish today are by air-freight). If high percentages like these were representative aquarists would hardly be able to pay for the animals arriving alive. Trade would be brought to a standstill automatically. These allegations disprove themselves by their lack of logic.

Nobody wants to conceal, however, that certain species are more delicate than others. Even if the CITES regulations do not yet impose any restrictions on the trade with coral fishes, the OFI (Ornamental Fish International, an organization representing the world wide aquatic industry) have admonished their members to make sure that *Chaetodon trifasciatus*, the redfin butterflyfish, is not imported and offered for sale anymore. This species is an extremely delicate, highly specialized feeder which is close to impossible to keep alive in an aquarium.

We think it is important that aquarists who find out by personal experience that certain species cannot be kept successfully in an aquarium consciously accept their responsibility and say **NO** as far as these species are concerned. Self-restraint is the best answer to emotional and subjective hostilities. Reputable aquarium shops should, of their own ac-

cord, not offer species for sale that are difficult to keep in an aquarium or cannot be kept there at all. It is irresponsible and also bad for business to sell animals that a customer will not be able to keep successfully. There are huge numbers of species that can thrive and in time possibly even reproduce in a aquaria for years and years.

It is important to point out in this connection the enormous progress that marine aquaristics have made during the last few years. Many species of fishes and invertebrates that we thought could not be kept in aquaria 10 to 15 years ago, may be offered conditions today that guarantee their well-being and a long life in the aquarium. The following statements by Peter WILKENS (with an interval of 14 years between them) bear witness to this: "...the stony corals .... are difficult to keep. Some colonies with large polyps live for a certain period of time, provided

For many of the butterflyfishes import restrictions are really appropriate. They are often specialized feeders that eat coral polyps; above *Chaetodon lunula* off the Maldives, below *Ch. fasciatus* in the Red Sea.

Underwater photos: G. Spies

It is entirely due to hobby aquarists that it has become possible today to keep and reproduce stony corals in a coral reef aquarium. Above: A colony of *Pocillopora damicornis*, eight months old, which grew from a larva or polyp bail-out in the aquarium. Below: The original colony of the *P. damicornis*, the young coral can be seen in front of it behind an *Acropora* sp.   Photos: D. Stüber

It is no problem to cut off a branch of the branching corals with a sharp knife or pair of scissors (here we have a gorgonian with zooxanthellae from the Caribbean). This branch is then placed in a hole which has been drilled into a piece of live rock. It will soon grow on the rock.   Photos: W.A. Tomey

they are fed with fine zooplankters. But sooner or later they will die of hunger (WILKENS,1973) "... "so today we find a considerable number of hobbyists who keep magnificent, genuine mini-reefs, where even such delicate species as *Acropora*-, *Stylophora*-, *Seriatopora*-, and *Echinopora*-stony corals thrive for years and even reproduce (WILKENS, 1990, English edition)"

New findings and modern technology have turned coral reef aquarists from consumers into serious hobbyists who are able to offer the animals that they keep good or even the best possible living conditions. Coral reef aquaristics has become a hobby that is no more restricted to the "chosen few". New experiences and scientific reports are published continually in popular, specialised and in scientific journals, and more and more books on this subject come out.

MOE (1978) describes coral reef aquaristics in the following way: "... an exciting and educational hobby enjoyed by millions of pe-

ople, supported by an extensive technical and industrial base aimed at permitting aquarists to keep their fishes under conditions as good as or better than many animals have in a well-planned zoo."

Coral reef aquaristics – more than just a hobby

Coral reef aquaristics have become very popular as a hobby. Some would-be conservationists keep claiming that it contributes to the destruction of the reefs but this is utterly wrong. Neither, however, is it a matter-of-course that everyone should agree with coral reef aquaristics. We think it is important to present its positive sides and argue for it rather than only to defend it whenever it comes under attack.

Many of the countries that are large exporters of coral reef organisms are among the poorest countries in the world. For them the trade in animals for coral reef aquaristics is a major source of income. Fish sold to the aquatic industry fetch considerably higher prices than do food fish. MOE (1978) remarks on this: "Not even Russian caviar ... is as valuable a fishery product as marine tropical fish... Assuming the average weight of the fish as 14.2 grams or 0.5 ounces, it represents a fishery product worth at least $65.00 per pound."

Good export chances and a stable market guarantee a considerable number of good jobs for the population in these countries. A UNESCO report (KENCHINGTON, 1985) estimates the number of people in Sri Lanka directly involved with the export of reef animals as high as 50.000.

To catch and export reef animals in a controlled and careful way is a profitable and considerate utilization of the resources. A

Anemone fishes are very popular with marine aquarists. Nowadays it is no problem any more to breed them in a marine aquarium.
Photo: G. Zurlo

publication of the World Wildlife Fund (ANON., 1981) summarizes a lot of ideas that most people – also people in the aquarium business – will agree with and which we fully support. In it guidelines are suggested for a future project for the export of aquarium animals from Bali, Indonesia. According to these guidelines the animals should be caught and treated in such a way that no harm is done to the reef biotope and no toxic substances are used. They say: "Foreign fish importers will, understandably, avoid purchasing supplies of fish which have a high mortality rate". Protected areas must be created, which may contribute to the recovery and regeneration of the fishing grounds. They will "help safeguard both the resources and the market and sustain the marine aquarium fish export industry."

Outside observers often smile condescendingly at aquaristics as a hobby that is left to school boys and other childish persons. There is no doubt that there are enthusiastic and highly interested aqua-

rists among youngsters between 10 and 15 years. Many of them become very much involved with this hobby and stick with it for a lifetime. More than any other hobby aquaristics offer a chance to experience nature and animals in our

homes. This leads to a growing interest in and a better understanding of nature outside one's own four walls.

It is not astonishing that many people whose first interest in nature was roused by aquaristics later

Anemone fish breed in an aquarium. They are as sound as a bell and perkily swim about in their anemone.
Photo: H.A. Baensch

Captive breeding of reef animals is proof of the growing success of marine aquaristics, as well as one way to reduce criticism from conservationists. It is, however, perhaps saddening for the third world countries that the aquarium industry now has the technology for producing more and more species ourselves. The commercial production will generally be located as close to the market as possible, in order to reduce freight costs. Here a small part of the facilities of the company C-Quest Inc. in Puerto Rico. They specialize in anemonefishes (*Amphiprion* and *Premnas*), of which they reproduce 10 different species. In addition they have successfully reared at least 14 other reef fishes, including *Pseudochromis aldabraensis* (below left) and *Gobiosoma evelynae* (below right).

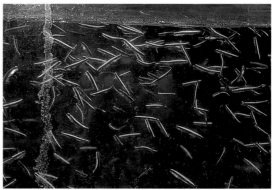

chose a scientific career. In his foreword to ALLEN (1980a) the world famous Austrian ethologist Dr. Konrad LORENZ, who always showed great interest in aquaristics, wrote: "In a time in which most people's thinking is becoming alienated from Nature in a very harmful way, it is encouraging to see an obvious steady increase in interest in marine animals and their care in saltwater aquariums. Both the care of marine fish and their scientific observation under natural conditions induce sensitivity and biological intuition in the aquarium owner and a faculty for observation in the diver interested in fish. Aquarium keeping and underwater observation are not "hobbies" in the usual sense, but rather serious occupations which require full participation. Thus

they are a "school" of general enjoyment of life whose educational value cannot be treasured enough."

Peter HUNNAM, an English marine biologist, has worked on the establishment of "underwater nature reserves", especially in coral reefs in Japan and in the Caribbean. He has also written an aquarium book (HUNNAM, 1981), in which we find the following statement: "Being a good aquarist entails more than looking after an aquarium adequately. One of the intriguing qualities of aquaria is that they raise many questions about underwater life as well as indicating a few answers. The aquarist is encouraged by indoor observations to go beyond the tank and petshop, explore the real world of nature, and penetrate the activities of

wild creatures and the ecology of aquatic habitats. Through first-hand field-work, or by study of natural history, the aquarist will be led to investigate the sources of specimens, their natural distribution and rarity, and their habits and relationships with other species. In addition to such ecological enquiries, he or she may proceed to learn more about the evolution of organisms, pondering the whys and wherefores of their form and colouring.

From these ventures, valuable knowledge is gained which makes a better aquarist. But its widest significance is to yield a better human being, more conscious of the natural surroundings over which mankind holds such power, of the dangers in environmental pollution and depletion, and of the

Hundreds of juvenile *Tridacna maxima* in the tanks of "Wau Island Mariculture Facility", Marshall Island.

Photo: J. Macaré

requirements that many species have in order to thrive or even survive on the planet. A dedicated aquarist will also rejoice in the beauty of wild creatures. There is staggering diversity, and yet every species of animal or plant is somehow perfect. Each has evolved as a vital unit within its own kind of environment. In endeavouring to recreate a suitable home for a gro-

up of aquatic organisms, the aquarist earns priceless insight into the laws and wonders of their watery lives."

It remains to be added that private aquaria often present animals in a much better condition and quality than do public aquaria, in spite of the fact that these usually are in the care of biologists or other academic staff trained in

the natural sciences. The extraordinary development of marine aquaristics is mainly due to the work of hobby aquarists. Public aquaria have, in general, only just started to make use of these new experiences during the last few years.

Finally we would like to emphasize the importance of reef aquaristics for science. The observation of reef animals in their natural surroundings is extremely time-consuming and mostly it is of utmost importance to be in the right place at the right time. How much easier then is it for an aquarist to keep and observe the animals continually in his own home for many years. It is very important that aquarists make notes on their perceptions, compare the results of their findings to scientific observations and publish them. A considerable number of observations and publications by aquarists have proved to be of outstanding importance for the scientific research in their field.

**Giant clam *Tridacna maxima* in the lagoon of Madang, Papua New Guinea.
Underwater photo: Dr. D. Brockmann**

Starfish, *Choriaster grannutatus*, at Pemba, Tanzania.   Underwater photo: P. Lange

List of References

Achterkamp, A. (1986): De eiwitafschuimer... ja-nee? *Het Zee Aquarium* **36** (3): 55-60.

Adey, W. H. (1983): The microcosm: A new tool for reef research. *Coral Reefs* **1** (3): 193-201.

Adey, W. (1994): Algal Turf Scrubbers and Model Ecosystems – A Continuing Dialog. *Aquarium Frontiers* (Spring 1994): 1-6.

Adey, W. H. & K. Loveland (1991): *Dynamic Aquaria – Building Living Ecosystems.* Academic Press, Inc., San Diego, USA.

Aldenhove, J. M. (1986): Local variation in mortality rates and life expectancy estimates of the coral-reef fish Centropyge bicolor (Pisces: Pomacanthidae). *Marine Biology*, Berlin, **92** (2): 237-244.

Allen, G. R. (1980a): *Butterfly and Angelfishes of the World.* Vol. II. Wilely Interscience, N.Y., USA.

Allen, G.R. (1980b): *Anemonefishes.* TFH Publications, Neptune, N.J., USA.

Allen, G.R. (1991): *Damselfishes of the world.* Mergus Verlag GmbH, Melle, Germany.

Allen, G. R & R. Steene (1994): *Indo-Pacific Coral Reef Field Guide.* Tropical Reef Research, Singapore.

Amir, A. P. (1982): Over wieren gesproken. Diatomen of kiezelwiertjes. *Het Zee Aquarium* **32** (12): 348-350.

Amir, A. P. (1987): Blauwwieren in het aquarium, waarom ? *Het Zee Aquarium* **37** (10): 116-117.

Anderson, R. C. (1990): *Living Reefs of the Maldives.* Novelty Printers and Publishers, Male, Rep. of The Maldives.

Anon. (1981): Guidelines needed for the commercial exploitation of coral reef fishes. Conservation Indonesia, *World Wildlife Fund*, **5** (1): 5-6.

Atkinson, M.J. (1987a): Alkaline phosphatase activity of coral reef benthos. *Coral Reefs* **6** (2): 59-62.

Atkinson, M.J. (1987b): Rates of phosphate uptake by coral reef flat communities. *Limnol. Oceanogr.* **37** (2): 426-435.

Atkinson, M. J. (1988): Are Coral Reefs Nutrient-limited ? *Proceedings of the 6th International Coral Reef Symposium*, Australia 1: 157-166.

Atkinson, M.J. (1991): Productivity of Enewetak Atoll reef flats predicted from mass transfer relationship. *Continental Shelf Research* **12** (7/8): 799-807.

Atkinson, M. J. & R.W. Bilger (1992): Effects of water velocity on phosphate uptake in coral reef-flat communities. *Limnol. Oceanogr.* **37** (2): 273-279.

Atkinson, M.J. & R.W. Grigg (1984): Model of a Coral Reef Ecosystem. II. Gros and Net Bentic Primary Production at French Frigat Shoals, Hawaii. *Coral Reefs* **3** (1): 13-22.

Atkinson, M.J. & D.F. Smith (1987): Slow uptake of 32P over a barrier reef flat. *Limnol Oceanogr.* **32** (2): 436-441.

Atkinson, M.J., B. Carlson & G.L. Crow (1995): Coral growth in high-nutrient, low pH seawater: a case study of corals cultured at Waikiki Aquarium, Honolulu, Hawaii. *Coral Reefs* **14** (4):215-223.

Baensch, H. A. & H. Debelius (1992): *Meerwasser Atlas.* Vol. I. Mergus Verlag GmbH, Melle, Germany.

Balderston, W. L. & J. M. Sieburth (1976): Nitrate removal in closed system aquaculture by columnar denitrification. *Appl. Environ. Microbiol.* **32**: 808-818.

Barnes, D. J. & B.E. Chalker (1990): Calcification and photosynthesis in reef-building corals and algae. In: Dubinsky, Z. (ed.) *Ecosystems of the world*, Bd. 25; Coral Reefs; Elsevier, Amsterdam, Oxford, New York, Tokyo; pp. 109 – 133.

Barnes, R. D. (1980): *Invertebrate Zoology.* Saunders College, Philadelphia, USA.

Barnes, R.S.K. & K.H. Mann (1980): *Fundamentals of aquatic ecosystems.* Blackwell Scientific Publ., U.K.

Baum, A. (1989): Nitratfilter im Seewasser. *DATZ* **42**: 1, 56.

Baumeister, W. (1988): Einsiedlerkrebse, I-IV. *DATZ* **41** (6): 156-157, (7): 215-217, (8): 278-279 and (9): 350-352.

Baumeister, W. (1990): *Meeresaquaristik.* Verlag Eugen Ulmer, Stuttgart., Germany.

Baylor, E.R, W.H. Sutcliffe & D.S. Hirshfiels (1962): Adsorbtion of phosphate onto bubbles. *Deep-Sea Res.* **2**: 120-124.

Becker, P. (1982): Algen im Seewasseraquarium? Technik oder Natur? *DATZ* **35** (3): 107-109.

Bennet, I. (1971): *The Great Barrier Reef.* Lansdowne Press, Dee Why West, NSW, Australia.

Bermert, G. & R. Ormond (1981): *Red Sea Coral Reefs.* Paul Kegan Intern. Ltd., London., U.K.

Bingman, C. (1995a): The effect of Activated Carbon Treatment on the transmission of Visible and UV Light Through Aquarium Water. Part 1. *Aquarium Frontiers (Summer 1995):* 4-5, 16-19.

Bingman, C. (1995b): Green-Fluorescent Protein: A model for coral host fluorescent proteins? *Aquarium Frontiers* (Summer 1995): 6-9.

Bingman, C. (1995c): Limewater; Part I. Precipitation of Posphate in Limewater and in the Aquarium. *Aquarium Frontiers* (Fall 1995): 6-9.

Birkholz, J. (1982): 4400 Liter Seewasser und gute Erfolge bei Pflege von Steinkorallen. *Das Aquarium* **16** (8): 425-429.

Birkholz, J. (1986): Üble Parasiten, die grüne Killerkugel. *Das Aquarium* **20** (1): 31-32.

Bishop, J. L. et al. (1976): Single-state nitrification- denitrification. *Jour. Wat. Poll. Cont. Fed.* **48** (3): 520-532.

Bohnsack, J. A. (1983): Resiliency of reef fish communities in the Florida Keys following a January 1977 hypothermal fish kill. *Environmental Biology of Fishes* **9** (1): 41-53.

Borowitzka, M.A. & A.W.D. Larkum (1986): Reef Algae. *Oceanus* **29** (2): 49-54.

Brockmann, D. (1991): Was ist Kalkwasser? *Das Aquarium* **269**: 23-26.

Brockmann, D. & A.J. Nilsen (1995a): A critical comparison of the most commonly used methods for dosing calcium in seawater aquariums. Part 1. *Aquarium Frontiers* (Summer 1995): 2-3, 24-25.

Brockmann, D. & A.J. Nilsen (1995b): A critical comparison of the most commonly used methods for dosing calcium in seawater aquariums. Part 2. *Aquarium Frontiers* (Fall 1995): 2-3, 24-25.

Brons, R. (1982): Kwallen in het zee aquarium. *Het Zee Aquarium* **32** (7/8): 197-203.

Brown, B.E. (1990): Coral bleaching. *Coral Reefs* **8**: (4) 153-232.

Brown, B.E. & Suharsono (1990): Damage and recovery of coral reefs affected by El Nino related seawater warming in the Thousand Islands, Indonesia. *Coral Reefs* **8** (4): 163-170.

Buddemeier, R. W. (1995): Carbonates and Strontium; A Response and Reanalysis. *Aquarium frontiers* 1 (Winter 95): 13-15.

Burgess, W.E., H.R. Axelrod & R.E. Hunziker III (1988): *Dr. Burgess' Atlas of Marine Aquarium Fishes*. TFH Publications, Neptune, N.J., USA.

Burns, T.P. (1985): Hard coral distribution and cold-water disturbance in South Florida: Variation with depth and location. *Coral Reefs* 4 (2): 117-124.

Cannon, L. & M. Goyen (1989): *Exporing Australia's Great Barrier Reef – a world Heritage Site*. The Watermark Press, Surry Hills, NSW., Australia.

Carr, N.G. & B.A. Whitton (1973): *The Biology of Bluegreen Algae*. Blackwell, Oxford, U.K.

Chardy, P., C. Chevillon & J. Clavier (1989): Major bentic communities of the south-west lagoon of New Caledonia. *Coral reefs* 7 (2): 69-76.

Choi, D.R. & R.N. Ginsberg (1983): Distribution of Coelobites (Cavity-Dwellers) in Coral Rubble Across the Florida Reef Tract. *Coral Reefs* 2 (3): 165-172.

Coles, S.L. & Y.H. Fadlallah (1991): Reef coral survival and mortality at low temperatures in the Arabian Gulf: new species-specific lower temperature limits. *Coral Reefs* 9 (4): 231-237.

Coles, S.L. & P.L. Jokiel (1977a): Effects of temperature on the mortality and growth of Hawaiian reef corals. *Marine Biology (Hawaii)* 43:201-208.

Coles, S.L. & P.L. Jokiel (1977b): Effects of temperature on photosynthesis and respiration in hermatypic corals. *Marine Biology (Hawaii)* 43:209-216.

Colin, P. L. (1978): *Caribbean Reef Invertebrates and Plants*. T.F.H. Publ., Neptune City, New Jersey, USA.

Culkin, F. (1985): The major constituents of sea water. In: *Chemical Oceanography*, vol. 1. J. Riley and G. Skirrov (eds.), Academic Press, London, U.K., pp. 121-161.

Dance, P.S. (1977): *Das große Buch der Meeresmuscheln*. Verlag Eugen Ulmer, Stuttgart, Germany.

Davis, P.J. (1984): The role of zooxanthellae in the nutritinal energy requirements of Pocillopora eydouxi. *Coral Reefs* 2 (4): 181-186.

Davis, P.J. & P.A. Hutchings (1983): Initidal Colonization, Erosion and Accretion on Coral Substrate. Experimental Results, Lizard Island, Great Barrier Reef. *Coral Reefs* 2 (1): 27-36.

Debelius, H. (1982): Erfolgreiches Seewassersystem: Das holländische Miniriff. *DATZ* 35 (5): 184-187.

Delbeek, C. J. & J. Sprung (1994): *The Reef Aquarium*. Ricordea Publication, Miami, USA.

Deuring, W. (1982): Zum Thema: Rotalgenbekämpfung im Seewasser-Aquarium. *Das Aquarium* 16 (6): 313-314.

Dinesen, Z.D. (1983): Pattern in the distribution of soft corals across the Great Barrier Reef. *Coral Reefs* 1 (4): 229-236.

Ditlev, H. (1980): *A Field Guide to the Reefbuilding Corals of the Indo-Pacific*. Dr. W. Blackhuys Publisher, Rotterdam, The Nederlands.

Dobler, K. (1990): Diskussion zum Biofilter – Wenn Mikroorganismen wählen könnten. *Das Aquarium* 24 (10):35-38.

Dodd, D.J.R. & D.H. Bone (1975): Nitrate reduction by denitrifying bacteria. *Water Res.* 9:323-328.

Done, T.J. (1982): Pattern in the distribution of coral communities across the Central Great Barrier Reef. *Coral Reefs* 1 (2): 95-107.

Doxtader, K.G. & M. Alexander (1966): Nitrification by heterotropic soil micro-organisms. *Proc. Soil. Sci. Amer.* 30: 351-355.

Drew, E.A. & K.M. Abel (1988a): Studies on Halimeda. I: The distribution and species composition of Halimeda meadows throughout the Great Barrier Reef Province. *Coral Reefs* 6 (3/4): 195-205.

Drew, E.A. & K.M. Abel (1988b): Studies on Halimeda. II: Reproduction, particularly the seasonality of gametangia formation in a number of species from the Great Barrier Reef Province. *Coral Reefs* 6 (3/4): 207-218.

Dring, M.J. (1986): *The Biology of Marine Plants*. Edward Arnold, London, U.K.

Dubinsky, Z. (ed.). (1990): *Ecosystems of the world*, vol. 25, Coral Reefs. Elsevier, N.Y., USA.

Ducklow, H.W. (1990): Biomass, production and fate of bacteria in Coral Reefs. In: Z. Dubinsky (ed.) *Ecosystems of the world*, vol. 25 Coral Reefs, Elsevier N.Y., USA, pp. 265-289.

Dunlap, W.C. & B.E. Chalker (1986): Identification and quantitation of near UV-absorbing compounds (S-320) in a hermatypic scleractinian. *Coral Reefs* 5 (3): 155-160.

Eager, E. & K. Peterson (1988): Great Barrier Reef Aquarium. *Australian Science Mag.* 3:16-57.

Edwards, A. & J. Rosewell (1981): Vertical Zonation of coral fishes in the Sudanese Red Sea. *Hydrobiologia* 79: 21-31.

Emmens, C.W. (1989): Waterquality in the Marine Aquarium. *FAMA* 12 (8): 92, 94,96, 98, 101, 130.

Escobal, P.R. (1995): Inside Protein Skimmers. *Aquarium Fish Magazine* 7 (5): 62-77.

Falkowski, P.G, P. L. Jokiel & R.A. Kinzinger III (1990): Irradiance and Corals. In: Z. Dubinsky (edt.) *Ecosystems of the world*, vol. 25. Coral Reefs, Elsevier N.Y., USA, pp 89-107.

Fautin, D.G. & G.R. Allen (1992): *A Field Guide to Anemonefishes and their Host Sea Anemones*. Western Australian Museum, Perth, Australia.

Fischer, W. & G. Bianchi (eds.) (1984): *FAO Species identification sheets for fishery purposes. Western Indian Ocean (Fishing Area 51)*. Rome, Food and Agricultural Organization of the United Nations, 6 vols.

Flügel, E. (1988): Halimeda, paleontological record and palaeoenviromental significance. *Coral Reefs* 6 (3/4): 123-130.

Fogg, G.E., W.D.P. Stewart, P. Fay & A.E. Walsby (1973): *The Bluegreen Algae*. Academic Press, N.Y., USA.

Fossä, S.A. (1988): *Akvarieindustri versus naturvern?* Upublisert rapport med begrenset distribusjon. 17p.

Fossä, S.A. & A.J. Nilsen (1994): Können Steinkorallen in Aquariensystemen wachsen? *Das Aquarium* 298: 26-30.

Fossä, S.A. & A.J. Nilsen (1995): *Korallenriff Aquarium*, vol. 1. 3. edition. Birgit Schmettkamp Verlag (BSV), Bornheim, Germany.

Fossä, S.A. & A.J. Nilsen (1996): *Korallenriff Aquarium*, vol. 2. 3. edition. Birgit Schmettkamp Verlag (BSV), Bornheim, Germany.

Fossä, S.A. & A.J. Nilsen (1995): *Korallenriff Aquarium*, vol. 3. 2. edition. Birgit Schmettkamp Verlag (BSV), Bornheim, Germany.

Fossä, S.A. & A.J. Nilsen (1995): *Korallenriff Aquarium*, vol. 4. 1. edition. Birgit Schmettkamp Verlag (BSV), Bornheim, Germany.

Fossä, S.A. & A.J. Nilsen (1996): *Korallenriff Aquarium*, vol. 5. 1. edition. Birgit Schmettkamp Verlag (BSV), Bornheim, Germany.

Furnas, M.J, A.W. Mitchell, M. Gilmartin & N. Revelante (1990): Phytoplankton biomass and primary production in semi-enclosed reef lagoons of the central Great Barrier Reef, Australia. *Coral reefs* 9 (1): 1-10.

George, D. & J. George (1979): *Marine Life*. Harrap, London, U.K.

Gladfelter, W.B. (1975): Sea anemones with zooxanthellae: Simultaneous contraction and expansion in response to changing in light intensity. *Science*, 189: 570-571.

Goreau, T.F. (1961): Problems of growth and calcium deposition in reefcorals. *Endeavour* 20: 32-40.

Goreau, T.F. (1963): Calcium carbonate deposition by coralline algae and corals in relation to their roles as reefbuilders. *Ann. N. Y. Acad. Sci.* 109: 127-167.

Goreau, T.F. et al. 1971 Reef Corals: Autotrophs or heterotrophs? *Biol. Bull.* 141: 247-260.

Graaf, F. de (1988): *Das Tropische Meerwasser Aquarium* 6. Auflage. Verlag J. Neumann – Neudamm GmbH & Co. KG, Melsengen, Germany.

Gundersen, K. (1966): The growth and respiration of Nitrosocystis oceanus at different partial pressures of oxygen. *J. Gen. Microbiol.* 42: 387-396.

Hansen, J.A., D.M. Alongi, D.J.W. Moriarty & P.C. Plooard (1987): The dynamics of microbial communities at davies Reef, central Great Barrier Reef. *Coral Reefs* 6 (2):63-70.

Hebbinghaus, R. (1994): Der Löbbecke-Kalkreaktor. *DATZ* 8: 517-522.

Heinz, T.K. (1983a): Rotalgenbekämpfung im Seewasser-Aquarium. *Das Aquarium* 17 (6): 319-320.

Heinz, T.K. (1983b): Algenfresser im Meeresaquarium – ein Nachtrag. *Das Aquarium* 17 (10): 542.

Heinz, T.K. (1990): Diskussion zum Biofilter. Das eine tun und das andere nicht lassen. *Das Aquarium* 24 (247): 44-46.

Hillis-Colinvaux, L. (1986): Have reefs been misnamed? *Oceanus* 29 (2): 43-48.

Hobson, E.S. (1974): Feeding relationship of teleostean fishes on coral reefs in Kona, Hawaii. *Fish Bull.* 74 (4): 915-1031.

Hoek, C. van den (1984): *Algen*. 2. Ausgabe. Thieme Verlag, Stuttgart, Germany.

Holleman, A.F. & E. Wiberg (1976): *Lehrbuch der anorganische Chemie*. Walter de Gruyter, N.Y., USA.

HOLLIDAY, L. (1989): *Coral reefs*. Salamander Books, Ltd., London. UK.

HUMANN, P. (1992): *Reef Creature Identification*. New World Publications, Jacksonville, Florida, USA.

HUMANN, P. (1993a): *Reef Coral Identification*. New World Publications, Jacksonville, Florida, USA.

HUMANN, P. (1993b): *Reef Fish Identification*. New World Publications, Jacksonville, Florida, USA.

HUMANN, P. (1994): *Reef Fish Identification*. Enlarged 2. edition. New World Publications, Jacksonville, Florida, USA.

HUNNAM, P. (1981): *Det levande akvariet*. Bonnier Fakta Bokfrlag AB, Göteborg, Sweden.

HÜSTER, R. (1985): "Rotalgen" im Seewasseraquarium. Ein weiteres Mittel zu ihrer erfolgreichen Bekämpfung. *Das Aquarium* **19** (2): 81-82.

HUTCHINGS, P.A. & P.D. WEATE (1977): Distribution and abundance of cryptofauna from Lizard Island, Great Barrier Reef. *Mar. Res. Indonesia* **17**: 99-112.

JANSEN, K. (1991): Zur Beleuchtung von Riffaquarien – HQI-1000 Watt: Aladins Wunderlampe oder nur sinnloser Stromfresser. *Das Aquarium* **25** (12): 24-27.

JACKSON, J.B.C. & J.E. WINSTON (1982): Ecology of crypticcoral reef communities,. I. J. Exp. *Mar. Biol. Ecol.* **57**: 135-147.

JAUBERT, J. (1989): An integrated nitrifying-denitrifying biological system capable of purifying sea water in a closed circuit aquarium. *Bulletin de l'Institut oceanographique, Monaco*, no special 5:101-106.

JENSEN, H.L. & K. GUNDERSEN (1955): Biological decomposition of aromatic nitro-compounds. *Nature* **175** (4451): 341.

JERIS, J.S. & R.W. OWENS (1975): Pilote-scale, high rate biological denitrification. *Jour. Wat. Poll. Contr. Fed.* **47** (8): 2043-2057.

JERLOV, N.G. (1968): *Optical Oceanography*. Elsevier, Amsterdam, the Nederlands.

JONES, M.S. (1992): The Living Coral Reef Ecosystem Exhibit. *AAZPA/CAZPA 1992 Annual Conference Proceedings* 381-387.

JOHNSON, P.W. & J.M. SIEBURTH (1976): In situ morphology of nitrifying-like bacteria in aquaculture systems. *Appl. Environ. Microbiol.* **31** (3): 423-432.

JOKIEL, P.L. (1980): Solar ultraviolet radiation and coral reef epifauna. *Science* **207**:1069-1071.

JOKIEL , P.L. & R.H. YORK (1982): Solar ultraviolet photobiology of the reef coral Pocillopora damicornis and symbiotic zooxanthellae. *Bull. Mar. Sci.* **32** (1): 301-315.

JOKIEL, P.L., R.Y. ITO & P.M. LIU (1985): Night irradiance and synchronization of lunar release of planula larvae in the reef coral Pocillopora damicornis. *Marine Biology* **88**: 167-174.

JONKLAAS, R. (1975): *Collecting marine tropicals*. TFH Publications Inc., N.J., USA.

KAL, E. (1982): Een eenvoudig system van nitraatafbraak. *Het Zee Aquarium* **32** (9): 242-245.

KAWAGUTI, S. (1969): Effect of the green fluorescent pigment on the productivity of the reef corals. *Abstract. Micronesia* **5**: 313.

KALUSCHKE, K. (1985): *Ökologie*, 2. Auflage, Biologische Arbeitsbücher, Band 25. Quelle & Meyer, Heidelberg, Germany.

KENCHINGTON, R. (1985): Coral-reef ecosystems: a sustainable resource. Nature and Resources, *UNESCO, Paris* **21** (2): 18-27.

KERSTITCH, A. (1989): *Sea of Cortez Marine Invertebrates – A Guide for the Pacific Coast, Mexico to Equator*. Sea Challengers, Monterrey, California, USA.

KESTER, D.R. & R.M. PYTKOWICZ (1967): Determination of the apparent dissociation constants of phosphoric acid in seawater. *Limn. Oceanogr.* **12**: 243-252.

KIPPER, H.E. (1989): *Das Optimale Meerwasser Aquarium* 3. Auflage, AD aquadocumenta Verlag GmbH, Bielefeld, Germany.

KNOP, D. (1987): Schmieralgen, ein unerschöpfliches Thema für Seewasser-Aquarianer. *Das Aquarium* **21** (3): 139-144.

KNOP, D. (1994): *Riesenmuscheln*. Dähne Verlag, Ettlingen, Germany. (English edition 1996 by Ricordea Publication, Miami, USA.

KOUMANS, F.P. (1933): On a new genus and species of Apogonidae. *Zool. Meded. (Leiden)* **16** (1-2):78.

KRISTIANSEN, H. (1969): Om naturlig vanns agressivitet og forskjellige metoder til bestemmelse av vannets aggressive egenskaper. *Vatten* **4**: 439-455.

KSIENSYK, H. (1982): Algen kontra Algen oder, wie man das Seewasser-Aquarium in "den Griff" bekommt. *Das Aquarium* **16** (7):371-374.

KÜHLMANN, D. (1984): *Das Lebende Riff*. Landbuch Verlag, Hannover, Germany.

KVALVÅGNÆS, K. (1982): Ornamental fish trade. The view from Indonesia. *InfoFish Marketing Digest, FAO*: 1982, November: 17-22.

LANDNER, L. (1985): *Water management and protection of the aquatic living resources in tropical and subtropical climates*. Tapir, University of Trondheim. In cooperation with The Nordic Council of Ministers, the Secretariat for Nordic Cultural Cooperation, Copenhagen, Denmark.

LATKA, R. (1991): Das "Lumilux-Riff", oder: Leuchtstoffröhren nur ein Kompromiß?" *Das Aquarium* **25** (262): 27-29.

LATKA, R. (1992): Was sind lebende Steine und welche Bedeutung haben sie für unsere Korallenriff-Aquarien? *Das Aquarium* **26** (1): 28-31.

LARSSON, A. (1984): Nagot om kalcium. *Blckfisken*. Organ far Saltforum Norden, (Sweden) **2** (4):12-19.

LESSER, M.P., W.R. STOCHAJ, D.W. TAPLEY & J.M. SHICK (1990): Bleaching in coral reef anthozoans: efects of irradiance, ultraviolet radiation, and temperature on the activities of protective enzymes against active oxygen. *Coral Reefs* **8** (4): 225-232.

LIESKE, E. & R. MYRES (1994): *Coral Reef Fishes*. Harper Collins Publishers, N.Y., USA.

LITTLER, D.S., M.M. LITTLER, K.E. BUCHER & J.N. NORRIS (1989): *Marine Plants of the Caribbean – A Field Guide fromFlorida to Brazil*. Airlife Publishing Ltd., Shrewsbury, U.K.

LONGHURST, A.R. (1981): *Analysis of Marine Ecosystems*. Academic Press, London, U.K.

LÜNING, K. (1985): *Meeresbotanik*. Georg Thieme Verlag, Stuttgart, Germany.

MAHAN, B.H. (1980): *University Chemistry*. 3. ed.. Addison- Wesley Publishing Company, Reading Mass.,USA.

MARSHALL, J.F. (1996): Calcification in Hermatypic and Ahermatypic Corals. *Science* **271**:637-639.

MARSHALL, J.F. & P.J. DAVIS (1988): Halimeda biotherms of the northern Great Barrier Reef. *Coral Reefs* **6** (3/4): 139-148.

McALLISTER, D.E. (1988): A glowing future for marine aquarium fishes ...the peaceful Philippine revolution under the seas. *Tropical Fish Hobbyist* **36** (12): 84-86.

MEBS, D. (1989): *Gifte im Riff*. Wissenschaftliche Verlagsgesellschaft mbH, Stuttgart, Germany.

MERGNER, H. (1979): Quantitative Analyse eines Rifflaguneareals bei Aqaba (Golf von Aqaba, Rotes Meer). *Helgol. Wiss. Meeresunters*. **32**: 476-507.

MERGNER, H. & H. SCHUHMACHER (1974): Morphologie, Ökologie und Zonierung von Korallenriffen bei bei Aqaba (Golf von Aqaba, Rotes Meer). *Helgol. Wiss. Meeresunters*. **26**: 238-358.

MERGNER, H. & H. SCHUHMACHER (1981): Quantitative Analyse der Korallen-Besiedlung eines Vorriffareals bei Aqaba (Golf von Aqaba, Rotes Meer). *Helgol. Wiss. Meeresunters*. **34**: 337-354.

MERGNER, H. & A. SVOBODA (1977): Productivity and seasonal changes in selected reef areas in the Gulf of Aquaba (Red Sea). *Helgol. Wiss. Meeresunters* **30**: 383-399.

MOE, M.A. Jr. (1978): The private oceans. *Sea Front.*, Miami **24** (4): 240-247.

MOE, M.A. Jr. (1993): *The Marine Aquarium Handbook. Beginner to Breeder*. Green Turtle Publications, Plantation, Florida, USA.

MOHAN, P.J. (1990): Ultraviolet ligth in the marine reef aquarium. *FAMA* **13** (1): 4-6, 156, 158, 160.

MULBARGER, M.C. (1971): Nitrification and denitrification in activated sludge systems. *Jour. Wat. Poll. Cont. Fed.* **43** (10): 2059-2070.

MUSCATINE, L. (1973): Nutrition of corals. In: O. A. JONES & R. ENDEAN (Red.). *Biology and Geology of Coral Reefs* 2: 77-115.

MUSCATINE, L., L.R. McCLOSKEY & R.E. MARIAN (1981): Estimating the daily contribution of carbon from zooxanthellae to coral animale respiration. *Limnol. Oceanogr.* **26**: 601-611.

MUSCATINE, L. (1990): Flux of Photosynthetic fixed Carbon in Corals. In: Z. Dubinsky (edt.) *Ecosystems of the world*, vol. 25 Coral Reefs, Elsevier N.Y. USA, pp 75-87.

MYERS, R.F. (1989): *Micronesian Reef Fishes*. Coral Graphics, Barrigada, Territory of Guam, USA.

NILSEN, A.J. (1983a): Miniriff, I-II. *Akvariet* **57** (9): 485-487 and (10): 543-546.

NILSEN, A.J. (1983b): Zooxantheller, viktige alger i saltvannsakvariet. *Akvariet* **57** (8): 430-432.

NILSEN, A.J. (1985): Belysningen i evertebratakvariet, I-II. *Akvariet* **59** (3):134-135 and (4):182-184.

NILSEN, A.J. (1987): Ein erfolgreiches Korallenriff-Aquarium. *Das Aquarium* **21** (220): 524-528.

NILSEN, A.J. (1988): Lebende Steine im Meerwasser-Aquarium. *Das Aquarium* **22** (9): 538-542

NILSEN, A.J. (1990a): The Successful Coral Reef Aquarium. Part 1, Protein Skimming. *FAMA* **13** (8):8-12.

NILSEN, A.J. (1990b): The Successful Coral Reef Aquarium. Part 2, Light. *FAMA* **13** (9):32-38.

NILSEN, A.J. (1990c): The Successful Coral Reef Aquarium. Part 3, Calcareous water. *FAMA* **13** (11): 32-37, 184.

NILSEN, A.J. (1990d): The Successful Coral Reef Aquarium. Part 4, Live Rock. *FAMA* **13** (12): 98-101, **14** (1):32-35, 182.

NILSEN, A.J. (1991a): The Successful Coral Reef Aquarium. Part 5, A large Reef Aquarium in Oslo. *FAMA* **14** (3):114-115, 119-122, 190.

NILSEN, A.J. (1991b): Ein Riffaquarium in Oslo mit ungewöhnlichen Dimensionen. *Das Aquarium* **25** (9): 27-32.

NILSEN, A.J. (1993): Two Aquaria Designed for Stony Corals. Part 1. *Aquarium Frontiers* (Fall 1993): 11-19.

NILSEN, A.J. (1994): Two Aquaria Designed for Stony Corals. Part 2. *Aquarium Frontiers* (Winter 1994): 1, 4-15, 17-18 (figs).

NILSEN, A.J. (1995): Two Aquaria Designed for Stony Corals. Part 3. *Aquarium Frontiers* (Spring 1995): 2-3.

OCEANUS (1986) The Great Barrier Reef: Science & Management. *Oceanus* **29** (2).

OMMEN, J. VAN (1992): Licht boven het zeeaquarium. *Het Zee Aquarium* **42** (3): 59-63.

PAUL, V.J. & K.L. VAN ALSTYNE (1988): Chemical defense and chemical variation in some tropical Pacific species of Halimeda (Halimedaceae; Chlorophyta). *Coral Reefs* **6** (3/4): 263-269.

PAWLOWSKY, E. (1994): Calcium im Korallenriff-Aquarium. *Das Aquarium* (301):28-35.

QUASTEL, J.J. et al. (1950): Oxidation of pyrivic-oxime by soil organisms. *Nature* **166** (4231): 940-942.

RANDALL, J.E., G.R. ALLEN & R.C. STEENE (1990): *Fishes of the Great Barrier Reef and Coral Sea*. Crawford House Press, Bathurst, Australia.

RAHARDJO, B. (1984): Brief account of coral reef fisheries and their management problems in Indonesia. *Biotrop Special Publications, Bogor, Indonesia*, (22): 63-66.

RECK, K. (1991): Sri Lanka: Was machst du nur mit deinen Korallenriffen ? *Das Aquarium* **25** (12):23.

REDAKTION "DAS AQUARIUM" (1981): Lieber Seewasseraquarianer, helfen Sie mit die "Rotalgen" zu bekämpfen. *Das Aquarium* **15** (2): 87-88.

REVELANTE, N. & M. GILMARTIN (1982): Dynamics of phytoplankton in the Great Barrier Reef lagoon. *J. Plank. Res.* (4): 47-76.

REYNEN, M. (1984): Bakterienfilter auch im Seewasser-Aquarium. *Das Aquarium* **18** (6): 307-310.

RICARD, M. (1977): Phytoplankton contribution to primary productivity in two coral reef areas of Fiji Islands and French Polynesia. *Proc. 3rd Int. Coral Reef Symp.* 1: 343-348.

RIETBERG, J. (1982): Het denitrificatiefilter (DNF). *Het Zee Aquarium* **32** (9): 239-241.

RISELEY, R.A. (1971): *Tropical marine aquaria; the Natural System*. George Allen & Unwin Ltd., London, U.K.

ROBERTS, H.H. & I.G. MACINTYRE (Red.) (1988): Halimeda. *Coral Reefs* **6** (3/4): 1-279.

ROBINSON, S. (1983-85): Collecting tropical marines. Series in *FAMA* **6-8**.

ROOS, P.J. (1967): *Growth and occurence of the Reef Coral porites asteroides Lamark in relation to Submarine Radiance Distribution*. Drukkerij Elinkwijk, Utrecht, The Nederlands.

ROUND, F.E. (1973): *The Biology of the Algae*. Edward Arnold (Publ.) Ltd., London, U.K.

RUETZLER, K. & D.L. SANTAVY (1983): The black band disease of Atlantic reef corals. I: Description of the cyanophyte pathogen. *PSZIN: Marine Ecology* **4**: 301-319.

SABATKE, J. (1985): Eine Filteranlage für das Meeresaquarium. *Das Aquarium* **19** (4): 199-200.

SALE, P.F. (1980): The ecology of fishes on coral reefs. *Ocean. Mar. Biol. Ann. Rev.* **18**: 367-421.

SAUER, K. (1989): *Richtige Aquarien- und Terrarienbeleuchtung*. Engelbert Pfriem Verlag, Wuppertal, Germany.

SCHIEMER, G. (1994): Hermit Crabs in the Reef Aquarium. *Aquarium Frontiers* (Summer 1994): 4-5, 10-11.

SCHILLER, C. & G.J. HENDL (1989): Evidence of enchanced microbial activity in the intertital space of branched corals: possible implications for coral metabolism. *Coral Reefs* **7** (4): 179-184.

SCHLAIS, J. (1979): Aiptasia: Nature's filter. *FAMA* **2** (5):51-53, 69-70.

SCHMIDT, H. (1984): Mein Aquarium, wie es mir gefällt. *Das Aquarium* **18** (10): 529-530.

SCHMIDT, M.M & P.G. HAEMSTRA (1986): *Smiths' Sea Fishes*. Springer Verlag, Berlin, Germany.

SCHMID, P. & D. PATSCHKE (1987): *Unterwasserführer Rotes Meer -Niedere Tiere*. Verlag Stephanie Nagelschmid, Stuttgart, Germany.

SCHOMISCH, W. (1989): Diskussion zum Biofilter. Ein Beitrag über die biologische Filtrung im Riffaquarium. *Das Aquarium* **23**: 696-701.

SCHOMISCH, W. (1991): Grundsätzliche Überlegungen zur Beleuchtung von Riffaquarien. *Das Aquarium* **25** (10): 23-28, 41.

SCHREEVE, J. (1996): Are Algae – Not Coral – Reefs' Master Builders ? *Science* **271**: 597-598.

SCHUHMACHER, H. (1976): Welche Rolle spielen Algen in Leben von Korallen. *Umschau* **76** (15): 491-493.

SCHUHMACHER, H. (1982): *Korallenriffe. Ihre Verbreitung, Tierwelt und Ökologie*, 2. Auflage; BLV Verlagsgesellschaft, München, Germany.

SCHUHMACHER, H. & H. MERGNER (1985a): Quantitative Analyse von Korallengemeinschaften des Sanganeb-Atolls (mittleres Rotes Meer). I. Die Besiedelungsstruktur hydrodynamisch unterschiedlich exponierter Aussen- und Innenriffe. *Helgol. Wiss. Meeresunters*. **39**: 375-417.

SCHUHMACHER, H. & H. MERGNER (1985b): Quantitative Analyse von Korallengemeinschaften des Sanganeb-Atolls (mittleres Rotes Meer). II. Vergleich mit einem Riffareal bei Aquaba (Nördliches Rotes Meer) am Nordrande des indopazifischen Riffgürtels. *Helgol. Wiss. Meersunters*. **39**: 419-440.

SHIBATA, K. (1969): Pigments and UV-absorbing substance in corals and blue-green algae living in the Great Barrier Reef. *Plant and Cell Physiol*. **10**: 325-335.

SHIMEK, R.L. (1995): What Benefit Does Strontium Supplementation Offer The Reef Aquarium ? *Aquarium Frontiers* (Winter 95): 7-13.

SIMKISS, K. (1964a): The Inhibitory Effects of some Meatbolites on the Precipitation of Calcium Carbonate from Artificial and Natural Sea Water. *J. Cons. Perm. Int. Explor. Mer.* **29**: 6.

SIMKISS, K. (1964b): Possible effects of Zooxanthellae on Coral Growth. *Experientia* **20**: 140.

SMITH, R.C & K.S. BAKER (1978): Penetration of UV-B and Biologically effective Dose-rates in Natural Waters. *Photochemistry and Photobiology* **29**: 311-323.

SOLTZ, D.L. & R.J. NAIMAN (1978): *The natural history of native fishes in the Death Valley system*. Natural History Museum of Los Angeles County, in conjunction with The Death Valley Natural History Association.

SOROKIN, Y.I. (1971): On the role of bacteria in the productivity of tropical oceanic waters. *Int. Rev. Ges. Hydrobiol.* **56** (1): 1-48.

SOROKIN, Y.I. (1973a): Microbiological aspects of the productivity of coral reefs. in: O.A.Jones and R. Endean (Editors), *Biology and Geology of Coral Reefs*, 2. Academic Press, N.Y., USA, pp. 17-45.

SOROKIN, Y.I. (1973b): Tropical role of bacteria in the ecosystem of the coral reef. *Nature* **242**: 415-417.

SOROKIN, Y.I. (1978): Microbial production in the coral-reef community. *Arch. Hydrobiol.* **83**: 281-323.

SPOTTE, S. (1979): *Seawater Aquarium, the Captive Enviroment*. John Wiley & Sons, N.Y., USA.

SPRUNG, J. (1993): A Review Of Algal Filtration: History & Future. *Aquarium Frontiers* (Fall 1993): 1-6.

SPRUNG, J. (1994): Algal Turf Scrubbers and Model Ecosystems – A Continuing Dialog. Comments by J. Sprung. *Aquarium Frontiers* (Spring 1994): 6-7.

STEEL, R. D. (1976): Light intensity as a factor in the regulation of the density of symbiotic zooxanthellae in Aiptasia tagetes (Coelenterata; Anthozoa). *Jour. Zool. London* **179**: 387-405.

STEEL, R.D. & N.I. GOREAU (1977): The breakdown of symbiotic zooxanthellae in the sea anemone Phyllactis (=Oulactis) flosculifera (Actinaria). *Jour. Zool. London* **181**: 421-437.

STEENE, R. (1978): *Butterfly and Angelfishes of the World*. vol. I. Australia. Wiley Interscience, N.Y., USA.

STÜBER, D. (1988): Zur Diskussion gestellt: Biologische Filterung im Riffaquarium ? *Das Aquarium* **22** (234): 737-739.

STÜBER, D. (1989): Die Vermehrung einer Seriatopora-Art. *Das Aquarium* **23** (1): 31-32, 37-38.

STÜBER, D. (1990a):Ein Kleines Juwel. Oder: Wie groß muß ein Meerwasser-Aquarium sein ? *Das Aquarium* **24** 254: 27-29.

STÜBER, D. (1990b): Was machen die da in Berlin eigentlich? *DATZ* **41** (8): 495-499.

SUK, W. (1990): Diskussion zum Biofilter. Warum keine biologische Filterung im Riffaquarium?. *Das Aquarium* **23** (240): 355-357.

TALBOT, F. (1984): *Readers' Digest book of the Great Barrier Reef.* Readers Digest Service Pty., Ltd., U.K.

TARDENT, P. (1979): *Meeresbiologie*. Thieme, Stuttgart, Germany.

TAYLOR, D.L. (1968): In situ studies on the cytochemistry andultrastructure of a symbiotic marine dinoflagellate. *Jour. Mar. Biol. Ass. U.K.* **48**: 349-366.

TAYLOR, D.L. (1969): On the regulation and maintenance of algae numbers in zooxanthellae – coelenterate symbiosis, with a note on the nutritional relationship in anemones. *Jour. Mar. Biol. Ass. U.K.* **49**: 1057-1065.

TAYLOR, D.L. (1973): The cellular interactions of algae invertebrate symbiosis. *Adv. Mar. Biol.* **11**: 1-56.

TAYLOR, L. (1978): Hawaiian fish emigrants. *Sea Frontiers, Miami* **24** (2): 91-100.

THEUNS, R.E. (1985): Spirulina, als voeding. *Het Zee Aquarium* **35** (10): 207-208.

THEUNS, R.E. (1986): Smeeralgen... indikatoren van slechte milieuomstandigheden? *Het Zee Aquarium* **36** (7/8): 152-154 and (9): 172-174.

THOMSON, D.A. & C.E. LEHNER (1976): Resilience of a rocky intertidal fish community in a physically unstable environment. *J. exp. mar. Biol. Ecol.* **22**: 1-29.

THORSON, G. (1964): Light as an ecological factorin the dispersal and settlement of larvae of marine bottom invertebrates. *Ophelia* **1** (1):167-208.

TITLYANOV, Y. & Y. LATYPOV (1991): Light-dependence in scleractinian distribution in the sublittoral zone of South China Sea Island. *Coral Reefs* **10** (3):133-138.

TRENCH, R.K. (1971): The physiology and biochemistry of a zooxanthellae symbiotic with marine coelenterates. *Proc. Royal Soc. London* **177**: 225-264

TRUSCH, B. & A. TRUSCH (1982): The soft coral community on a sheltered reef quadrat at Laing Island (Papua New Guinea). *Mar. Biol.* **65**: 321-332.

TATE, R.L. (1977): Nitrification in histosols: A potential role for the heterotrophic nitrifier. *Appl. Environ. Microbiol.* **33** (4): 911-914.

TYREE, S. (1994): Sexual Reproduction and Recruitment of the Stony Coral Pocillopora verrucosa (Ellis and Solander, 1786) with discussion of Spawning Introduction Techniques. Part 1. *Aquarium Frontiers* (Spring 1994): 13-26 and Part 2 (Summer 1994):12-17.

VERON, J.E.N. (1986; 2. edition 1993): *Corals of Australia and the Indo- Pacific*. Angus & Robertson Publishers, North Ryde NSW, Australia & London, U.K.

VINE, P. (1986): *Red Sea Invertebrates*. Immel Publishing, London, U.K.

WALLACE, R.A., J.L. KING & G.P. SANDERS (1986): *Biology the science of life*. 2. Edition. Scott, Foresman and Company, USA.

WALLS, J.G. (1982): *Encyclopedia of Marine Invertebrates*. TFH Publ., Neptune City, New Jersey, USA.

WEBB, K.L. & W.J. WIEBE (1978): The kinetics and possible significance of nitrate uptake by several algae-invertebrate symbioses. *Mar. Biol.* **47**: 21-27.

WELLS, F.E. & C. BRYCE (1988): *Seashells of Western Australia*. Western Australia Museum, Perth, Australia.

WEINBERG, S. (1976): Submarine Daylight and Ecology. *Marine Biology (Berlin)* **37**: 291-304.

WELLS, S., M. JENKINS & C. SHEPARD (edts). (1988): *Coral Reefs of the World*. 3 vol. Belhaven Press, USA.

WENDLER, E. (1986): Ozoneinsatz im Meerwasser-Aquarium. *Das Aquarium* **20** (208): 543-544 and (209): 595-599.

WICKENS, J.F. & M.M. HELM (1981): Sea water treatment. In: Hawakins, A. D. *Aquarium Systems*. Academic Press, London, U.K. pp. 63-128.

WILKENS, P. (1973): *The saltwater aquarium for tropical marine invertebrates*, vol I. Engelbert Pfriem Verlag, Wuppertal, Germany.

WILKENS, P. (1980): *Niedere Tiere im tropischen Seewasser Aquarium*, vol II. Engelbert Pfriem Verlag, Wuppertal, Germany.

WILKENS, P. (1982a): Meerwasser (I): Salzgehalt und Dichte. *Das Aquarium* **16** (11): 595-597.

WILKENS, P. (1982b): Meerwasser (II): pH-Wert und Pufferkapazität. *Das Aquarium* **16** (12): 649-651.

WILKENS, P. (1983a): Meerwasser (III): Problem-Element Calcium. *Das Aquarium* **17** (3): 140-146.

WILKENS, P. (1983b): Meerwasser (IV): Spurenelemente. *Das Aquarium* **17** (10): 537-539.

WILKENS, P. (1983c): Meerwasser (V): Spurenelemente, II. *Das Aquarium* **17** (11): 593-594.

WILKENS, P. (1983d): Borstenwürmer, Plage im Meeresaquarium. *Das Aquarium* **17** (2): 84-87.

WILKENS, P. (1985a): Leser schreiben uns: Grünfadige Algen im Meeres-Aquarium. *Das Aquarium* **19** (7): 366-367.

WILKENS, P. (1985b): "Rotalgen" im Seewasser. Anmerkungen zum Bericht von Rudolf Hüster in Heft 188, 2/85. *Das Aquarium* **19** (8): 423-424.

WILKENS, P. (1985c): "Lebenselixier Licht" im Meeresaquarium. *Aquarien Magazin* **19** (8): 320-323.

WILKENS, P. (1990): *Invertebrates: Stone and False Corals, Colonial Anemones*. Engelbert Pfriem Verlag, Wuppertal; Germany.

WILKENS, P. & J. BIRKHOLZ (1986): *Invertebrates -, Tube-, Soft- and Branching Corals*. Engelbert Pfriem Verlag, Wuppertal; Germany.

WILLIAMS, D.M.B., G. RUSS & P.J. DOHERTY (1986): Reef fish: large-scale distribution and recruitment. *Oceanus* **29** (2): 76-82.

WILSON, E.O. et al. (1978): *Life on Earth*. 2. edition. Sinauer Associates, Inc., Sunderland, Massachusetts, USA.

WILSON, B. (1993): *Australian Marine Shells*, vol. 1-2. Odyssey Publishing, Kallaro, Western Australia.

WOELKERLING, W.J. (1988): *The Coralline Red Algae*. Oxford University Press, London, U.K.

WOOD, E.M. (1983): *Corals of the World*. TFH Publications, Neptune City, New Jersey, USA.

WRAY, J.L. (1977): *Calcareous algae*. Elsevier, Amsterdam, The Nederlands.

YAMAZATO, K. (1970): Calcification in the solitary coral, Fungia scutaria Lamarck, in relation to enviromental factors. *Bull. Sci. Engag. Div. Univ. Ryukyus* **13**:1-122.

YONGE, C.M. (1936): Mode of life, feeding, digestion and symbiosis with zooxanthellae in the Tridacnidae. *Sci. Rep. Great Barrier Reef Exped.* **1** (11): 283-321.

YONGE, C.M. (1968): Living corals. *Proc. Royal Soc.* **169**: 329-344.

YONGE, C.M. & A.G. NICHOLS (1931): Studies on the physiology of corals. IV: The structure, distribution and physiology of zooxanthellae. *Sci. Rep. Great Barrier Reef Exped.* **1**: 135-212.

Natural Monument

Great Barrier Reef

A steep reef slope.   Underwater photo: G. Spies

Index

All scientific genera and species names are printed in *italics*. Page numbers printed in **bold** types refer to illustrations and/or major discussions of the topic.

Abalones 187
Abudefduf
- *sexfasciatus* **44**
- *vaigiensis* **44**
Acanthaster planci 31
Acanthodendrilla **175**
Acanthophora spicifera 312; **313**
Acanthopleura 32
- *granulata* **92**; 187
Acanthurus 35; 288-289
- *olivaceus* **26**
- *sohal* **290**
Acclimatisation **165-166**
- container for **165**
Acetabularia 283; **284**; 285
Acropora **27**; **28**; 35; 36; 37; **42**; **69**; **79**; 177-178; **186**
- Berlin **178**
- *gemmifera* **40**
- growth forms 37
- *microphthalma* **214**
- *pulchra* **103**
Acroporidae 177
Actiniaria 176
Actinic blue lamps 207
Actinodendron arboreum **139**
Activated Carbon **257-258**
Adsorbate 259
Aeoliscus strigatus **41**
Aerobic 242-243
Ahermatypic corals 178
Aiptasia 255
Algae 23; 24; 25; 26-27; 35; 123; 200; 267; **271-324**
- biochemical characteristics 274
- Brown 32; 273; 274; **302-307**
- Calcareous 26; 123; 164; **288**; **296-299**; 311; **312-318**
- distribution on reef 280
- during the break in period 162-163; **164**
- ecological importance 273
- effect of grazing 30-31
- Filamentous 31; **163**; 164; 254; **282-283**; **287-292**
- Green 274; **282-302**
- need for carbon 223-224
- Parasitic **272**; 277
- Planctonic 25; 26-27; 48
- Red 32; 273; 274; **307-318**
- reproduction **273-274**; **282-283**; 299; 304; 308; 322
- Symbiotic 27; 200; 273; 277; **319-324**
- Turf **26**; **272**; 273; 308; **309**
Algae eaters 163; 187; **288-290**

Algae filter **254-255**
Algae zone 31; **32**
Alpheus 142
Aluminium 262
Amblyeleotris **39**
- *sungami* **139**
Ammonia 23; 242; **243-244**
- in a new tank 162
Ammonium 242; **243-244**
Amphipoda **183**
Amphiprion 36
- *clarkii* **75**
- *melanopus* **42**
- *nigripes* **329**
- *ocellaris* **75**
- *perideraion* **75**
Amphiroa **314**; **316**; **317**
- *brasiliana* 316
- *fragilissima* 316
- *rigida* 316
- *tribulus* 316
Amphitrite **182**
Anaerobic 242-243; 246
Anemone fish 36; **75**; **343**
- Dusky **42**
- Maldives **329**
Anemonia majano **176**
Angelfish 37; 128; 184; 290
- Ascension 91; **97**
- Blue-Girdled **73**
- Cherub 91
- Clarion **89**
- Emperor **62**; **64**; **327**
- Flame 81; **148**
- hybrid **96**
- Regal **45**
- Shepard's 81
Annelids 180
Antennarius 105
Aphroditidae 181
Aphroditiformia 181
Aquaria Vattenmuseum **131**; **156-157**
Aquarium construction **107-108**
Arachnids 185
Aragonite 13; **322**
Arca 186; **187**
Artificial decorations **116**
Ascension 90; 91; 97
Ascidiacea 190
Assessor macneilli **57**
Astraea **289**; 290
Astreopora 37
Atlantic Ocean 15
Autotrophic
- ecosystem 23; 25
- organisms 20; 243
Avrainvillea 292; **293**; **294**
Bacillariophyceae 274; **275-276**
Background **118**
Bacteria **48-50**; **242-243**; 254; 276

Bacterium 243
Bahamas **96**
Bangiales **308**
Barbados **14**
Barium 238
Barnacles 32; 184
Barracuda **43**
Barriers, Zoogeographical 58; 88
Batfish 127; 131
- Orbiculate **130**
Batophora **284**; 285
- *oerstedii* 285
Beach **31-32**; **38-39**
Belau **80**
Bequia **37**
Bermudas 90
Bigeyes 91
Biomass 30; 48
Bivalves 32; 186
Black light lamps 207-208
Black-band-disease 277
Bleaching **212**; **214**
Blennidae 32; 289
Blenny 32
- Jeweled **163**; 289
Blue Coral **179**
Blue light 200-201; 207-208; 279; 288
Blue-green algae 32; 48; 164; 271; **273**; 274; **276-280**
Bodianus anthioides **143**
Bonaire **90**; **96**; 281
Boodlea 280
Bora Bora **83**
Boron 238
Botrylloides **190-191**
Botryllus **190-191**
Bottom media **118**
Box crab **39**
Break in period **162-165**; 167
Briareum **176**
Bristle worms **180**
Bristletooth, Goldring 87
Brittle stars 32; **167**; 190
Bryopsis 26; **163**; 164; 280; **284**; 287
- *plumosa* 287
Bryozoa 54; **189**
Bubble algae 35
Buffer capacity **223-224**; 224-227; 243
Butterflyfish 37; 128
- Blackbacked **130**
- Longnose 88
- Reticulated **87**
- West African **99**
C-Quest Inc **344**
Cable ties 114; **120**
Calappa **39**
Calcareous reactor **230**
Calcinus
- *californiensis* 290
- *tibicen* **289**; 290

Gorgonians, soft corals and sponges at Bega Lagoon, Fiji. Underwater photo: E. Svensen

Calcium 224-227; **227-228**; 238; 288; 298
- methods of addition **228-235**
Calcium carbonate synthesis **319**; 322
Calcium chloride 227; **229**
Calcium hydroxide 224; 227; 230
Calcium oxide 224; 230
Callipallene **186**
Calloplesiops altivelis **155**
Calothrix 280
Cape Verde 98
Caphyra rotundifrons **292**
Capnella 35; 36
Captive breeding **344; 345**
Caranx sexfasciatus **42**
Carbon dioxide **228**; 228-235; 272
Carbon filtration **257-258**
Carbonate 223; 227; 272
Carbonate hardness **224-227**; 288; 314
Carbonic acid 223

Cardinalfish, Pyjama- **148**
Caribbean 15; **59**;88; **90-91**
Caribbean Sea 90
Carnivors 30
Carotenoids **197-198**; 274
Carposporophytes **308**
Carteriospongia foliascens 324
Caryophylliidae 177
Catalaphyllia jardinei **141**; 142
Caulerpa 32-35; 123; 141; 254; 280;
299-302
- *brachypus* **271**
- *cupressoides* **301**
- *macrodisca* **300**
- *mexicana* **300**; 301
- *nummularia* **300**
- *peltata* **300**
- *prolifera* 299; **300**
- *racemosa* **24**; 300; **302**; 303

- *scalpelliformis* **301**
- *sertularoides* **301**
- *taxifolia* **301**
- *verticillata* **300**
Caulerpales **287-302**
Cave aquarium **149-155**
Caves **36; 46-47; 149-155**
Centropyge 133; 184; 290
- *argi* 91
- *bicolor* 336
- *loriculus* 81; **148**
- *resplendens* 91; **97**
- *shepardi* 81
Cephalopholis argus **43**
Cephalopoda 186
Ceramiales **309;311**
Ceramium 26; 280; 309; **311**
Ceratodictyan 280
Cerianthus 128

Chaetodipterus
- *faber* 88
- *zonatus* 88
Chaetodon
- *falcifer* **88**
- *fasciatus* **340**
- *luciae* **99**
- *lunula* **340**
- *melannotus* **130**
- *reticulatus* **87**
- *trifasciatus* **25**; 339
Chaetomorpha **302**
- *crassa* 302
- *linum* 302
Chaetopteridae **181**
Chelicerata 185
Chelidonura varians **38**
Chelmon rostratus 182
Chironephthya 37
Chitons 32; 187
Chlorodesmis 280
- *fastigiata* **292**
Chlorophyll **197-198**; 274
Chlorophyta 274; **282-302**
Chnoospora 280
Chordata 190
Chromis **83**; 128
- *viridis* 36
Chromodoris elizabethae **46**
Ciliates **50-51**; **173**
Ciliophora 50
Cinachyra **297**
Cirratulidae **181**
Cirripedia 32; 184
CITES 106; 178; **336-337**; 339
Cladiella 35
Cladophora 26
Cladophorales **302**
Cladophoropsis **285**; 292; **293**
Clams, Boring 186; **187**
Cleaner shrimp **47**; **152**
Clibanarius 32
Clipperton Island 88
Clove polyps 176
Cnidaria 175-179
Cobalt 238
Codium **292**; **294**
- *fragile* 292
- *spongiosum* 292
Coenobita **38**
Collospongia auris **324**
Colonial anemones 30; 176
Colour temperature 205
Community aquarium 128; **132-133**
Compatibility 128
Conductivity **219**
Conservation 106; 192; **327-345**
Consumers 23; **30-31**
Cooling **215**
Copepoda **183**
Coral crabs **184**
Coral Sea **26**; **42**; **44**; **110**; **138**
- Boomerang Reef **76**
- Flinders Reef **17**; **150**; **315**
- Osprey Reef **25**
Coral skeletons
- artificial **117-118**
- for decoration **116-118**; 336
Corallinaceae 26
Coris 118
Corythoichthtys nigripectus **102**
Cowries 187; 290
Crabs **39**; **184**; **271**; **292**
Crown of Thorns starfish 31
Crustacea 30; **183-185**
Crustaceans 30; 32; **183-185**
Cryptocentrus **329**
- *cinctus* **148**; **253**
Cryptonemiales **312**
Ctenochaetus 288
- *strigosus* **87**
Cuba **95**
Cumacea 184
Currents **264-266**; **268**
Cyanide 106; 166; 327; **328-331**
Cyanobacteria 276
Cyanophyta 274; **276-280**
Cymodocea serrulata 140
Cymopolia barbata **284**; 285
Cypraea 187; 290
Damselfishes 35
Dartfish, Decorated **148**
Dascyllus marginatus **63**
Dasycladales **283-285**
Dasycladus vermiculatus **284**; 285
Decapoda **184**
Decomposing organisms 23; **48-50**; 180; 241-247
Decoration
- live organisms as **119-123**
materials 112; 252
Dendronephthya 37; **64**; **65**; **82**; **102**; 127; 152-154; **159**
Dendropoma maxima 186
Denitrification 246; 253-254
Denitrification filter 252; 253-254
Density 218-220; 238
Derbesia **163**; 164; **273**; **287**
Derbesia marina **282-283**; 287
Detritus eaters 50; 180; 184; 190
Diadema 35; 290
Diatoms 164; 237; 274; **275-276**
Dictyopteris 304-305
Dictyosphaeria 280; **286**
Dictyota 32; 280; 304; **305**
- *bartayresii* 304
- *ciliolata* 304
- *dichotoma* 304
- *mertensii* **281**
Dictyotales **304-305**
Didemnum molle **45**; **323**; 324
Dinitrogen 23
Dinoflagellates **275**; **319-323**
Dinophyceae 27
Dinophyta 274; **319-323**
Diodogorgia nodulifera **152**
Diorama 118; 140
Diploidy **304**
Disco sphere-globe **105**
Dissimilation 243; **246-247**
Distichopora violacea **28**
Diving 338
Doryrhamphus excisus 88
Dragonets 184
Dutch mini-reef **266-267**
Dynamite fishing **331-332**; 338
East Africa **66**
Easter Island **58**; 59
Eastern Pacific 15; **59**; **88-89**
Echeneididae 91
Echinodermata 30; 189-190
Echinoderms 30; 189-190
- acclimatisation of 165
Echinometra **40**; **289**; 290
- *mathaei* 32
Echinopora 36
Echinostrephus molaris **29**
Ecsenius 289
Einstein **199**
Endemisms 58; 60; 87
Energy budgets 199
Enhalus acoroides 140
Enteromorpha 32; 280; 283; **284**
- *clathrata* 283
Entoprocta 189; **190**
Epinephelus adscensionis **100**
Epitoke **180**
Epoxy 107
- Underwater 112; **120-122**; 172
Euchema 311; **312**
Eucrossorhinus dasypogon **57**
Eunicidae 180
Euphyllia
- *ancora* **272**
- *divisa* **321**
- *glabrescens* **177**
Euplotes **173**
Evaporation 220
Fairy Basslet 69
Faros **17**
Favia 35; 36; 37; 179
Faviidae 179
Favites 35; 36; 37; 179
Favoistes **14**
Feather Star **45**
Feldmannia 280
Fiji **12**; **36**; **829**
Filefish, Orangespotted **129**
Filtration 242; **251-268**
- Biological **251-257**
- combination of filters **266-268**
Fire Coral **28**
Fish aquarium **129-131**
Fishes 30
- Species distribution **60**
Flagellates 49; 50-51
Flatworms **179**
Florida 91; **141**
Fluorescent lamps **205-208**
Flux of light **199**
Food chain 24
Foraminiferans 49-50; **173**; 174-175; **273**
Forcipiger flavissimus **88**
Fore-reef 31; **36**
French Polynesia **83**
Fromia monilis **291**
Fucales **306-307**
Fucus **304**
Fungia 37
Galapagos 88
Galaxaura **25**; 309; **310**
- *marginata* 309; **310**
- *subverticillata* 309; **310**
Galaxea 37
Gametangia **299**
Gametophytes 282; 304; 308
Gardeneel, Spotted **139**
Gastropods 186
Gelidiales **308-309**
Gelidiella 280
Gelidium **309**
Geology **13-15**
Giant clams **29**; 60; **336**
Gigartinales **311-312**
Glasseye **99**
Gliffordia 280
Gnatostomulida **180**
Gobies 32
Gobiidae 32
Gobiosoma evelynae **344**
Goniastrea 35; 36; 37; **41**; **79**; **179**
Goniopora **138**; **159**
Gonodactylus 185
Gorgonians **150**; 152; **342**
Gramma loreto 91; 133
Gravel 118
Great Barrier Reef **6**; 17; **76-79**
- Agincourt Reef **111**; **113**
- Alexandra Bay **77**
- Harrier Reef **27**
- Hastings Reef **54**
- Low Island **79**
- Myrmidion Reef **145**
- Pompey/Hardline Complex **56**
- Wheeler Reef **40**
- Wistari Reef **78**

Great Barrier Reef Aquarium	255	Indonesia	328	Mangrove trees
Grouper	37; 94; **100**; 131	- Sulawesi	**13**; **16**; **39**; **41**; **43**; **72**; **141**	Mantis shrimp
- Peacock	**43**	Invertebrates	119-123	Marianas
Guam	**81**	Iodine	**237**; 238	Marshall Islands
Gulf of California	89	Irradiance of light	**199**	*Martensia*
Gulf Stream	91	Isopoda	184	- *pavonia*
Gymnodinium microadriaticum	319; **320**	Isotherm	57; **58**	Mechanical filters
Gymnothorax		*Jania*	**314**; 315	Mediterranean
- *favagineus*	**152**	- *adherens*	315	*Megalomma*
- *javanicus*	**28**; **45**	- *rubens*	315	Mercury vapour lamps
Halimeda	26; 32; 141; 280; **296-299**; **303**	Jaubert System	118; 140; **250**; **256-257**;	*Mesophyllum*
- *copiosa*	297		266	Metal halide lamps
- *cryptica*	297	Jawfish		Metal pollution
- *discoidea*	**299**	- Bluespotted	89	Micro-atoll
- *distribution in reef*	*298*	- Yellowhead	91	*Microleus*
- *gracilis*	297	Jellyfish	**176**	Microorganisms
- *incrassata*	**297**; 298	*Johnrandallia nigrirostris*	89	*Microspathodon chrysurus*
- *lacrimosa*	297	Joul	**199**	*Millepora*
- *monila*	297	Kalkwasser	**224-227**; **229-232**; 262;	- *dichotoma*
- *opuntia*	**297**; 298		288; 314	Millisiemens
- *tuna*	297; 298; **299**	Kelvin	205	Mineralisation
Haliolistes	14	Key Stone	**15**	*Mitra*
Haliotes	187	KH	**224-227**	Mitres
Halodule		King Crab	105	Mitridae
- *beaudettei*	140	Labridae	35	Mollusca
- *pinifolia*	140	Lactose	254	Molly Miller
Halymenia	**312**; 313	*Laminaria*	304	Monaco Oceanographic Museum
Hamlet		*Laurencia*	280	Monera
- Barred	**94**	- *obtusa*	**281**	Monoculture filter
- Butter	**94**	Lava	116	*Montastrea*
Hatchet fish	64	*Lepidonotus carinulatus*	181	*Montipora*
Hawaiian Islands	59; 61; **84-87**	*Leptoria*	**55**	- *digitata*
Heating	**214-215**	Lessepsian immigrants	58	Moonlight
Heliopora coerulea	178; **179**	*Leveillea*	280	Moray eels
Helioporacea	178	*Liagora*	309; **310**	*Muraena melanotis*
Herbivors	30-31; 163; 288-290	*Licmophora*	**275**	mV
Hermatypic corals	178; 323	Light	**195-211**; 321	*Myrionema*
Hermit crabs	32; **38**; 92; 118; **289**; 290	- absorption	**196-198**	*Myripristis*
Herpolitha	37	- in the aquarium	**203-211**	- *jacobus*
Heteractis	36	- indirect	200	*Naso*
- *magnifica*	**42**	- intensity	35; 36-37; **198-201**	Natural System
Heterocentrotus	35	- measuring	199	*Nausithoe*
Heteroconger hassi	**139**	- penetration of	**200**; 258	Nemaliales
Heterocysts	276	- spectrum	195-196; 200	*Nemateleotris*
Heterokontophyta	**275-276**; **302-307**	Lime burning	106; 337	- *decora*
Heteropriacanthus cruentatus	**99**	Limestone, for decoration	**116**	- *magnifica*
Heterotrophic		Limestone-reactor	**232-235**	Nematoda
- ecosystem	23	Limpets	187; **188**	*Neogoniolithon*
- organisms	20; 243	*Limulus*	185	- *spectabile*
Heteroxenia	37	*Linckia laevigata*	**41**; 79	- *strictum*
Histrio histrio	91	Line Islands	84	*Neomeris*
Holacanthus		Lionfish	44	- *annulata*
- *ciliaris x bermudensis*	**96**	*Liopropoma aurora*	87	*Nephthea*
- *clarionensis*	89	Lithium	238	Nephtheidae
- *limbaughi*	89	*Lithophaga*	186	Nereidae
- *passer*	89	*Lithophyllum*	280; **315**; 316	*Nerita*
Holaxonia	**64**; **152**; **153**	Live Rock	13; **105**; 162; **169-193**	Nitrate
Holocentrus rufus	**97**	- biological effects	242-243; 246; 280	
Homotrema rubrum	173; **174-175**	- drilling and sawing	114; 172	- in a new tank
Hormothamnion	280	- in biofilters	252-253	Nitrate reduction
Horseshoe crabs	185	- organisms on	**172-191**; 275	Nitrification
HQI-lamps	208	- treatment of	**170-172**	Nitrite
HQL-lamps	208	- use as decoration	**112-116**	- in a new tank
Hydnophora exesa	**203**	*Lobophora*	32; 280; **306**	*Nitrobacter*
Hydrocharitaceae	25	- *variegata*	**281**; 305	Nitrogen
Hydroclathrus	280	*Lobophyllia*	36; 37; **54**	Nitrogen cycle
Hydrodynamics	**264-266**	*Lophosiphonia*	280	*Nitrosomonas*
Hydrogen carbonate	223; 224-228;	Lord Howe Island	59; **77**	Normal foam
	229; 272	Lumen	**199**	Nudibranch
Hydroidea	175	*Lutjanus kasmira*	**139**	Nutrients
Hydroids	175	Lux	**199**	- Algae-
Hydrolithon	**285**	*Lyngbya*	**273**; 277; **279**; 280	- Inorganic
Hydrometer	219	- *aestuarii*	277	- Organic
Hydrotechnology	**264-266**	Lbbecke reactor	233	*Ochtodes*
Hydrozoa	**43**; 175; 176	*Madracis*	98	*Ocypode saratan*
Hypnea	26; 280; 311; **312**	Malacostraca	183; 184	*Odontella*
Hypoplectrus		Maldives	3; **17**; **18**; **30**; **68-69**; 112	*Odontodactylus scyllaris*
- *puella*	**94**	- Embudu	**38**	OFI
- *unicolor*	**94**	- Kuredu	**195**	Oil spills
Indo-Pacific	15; **59-61**	- Latheef Reef	**46**; **150**	Omnivors

Mangrove trees	**136**; 140; **141**
Mantis shrimp	**185**
Marianas	81
Marshall Islands	**81**
Martensia	311
- *pavonia*	311
Mechanical filters	**257**
Mediterranean	58; 91
Megalomma	**331**
Mercury vapour lamps	**208**
Mesophyllum	311; **314**; 316; **318**
Metal halide lamps	**208-211**
Metal pollution	262
Micro-atoll	31; **35**
Microleus	277-278
Microorganisms	**48-50**
Microspathodon chrysurus	90
Millepora	**28**; **36**; **65**; **110**; 176
- *dichotoma*	**43**
Millisiemens	219
Mineralisation	**243-244**
Mitra	**187**
Mitres	186-187
Mitridae	186
Mollusca	30; **186-189**
Molly Miller	91
Monaco Oceanographic Museum	**256**
Monera	48
Monoculture filter	254
Montastrea	98
Montipora	37; **178**
- *digitata*	**141**
Moonlight	**201-202**
Moray eels	**28**; 37; **45**; 99; **100**; **152**
Muraena melanotis	**99**; **100**
mV	**249**
Myrionema	**175**
Myripristis	36; **47**; 127
- *jacobus*	**101**
Naso	288
Natural System	256; **266**
Nausithoe	**175**; **176**
Nemaliales	**309**
Nemateleotris	
- *decora*	**148**
- *magnifica*	**144**
Nematoda	**48**; **49**; 180
Neogoniolithon	315
- *spectabile*	315
- *strictum*	315
Neomeris	**285**
- *annulata*	**284**; 285
Nephthea	35; 36
Nephtheidae	**149**
Nereidae	**180**
Nerita	32; 290
Nitrate	23; 24; 25; 221; 236; 244;
	245-246; 262
- in a new tank	162
Nitrate reduction	246
Nitrification	243; **244-246**
Nitrite	23; 244; **245-246**
- in a new tank	162
Nitrobacter	50; 162; **244**
Nitrogen	22; 23; 50; 242; 276
Nitrogen cycle	50; 162; 242; **243-247**
Nitrosomonas	50; 162; **244**
Normal foam	258
Nudibranch	**38**; **46**; 187; **241**
Nutrients	50; 279-280; 288; 321-322
- Algae-	272
- Inorganic	23; 25; 236; **241-247**
- Organic	24
Ochtodes	311; 312; **313**
Ocypode saratan	**39**
Odontella	**275**
Odontodactylus scyllaris	**185**
OFI	339
Oil spills	337
Omnivors	30

Ophioblennius	
- *atlanticus*	88
- *steindachneri*	88
Ophiuroidea	190
Opistognathus	118
- *aurifrons*	91
- *rosenblatti*	89
Oscillatoria	277; **278**; **279**
Osmoregulation	**219-220**
Ostreobium	**272**
Over-exploitation	**332-336**
Oxidation	247-249
Oxygen	24; **25**; **236**; 242; 244; 246
Oxymonacanthus longirostris	**129**
Ozone	249; 263-264
Ozonisation	**263-264**
Padina	32; 280; 305; **306**
- *sanctaecrucis*	**281**
Paguristes cadenati	290
Palau	80
Palolo siciliensis	**181**
Palolo worm	181
Pangaea	14
Papua New Guinea	**14**; **73**; **326**
PAR	**200**
Paragoniolithon	280
- *conicum*	318

Paranthias furcifer	89
Parapriacanthus	**64**
Parasites	183-184; **186**; 187
Peanut-worms	**183**
Peltodoris	**241**
Penaeidae	**38**
Penedos de Sao Paolo	90
Penicillus	141; **294-296**
- *capitatus*	**295**; 296
- *dumetosus*	296
- *pyriformis*	296
Pericelis	**179**
Periclimenes	
- *brevicarpalis*	**139**; **142**
- *yucatanicus*	**330**
Peyssonnelia	280; **317**; **318**
pH	**222-223**; 228; 231; 243; 244; 314
Phaeophyceae	274; **302-307**
Phaeophyta	273
Philippines	328-331
- Cebu	**74**
Phimochirus operculatus	290
Pholas	**186**
Phormidium corallyticum	277
Phosphate	236; **247**; 262; 322
Phosphorus	22; 23
Phosphorus cycle	**247**

Photosynthesis	**19-20**; **198**; 200; 224; 271-272
Phycobilines	**197-198**; 274
Phyllochaetopterus	**181**
Phymanthus	141; **142**
Phytoplankton	48
Pigments	**197-198**; **274**; 322
Pilumnus	**184**
Pipefish	184
- Bluestripe	88
Pistol shrimp	118; 142; **148**
Plankton	48
Platax	127; 131
- *orbicularis*	**130**
Platygyra	35; 36; 37
Platyhelminthes	179
Plerogyra	37
- *sinuosa*	**269**
Plesiopidae	**57**; 60
Pocillopora	37; **83**; 178
- *damicornis*	**103**; 178; 197; **341**
- *eydouxi*	**325**
- *meandrina*	**86**
Pocilloporidae	177; 178; 184
Pollution	337
Polycarpa	**45**; 191
Polychaeta	30; **180-183**

Orbiculate Batfish, *Platax orbicularis*, and Cleaner Fish, *Labroides dimidiatus*, at Pemba.

Underwater photo: P. Lange

Polycladia	179
Polymnia	182
Polynoidae	181
Polyp, Primary	177
Polyphysa	283; **284**; **285**
Polyplacophora	187
Polysiphonia	280
Polyurethane foam	116; **117**; **156-157**
Pomacanthus	
- *imperator*	**64**; **327**
- *navarchus*	**73**
- *paru*	**90**
- *zonipectus*	89
Pomacentridae	35
Porites	35; 36; 37; 98; **179**
- *cylindrica*	**79**
Poritidae	179
Porolithon	280; 317
Porphyra	308; **309**
- *tenera*	308
Potassium iodide	237
Powerhead pumps	264
Prawngoby, Yellow	**148**
Predation	128; 129; 184
Priacanthus	91
Prionurus laticlavius	89
Procaryotes	271
Prochlorophyta	324
Producers	20; **25-29**
Production	
- Bacterial	50; 51
- Primary	23; **25**; 51
Protein foam	258
Protein skimming	**258-261**; 288
- effects on phosphate	**247**
Protista	48
Protoreaster nodusus	38
Protozoa	48; 174-175
Protula	**241**
Psammocora contigua	**177**
Pseudanthias	35; **74**; 128
- *squamipinnis*	36; **69**; 325
Pseudobiceros	179
Pseudoceros	179
Pseudochromidae	60
Pseudochromis	133
- *aldabraensis*	**344**
- *fridmani*	**62**258
Pterois	131
- *antennata*	**47**
- *miles*	**44**;
Puerto Rico	**92-93**; **344**
Pumps	264-266
PUR	**200**
PVC-tubes	**114-115**; 172
Pycnogonida	**185-186**
Pygoplites diacanthus	36; **45**
Quanta	**199**
Quantum units	199
Ra-index	205
Ralfsia	280
Ray	131
- Bluespotted	**144**
Razor fish	**41**
Red Sea	16; 20; 58; 61; **62-65**; 126; 127
- Hurghada	**62**
- Sinai	**45**
Redox potential	172; **247-249**; 280
Reduction	247-249
Reef edge	31; **36**; **42-43**
Reef flat	31; **32-35**; **40-41**
Reef gorge aquarium	**145-148**
Reef pinnacles	31; **35**; 36
Reef profile aquarium	**156-157**
Reef slope	31; **36**; **44-45**
Reefs	
- Algae	26
- atolls	15; **19**
- Bank	15; **17**
- Barrier	15; **17-18**

- dangers to	**336-338**
- destroyed by cyclone	**25**
- distribution of	19; 57
- Fossil	**13-15**
- Fringing	15
- Oceanic	15
- Platform	15; **16-17**
- productivity of	332-333
- Shelf	15
- zones of	**31-47**
Reproduction	201; **341**; **344**; **345**

Rubidium	238
Rugosa	14
Rypticus saponaceus	**100**
Sabellastarte	**331**
- *indica*	**182**
Sabellidae	**154**; **181-182**; **331**
Salarias fasciatus	**163**; 289
Salinity	**218-220**; 238
Samoa	**83**
Sand zone	31; **38-39**; **138-144**
Sand zone aquarium	**138-144**

A Modern Coral Reef Aquarium.

Respiration	20
Reverse osmosis	**262-263**
Revilla Gigedo	88
Rhinomuraena quaesita	**147**
Rhipocephalus	**294**; 296
Rhizophora	140; **141**
Rhodophyta	273; 274; **307-318**
Ribbon eel	**147**
Ringed worms	180
Rio de Janeiro	90
Rocks	116
Rotenone	328

Sao Tome	98; **99-101**
Sarcomastigophora	49
Sarcophyton	35
Sargassum	26; 32; 280; 306; **307**
Sargassumfish	91
Sargocentron	
- *rubrum*	**155**
- *spiniferum*	**46**
Scaleworm	**181**
Scartella cristata	91
Schizothrix	**277**
- *calcicola*	276

Scleractinia	14; 30
Scleraxonia	**44**; **176**
Scleronephthya	37
Scutus anguis	187; **188**
Scyphozoa	176
Sea anemones	36; 176
Sea grass	140
Sea lettuce	282
Sea Mouse	181
Sea of Cortez	**89**
Sea pens	118

Siderastrea	98
Siganidae	58; 60
Siganus rivulatus	58
Silicates	**236-237**; 262; 275
Silicon	238; 275
Single-celled organisms	**49-50**
Sinularia	35; 37; **158**
- dura	**316**
Siphonocladales	**285-287**
Siphonogorgia	37
Sipunculida	**183**

Sphaeramia nematoptera	**148**
Sphyraena	**43**
Spionidae	182; **183**
Spondylus	**29**; **47**
Sponges	**29**; **44**; **93**; 122; **139**; **174**; 175;
	249; **277**; **297**; 323; **324**
- acclimatisation of	165
Spongites	**315**; 317-318
- onkodes	318
- pachiderma	318
Sporangium	**282-283**
Sporolithon	**285**
Sporophytes	282; 304; 308
Squilla	185
Squirrelfish	
- Long-Jawed	**46**
- Longspine	**97**
- Russet	**155**
Starfish	**38**; **98**; **190**; **291**
- Blue	**41**; **79**
Stenopus hispidus	**47**; **152**
Stichodactyla	36
- gigantea	141; 143
Stolonifera	176
Stomatella	187; **188**
Stomatopoda	185
Stony corals	30; 35; 37; **319**; 323;
	339; 342
- attaching to rock	**120-122**
- genera distribution	**60**
- growing from live rock	**176-178**
- protection of	**336-337**
Strontium	**235-236**; 238
Strontium chloride	236
Styelidae	190
Stylophora	35; 37
Stypopodium zonale	**281**; **305**
Styrofoam	116
Subergorgia mollis	**44**
Subgravel filters	256
Suez Canal	58
Surgeonfishes	35; **288-289**
Swiftia exserta	**152**
Sycon	**249**
Syllidae	**180**
Symbiodinium	319
Symphyllia	**269**
Synalpheus	**142**
Synanceia verrucosa	105
Synchiropus	184
Syngnathidae	184
Syringodium	
- filiforme	140
- isoetifolium	140
Tabulata	14
Tachypleus	185
- gigas	105
Taeniura lymma	**144**
Tanaidacea	**183**
Tanzania	**66**
Tapwater	262
Temperature	57-58; **213-215**; 244
Terebelidae	**182**
Terebella	182
Tethys Sea	14
Tetrasporophytes	308
Thailand	
- Andaman Islands	**70**
- Ko Hi	**71**
Thalassia	25-26
- hemprichii	140; **141**
- testudinum	140
Thor amboinensis	**330**
Threadworms	180
Titanoderma	316
Tourism	**337**; 338
Toxins	242; 244; 245; **309**
Trace elements	162; **218**; 237; **238**
Trachyphyllia geoffroyi	**157**

Photo: G. Pilling

Sea Spiders	**185-186**
Sea squirts	**29**; **45**; 122; **190-191**;
	323; 324
Sea urchins	**29**; 32; 35; **289**; 290
Semi-biological system	**267**
Seriatopora	36; 37; **54**
Serpulidae	**181-182**
Seychelles	**67**
Sharks	**57**; **131**
Shells	118
Shrimps	**38**; 184; **330**
Sibling species	88-89

Sipunculoidea	30
Slime algae	163; **278-280**
Snails	32; 35; **167**; **186-188**; **289**; 290
Snapper, Bluelined	**139**
Soapfish	**100**
Sodium carbonate	227
Sodium cyanide	328
Soft corals	37; **98**; 122
Soil erosion	338
Soldierfish	127
- Blackbar	**101**
Solomon Islands	**81**

Trade
- claimed losses **339-342**
- in aquarium organisms   61; 81; 89; 91;
          98; 103-106; 127; **327-345**
- in corals   117; **336-337**
- in live rock   **192-193**; 337
Trevally   42
Trickle filter   254
Tridacna   35; **323**; 336; **345**
- *gigas*   **40**
- *maxima*   29; **345**
Tridacnidae   60; 323
Tripneustes gratilla   32
Trochus   35
Tubastraea   36; **100**; 119-120; **178**
- *coccinea*   **122**
Tube anemones   128
Tube worms   154; **181-182**; 186; **241**
Turbellaria   179
Turbinaria (algae)   280; **307**
- *turbinata*   281
Turbinaria (coral)   **103**; **286**; 307
Turbo   35; 187; **188**
Turtle weed   292
Tydemania expeditionis   **293**
Udotea   141; 293; **294**
- *cyathiformis*   293; **295**
- *flabellum*   293; **294**
- *occidentalis*   293
- *wilsoni*   293

Ulotrichales   **282-283**
Ulva   26; 32; 282; 308
- *fasciata*   283
- *lactuca*   282
Ulvaria oxysperma   283
Urea   242
Uric acid   242
UV filter   204
UV sterilizers   196; **264**
UV-A   **196-198**; 279; 288
UV-B   **196-198**
- penetration of   **199**
UV-C   **196-198**
UV-light
- biological effects   197-198; 204; 214
- protection   **195**; **196-197**; 199; 201; 204
Valenciennea sexguttata   **39**
Valonia   280; 285; 286
- *aegagrophila*   286
- *macrophysa*   **286**
Vanadium   238
Ventricaria ventricosa   35; **285**; 286
Vermetidae   186; **189**
Virgin Islands   94
Waikiki Aquarium   **129**; **136**
Wastes   241-242
Water   **217-239**
- artificial seawater   **220-222**
- composition of seawater   **217-218**
- natural seawater   220; 238

- tapwater   262
Water changes   **264**
Water motion   266
Wavemakers   266
West Africa   59; 91; **98**
Western Atlantic   15; 90
Wonder Coral   **141**
Wrasses   35
Xanthidae   **184**
Xenia   35; 37; **40**
Yamadaella   280
Zebrasoma   288
- *flavescens*   **166**
- *gemmatum*   **288**
- *scopas*   288
- *veliferum*   **167**; 288
- *xanthurus*   5; **167**; 288; **290**
Zoanthiniaria   30; **176**
Zoanthus sociatus   **187**
Zoogeographical regions   **59**
Zoogeography   **57-61**; **88-91**; **98**
Zooplankton   48
Zoospores   **282-283**
Zooxanthellae   20; 27; 122; 196-197;
          204; 214; 224; 273; 287; **319-323**
- importance of light   321
- nutrient translocation   321-322
- nutrient uptake   321
- reproduction   **322**

Stonogobiops nematodes.

Photo: G. Söntgen

The Monthly Magazine
for
German Reading People

order your free copy

Birgit Schmettkamp Verlag
P.O.Box 31 62 · D-53314 Bornheim · Germany
Phone: ++49-2227-1557; Fax ++49-2227-7662

The Encyclopaedia

on

The Modern Coral Reef Aquarium

in four volumes

Contents of Volume 2
Cnidarians:

- Hydroids
- Jellyfish
- Black Corals
- Pipe Corals
- Soft Corals
- Gorgonians
- Blue Corals
- Sea Pens
- Anemones
- Colonial Anemones
- Mushroom Anemones
- Stony Corals etc.

ISBN 3-928819-23-2

Year of publication: fall 1997

Volume 3

The Modern Coral Reef Aquarium

Svein A. Fosså
Alf Jacob Nilsen

Birgit Schmettkamp Verlag

Contents of Volume 3
Invertebrates:
- Microorganisms ● Sponges
- Marine Worms ● Molluscs
- Sea Stars ● Sea Quirts
- Starfish ● Shrimps
- Crabs etc.

ISBN 3-928819-28-3
Year of publication: fall 1998

Volume 4

The Modern Coral Reef Aquarium

Svein A. Fosså
Alf Jacob Nilsen

Birgit Schmettkamp Verlag

Contents of Volume 4
Fishes:
- Systematic and Nomenclature
- Reproduction
- Coral Reef Fishes

ISBN 3-928819-22-4
Year of publication: fall 1999

Birgit Schmettkamp Verlag

P.O.Box 31 62 · D-53314 Bornheim · Germany
Phone: ++49-2227-1557; Fax ++49-2227-7662

Reef edge at low tide at Bunaken, Indonesia. Photo: A. J. Nilsen

Reef edge in the Red Sea. Underwater photo: Dr. D. Brockmann

Zebra Pipe Fish, *Doryrhamphus dactyliophorus.*

Photo: G. Spies